GLOBAL HANDBOOK ON FOOD AND WATER SAFETY

ABOUT THE AUTHORS

SONIA YUSON-DE LEON is a professor in the Department of Food Science and Nutrition at the University of the Philippines (UP) in Quezon City. She holds a Bachelor of Science in Food Technology (cum laude) from the UP, a Ph.D. in Food Technology from the University of Massachusetts, and a Masters of Business Management from the Asian Institute of Management. Over the last four decades, she has researched and written technical articles and more than fifteen books on food science and technology, including *Food Safety and Sanitation for Philippine Consumers*. She has worked on installing, maintaining, and evaluating food safety systems in various firms throughout the Philippines. She has participated in Codex food hygiene meetings and is presently working with the Department of Agriculture as technical consultant on Food Hygiene–related issues in Codex.

SUSAN MEACHAM, Ph.D., R.D., chair of the Department of Nutrition Sciences at the University of Nevada Las Vegas (UNLV), and director of the American Dietetic Association accredited Didactic Program in Dietetics at UNLV, obtained a Ph.D. in Human Nutrition and Foods from Virginia Polytechnic Institute and State University and currently teaches complementary and integrative medical nutrition therapy and metabolism courses. Dr. Meacham also works with the Nevada Nutrition Education and Research Program in the School of Medicine at UNLV, the School of Dentistry at UNLV. As a member of the UNLV Cancer Research Institute, she compares dietary intake methodologies, determines the essentiality of trace minerals and reviews the effectiveness of complementary and integrative therapies for chronic disease prevention. Dr. Meacham is on the editorial board of *Today's Dietitian* and consults at Canyon Ranch Spa Club at the Venetian Hotel in Las Vegas. Meacham, past president of numerous local dietetic associations, is a founding member the Nevada Chapter of the Society of Public Health Educators (SOPHE).

VIRGINIA S. CLAUDIO, Ph.D, MNS, R.D., earned a B.S.H.E. degree (Foods and Nutrition) from the University of the Philippines; her dietetic diploma at the Indiana University Medical Center, and a Masters degree in Nutritional Science from Cornell University, New York. She finished her Ph.D. at Kansas State University as a General Foods Fellow. Mrs. Claudio has twenty years of teaching experience. As an associate professor at Chicago State University, Texas A&I, California State University, and the Charles R. Drew University School of Allied Health at Los Angeles, she conducted research in addition to her teaching duties. Additionally, she worked as a dietitian for twenty-two years in United States' hospitals, nursing homes, medical clinics, and university food services. As Foodservice Director, her administrative duties included enforcing the policies for food sanitation and safety and coordinating quality assurance activities. As an R.D. consultant for group home facilities, she monitored proper food handling of support personnel. Currently, she is a private practitioner in Las Vegas, Nevada, in medical nutrition services and continues to write textbooks. This volume is her twelfth book.

GLOBAL HANDBOOK ON FOOD AND WATER SAFETY

For the Education of Food Industry Management, Food Handlers, and Consumers

By

SONIA Y. de LEON, PH.D., M.B.M.

SUSAN L. MEACHAM, PH.D., R.D.

VIRGINIA S. CLAUDIO, PH.D., R.D.

CHARLES C THOMAS • PUBLISHER, LTD.
Springfield • Illinois • U.S.A.

Published and Distributed Throughout the World by

CHARLES C THOMAS • PUBLISHER, LTD.
2600 South First Street
Springfield, Illinois 62704

ISBN 0-398-07402-X (hard)
ISBN 0-398-07403-8 (paper)

Library of Congress Catalog Card Number: 2003042625

With THOMAS BOOKS *careful attention is given to all details of manufacturing and design. It is the Publisher's desire to present books that are satisfactory as to their physical qualities and artistic possibilities and appropriate for their particular use.* THOMAS BOOKS *will be true to those laws of quality that assure a good name and good will.*

Printed in the United States of America
SR-R-3

Library of Congress Cataloging-in-Publication Data

De Leon, Sonia Yuson.
Global handbook on food and water safety : for the education of food industry management, food handlers, and consumers / by Sonia Y. de Leon, Susan L. Meacham, Virginia S. Claudio.
p. cm.
Includes bibliographical references and index.
ISBN 0-398-07402-X (hard) -- ISBN 0-398-07403-8 (pbk.)
1. Food service--Sanitation--Handbooks, manuals, etc. 2. Food--Safety measures--Handbooks, manuals, etc. 3. Food--Sanitation--Handbooks, manuals, etc. 4. Food industry and trade--Safety measures--Handbooks, manuals, etc. 5. Food--Toxicology--Handbooks, manuals, etc. 6. Food handling--Safety measures--Handbooks, manuals, etc. 7. Water-supply--Safety measures--Handbooks, manuals, etc. 8. Water-supply--Sanitation--Handbooks, manuals, etc. 9. Water--Toxicology--Handbooks, manuals, etc. I. Meacham, Susan L. II. Claudio, Virginia Serraon, 1932- III. Title.

RA1216.D45 2003
363.72'96--dc21

2003042625

Dedicated to our families for their moral support in writing this book.

DISCLAIMER

PREFACE

The world is now referred to as the "global village," and the globalization of food trade has made food from distant lands very accessible to consumers in a very short period of time. With the increased volume and value of international trade, some new problems have surfaced, such as emerging food pathogens that the present regulatory systems have difficulties in detecting and controlling. The World Health Organization (WHO) has proclaimed, "Access to food, water, and sanitation is a fundamental human right and is vital for the dignity and health of all people." Providing this global village safe food and water is indeed one of the main challenges of the millennium.

Most illnesses and death from food and waterborne diseases are preventable. Pathogenic microbial growths, and physical and chemical hazards, are controllable. We have written this book to help in preventing food and waterborne diseases.

This book is for consumers and food handlers throughout the food chain, from the farm and sea to the consumer's table. It gives guidelines for management, for trainers of food handlers, and for consumers. If we can save one life, and prevent one foodborne or waterborne illness, the effort expended in writing this book will have been well worth it!

–THE AUTHORS

INTRODUCTION

This book is a practical reference on food and water safety for food managers, trainers/educators, food handlers, and consumers worldwide. There are four parts, each with unique features and learning goals.

The first two chapters of the text emphasize the importance of food and water safety on health and life maintenance. The remaining chapters are the whys and means in ensuring food and water safety. Each chapter has an introductory paragraph that states the objective(s) and scope of the chapter text. Definitions of useful terms, tables, and figures/illustrations serve to make the key points better understood and easier to remember. At the end of each chapter is a bibliography for that chapter. This list of references gives the reader a chance to delve into areas of interest and read further for more information. Review questions at the end of the chapters enhance the learning experience.

A unique feature of this book is a section presenting foodborne disease outbreaks. An introductory page explains the selection of fifty cases presented in this text as representative samples of literally hundreds of foodborne disease outbreaks that can be found in the literature. These sample cases are also important learning tools for problem-solving and evaluating foodborne illnesses.

The appendices supplement the text, giving additional information in a brief, concise manner, such as tables, charts, and sample forms. The list of selected web sites on food and water safety concludes the appendix material.

This book is unique because:

- It explains **water safety** in more detail, whether it is used for drinking and cooking or in recreational water facilities.
- It contains numerous examples of **foodborne disease outbreaks** (FBDOs) worldwide with a variety of etiologic agents that cause the illnesses from contaminated food or water.
- It offers guidelines to supply safe food and water for emergencies that include preparedness in case of **bioterrorism, power outage, floods, hurricanes, and other disasters.**

- Each chapter has **practical guidelines about food and water safety** when handling foods throughout the food chain.
- Chapter 14 deals with **challenges for the future** to ensure a safe water and food supply.
- The last chapter (Chapter 15) presents fifty foodborne disease outbreaks from different parts of the world caused by a variety of etiologic agents.

In light of global trade and increasing cultural diversity in food consumption, this book is a valuable addition to one's library. We encourage readers to share with the authors their suggestions to enhance the next revision of this volume.

ACKNOWLEDGMENTS

The authors gratefully acknowledge the assistance of those without whom this book would not have been possible:

- Our research assistants: Aaron Darnton, Kim Darnton, Farah Galvez, Megielyn Gonzalez, Leonor Gubuan, Karen Kintana, Erinn Pengson, Grace Revere, Sheela Revilla, Karen Roscom, and Lara Vivas
- Our word processors: Robin Toles and Sandra M.Tucknott
- Our illustrators: Brian Rose, Farah Galvez, and Linton T. Gonzaga
- Dr. Leslie Johnson for her professional assistance
- Our colleagues: Libia Chavez and Mila Dolores for their valuable input in the Food Safety Systems chapter
- The librarians from the Health Science Library at the Clark County Library District, West Charleston, Las Vegas, Nevada location

SPECIAL THANKS

- To Linda L. Cox for compiling the glossary and editing the whole book from cover to cover.
- To James M. Jay, Professor Emeritus, Wayne State University, Detroit, Michigan, and Adjunct Professor at the University of Nevada, Las Vegas, Nevada for his technical expertise.

CONTENTS

FIGURES

TABLES

GLOBAL HANDBOOK ON FOOD AND WATER SAFETY

Chapter 1

IMPORTANCE OF FOOD AND WATER SAFETY

1.0 INTRODUCTION

Food and water safety is an essential public health issue for all countries. Every person must eat and drink to sustain life, but life will be shortened or the quality of a person's health will suffer, if food or water contaminated with a foodborne pathogen or its toxin has been consumed. No one in either developed or developing countries is spared from contracting foodborne diseases.

The following statements from international health organizations highlight the importance of food and water safety:

"Access to food, water, and sanitation is a fundamental need and a human right. It is vital for the dignity and health of all people."[1]

"Access to safe food, water, and sanitation is the foundation of development."[2]

"Access to nutritionally adequate and SAFE food is a right of each individual."[3]

The last statement was initiated during a joint international conference of the Food and Agriculture Organization and World Health Organization (FAO/WHO) in 1992. In May 2000, the World Health Assembly, which is the governing body of WHO, adopted a resolution that directs future priority issues on food safety and increases involvement with the Codex Alimentarius Commission.

2.0 FOOD AND WATER SAFETY: EFFECTS ON HEALTH

Disease caused by contaminated food and water is one of the most widespread and growing health problems, both in developed and developing countries. The global incidence of foodborne disease is difficult to estimate because many are not reported; however, available statistics are useful in showing general trends.

2.1 Epidemiology

In developed countries, the percentage of people suffering from foodborne disease increases by 30 percent each year. In the United States alone, about 76 million cases are estimated to occur annually. In developing countries, diarrheal disease is a major cause of malnutrition among infants and children under five, of which 70 percent is attributed to contaminated food and water.[4]

Globally, there are 50 million deaths per year of which 80 percent are in developing countries. Half of the mortality in developing countries is due to infectious diseases and parasites.[5]

The United States of America (USA) has one of the safest food and water supplies in the world. Nonetheless, in the United States, *on a daily basis,* the estimated number of deaths (25) and illnesses (16,000) are alarming.[6]

The number of persons potentially affected per incidence of a foodborne disease could range from one individual, an entire family, a community, or as many as hundreds and thousands of people. Table 1.1 lists some examples of food poisoning outbreaks, showing the number of deaths in each incidence.

The Centers for Disease Control and Prevention (CDC), of the US, documents cases of foodborne illnesses that are reported worldwide. Their weekly reports are available at the web site http://www.cdc.gov/mmwr. The problem of waterborne diseases is related to the fact that more than 1 billion people or one-sixth of the world's population do not have access to safe drinking water, and nearly 2.4 billion, or 40 percent of the world's population, lack proper hygienic sanitation systems. Almost all of these problems are seen in the developing countries.[12]

Chapter 2 deals with water safety and cites more statistics and control systems for water supplies globally.

2.2 Effects of Foodborne Illnesses on Health

The full impact of foodborne diseases on health cannot be fully appreciated if based solely on the number of people affected. The severity and duration of the illness are important to know, as well as the onset or incubation period when the signs and symptoms start to appear. These factors vary according to the kind of infection or intoxication, the virulence of the etiologic agent, the dose or number of microorganisms, the age and health status of the victim, and pre-existing medical conditions that reduce a person's immune system or resistance to disease. The young, elderly, pregnant women, persons undergoing chemotherapy, and individuals suffering from malnutrition, HIV/AIDS, cancer, anemia, and tuberculosis are at higher risks to contract foodborne illnesses sooner than the average, healthy adult.

To illustrate the wide variety of signs and symptoms manifested in each of the common foodborne diseases, the succeeding tabulated

Table 1.1
EXAMPLES OF FOOD POISONING OUTBREAKS

Location	*Year*	*Disease*	*Cases*	*Deaths*	*Reference*
Cairo	1991	Botulism	91	18	Rakha, 1992[7]
China	1988	Hepatitis A	292,000	32	Christian, 1990[8]
India	1974	Aflatoxic hepatitis	n.a.	100	Krishnamachari et al., 1982[9]
Latin America (10 Countries) n/a*	1991	Cholera	300,000	3,170	Dawson & Costaarrica, 1992[10]
USA 1998[11] (Wisconsin)	1993	Cryptosporidiosis	400,000	104	Scott & Sockett,

*Not Available

data (Tables 1.2 to 1.6) have been compiled from the latest CDC publication prepared as a primer for physicians for the diagnosis and management of foodborne illnesses.[13]

Note from the tables that the classical signs and symptoms of most foodborne diseases generally include vomiting, diarrhea, abdominal pain, gastroenteritis, fever, fatigue, and general weakness. If the episode lasts only a day or two, and the illness is mild, the person affected does not seek medical help, but often mistake the symptoms for an intestinal flu. Many cases are therefore unreported, and of those reported, usually the investigation and final diagnosis cannot be completed.

Some foodborne illnesses of longer duration could affect other organs of the body, such as the liver, kidneys, heart, central nervous system, the lungs and respiratory system, and the skin.[14]

More details on the effects of foodborne diseases on health are given in Chapter 5, which discusses the microbiological hazards of food safety. Information on the incubation period, duration of the illness, foods associated or implicated with its occurrence, how transmitted, and preventive measures, are also included in Chapter 5. The signs and symptoms of foodborne illnesses caused by bacteria, parasites, viruses, chemicals and biological toxins are generally summarized here.

3.0 FOOD AND WATER SAFETY: SOCIOECONOMIC CONSIDERATIONS

The grief, anguish, pain, and misery suffered by the victim, family members, and caregivers of those suffering from foodborne illnesses cannot be measured in monetary value. The worst scenario is when the final result of the episode or illness is death. Some of the economic losses could be measurable and are documented, but are often underestimated because the indirect costs associated with the foodborne illness are not always observable or determined immediately.

The following outline summarizes the various costly factors related to foodborne illness:[15]

Table 1.2
SIGNS AND SYMPTOMS OF FOODBORNE ILLNESSES CAUSED BY BACTERIA

Etiology Agent	*Signs and Symptoms*
Bacillus cereus (diarrheal toxin)	Abdominal cramps, watery diarrhea, nausea
Bacillus cereus (emetic toxin)	Sudden onset of severe nausea and vomiting
Campylobacter jejuni	Diarrhea, cramps, fever, and vomiting; diarrhea may be bloody
Clostridium botulinum (children and adults)	Vomiting, diarrhea, blurred vision, diplopia, dysphagia, and descending muscle weakness
Clostridium botulinum (infants)	Infants under 12 months: lethargy, weakness, poor feeding, constipation, hypotonia, poor head control, poor gag and suck
Clostridium perfringens	Watery diarrhea, nausea, abdominal cramps
Enterotoxigenic	Watery diarrhea, abdominal cramps
E. coli (ETEC)	Some vomiting
Listeria monocytogenes	Fever, muscle aches, and nausea or diarrhea. Pregnant women may have mild flu-like illness, and infection can lead to premature delivery or stillbirth. The elderly or immunocompromised patients may have bacteremia or meningitis.
Salmonella spp.	Diarrhea, fever, abdominal cramps, vomiting. *S. Typhi* and *S. Paratyphi* produce typhoid with insidious onset characterized by fever, headache, constipation, malaise, chills, and myalgia; diarrhea is uncommon. Vomiting is usually not severe.
Shigella spp.	Abdominal cramps, fever, and diarrhea. Stools may contain blood and mucus.
Staphylococcus aureus	Sudden onset, severe nausea and vomiting; abdominal cramps; diarrhea and fever may be present
Vibrio cholerae	Profuse watery diarrhea and vomiting, which can lead to severe dehydration and death within hours
Vibrio parahaemolyticus	Watery diarrhea, abdominal cramps, nausea, vomiting
Yersinia enterocolitica	Appendicitis-like symptoms (diarrhea and vomiting, fever, and abdominal pain)

3.1 Costs That May Be Incurred by the Sick Individual or Caregiver/Family

- Loss of family income
- Loss of opportunities for advancement
- Increased insurance
- Medical expenses to include physical rehabilitation and long-term care
- Cost for pediatric and geriatric care
- Cost of special dietary needs
- Loss of productivity, leisure, and travel opportunities
- Funeral expenses as applicable

Table 1.3
SIGNS AND SYMPTOMS OF FOODBORNE ILLNESSES CAUSED BY PARASITES

Etiology Agent	*Signs and Symptoms*
Cryptosporidium parvum	Cramping, abdominal pain, watery diarrhea. Fever and vomiting may be present and may be relapsing.
Cyclospora cayetanensis	Fatigue, protracted diarrhea, often relapsing
Entamoeba histolytica	Bloody diarrhea, frequent bowel movements (looks like *Shigella*), and lower abdominal pain
Giardia lamblia	Acute or chronic diarrhea, flatulence, bloating
Toxoplasma gondii	Generally asymptomatic, 20 percent may develop cervical lymphadenopathy and/or a flu-like illness. In immunocompromised patients, central nervous system (CNS) disease, myocarditis, or pneumonitis is often seen. Severe damage to fetus.
Trichinella spiralis	Nausea, vomiting, diarrhea, abdominal discomfort followed by fever, myalgias, periorbital edema

Table 1.4
SIGNS AND SYMPTOMS OF FOODBORNE ILLNESSES CAUSED BY VIRUSES

Etiology Agent	*Signs and Symptoms*
Hepatitis A	Diarrhea, dark urine, jaundice, and flu-like symptoms (fever, headache, nausea, and abdominal pain)
Norwalk-like viruses	Nausea, vomiting, watery large-volume diarrhea–fever is rare
Rotavirus	Vomiting, watery diarrhea, low-grade fever. Temporary lactose intolerance may occur. Infants and children, the elderly, and the immunocompromised are especially vulnerable.
Other viral agents (astroviruses, calciviruses, adenoviruses)	Nausea, vomiting, diarrhea, malaise, abdominal pain, headache, fever

3.2 Business and Industry Costs

- Legal liability costs
- Insurance costs
- Costs of product recall or discarded rejects
- Poor publicity and stock value suffers
- Loss of reputation
- Costs of investigation, cleaning up, and education
- Loss of business

3.3 Costs to the Nation and Government

- Expenses for plant or on-site inspection
- Surveillance costs
- Legislation
- Medical costs
- Prosecution costs
- Health care/welfare benefits awarded to the qualified person

Table 1.5
SIGNS AND SYMPTOMS OF FOODBORNE ILLNESSES CAUSED BY CHEMICALS

Etiology Agent	*Signs and Symptoms*
Antimony	Vomiting, metallic taste
Arsenic	Vomiting, colic, diarrhea.
Cadmium	Nausea, vomiting, myalgias, increase in salivation, stomach pain
Copper	Nausea, vomiting, blue or green vomitus
Lead	High blood pressure, kidney problems.
Mercury	Numbness, weakness of legs, spastic paralysis, impaired vision, blindness, coma. Pregnant women and the developing fetus are especially vulnerable.
Nitrite poisoning	Nausea, vomiting, cyanosis, headache, dizziness, weakness, loss of consciousness, chocolate-brown colored blood
Pesticides (organophosphates or carbonates)	Nausea, vomiting, abdominal cramps, diarrhea, headache, nervousness, blurred vision, twitching, convulsions
Sodium fluoride	Salty or soapy taste, numbness of mouth, vomiting, diarrhea, dilated pupils, spasms, pallor, shock
Thallium	Nausea, vomiting, diarrhea, painful paresthesias, motor polyneuropathy, hair loss.
Tin	Nausea, vomiting, diarrhea
Zinc	Nausea, vomiting, diarrhea, myalgias, stomach pain

- Costs of clean-up and education
- Losses from tourism and food export trade, as applicable

The following data are selected examples to illustrate the impact of economic losses experienced by a family, community, or nation due to foodborne diseases.

- Based on 1985 figures, the total cost resulting from intestinal infectious diseases alone in the United States was estimated to be above $25 billion for that year.[15]
- In 1997, the United States Department of Agriculture (USDA) estimated that from just six types of foodborne pathogens, the medical costs and loss of productivity reached as high as $6.7 billion.[16]
- The cholera epidemic in 1991 cost Peru more than $700 million in lost exports of their fish and fishery products (industry). Tourism dropped and many restaurants closed.[16]
- In 1993, four restaurants were involved in an *Escherichia coli* outbreak in the United States. The company paid almost $5 million to cover total outbreak costs for forty-eight infected persons.[17]
- In 1999, when dioxins were found in poultry in Belgium, it led to widespread disruption of trade and loses of hundreds of millions of Euros.[18] The med-

Table 1.6
SIGNS AND SYMPTOMS OF FOODBORNE ILLNESSES CAUSED BY BIOLOGICAL TOXINS

Etiology Agent	*Signs and Symptoms*
Ciguatera fish poisoning (ciguatera toxin)	Abdominal pain, nausea, vomiting, diarrhea, neurologic, paresthesias, reversal of hot or cold pain, weakness. After 2 to 5 days, bradycardia, hypotension, increase in T wave abnormalities.
Mushroom toxins, short-acting (museinol, muscarine, psilocybin, coprius artemetaris ibotenic acid)	Vomiting, diarrhea, confusion, visual disturbance, salivation, diaphoresis, hallucinations, disulfiram-like reaction, confusion, visual disturbance
Mushroom toxin, long-acting (amanital)	Diarrhea, abdominal cramps, leading to hepatic and renal failure.
Pufferfish (tetrodotoxin)	Paresthesias, vomiting, diarrhea, abdominal pain, ascending paralysis, respiratory failure.
Scombroid (histamine) poisoning	Flushing, rash, burning sensation of skin, mouth and throat, dizziness, urticaria, paresthesias.
Shellfish toxins (diarrheic, neurotoxic, amnesic)	Nausea, vomiting, diarrhea, and abdominal pain accompanied by chills, headache, and fever.
Shellfish toxins (paralytic shellfish poisoning)	Diarrhea, nausea, vomiting leading to paresthesias of mouth, lips, weakness, dysphasia, dysphonia, respiratory paralysis

ical costs and value of lives from just five foodborne illnesses in England and Wales were estimated at £300 to 700 million annually in 1996.[19]

It is estimated that about 2 to 3 percent of cases of foodborne diseases lead to long term illnesses, which are far more damaging to human health and the economy than the initial disease. For example, certain strains of *E. coli* cause kidney failure in infants and young children; Salmonellosis may lead to reactive arthritis and serious infections; *Campylobacter* is the most common precipitating factor for Guillain-Barre syndrome; Listeriosis can cause meningitis, stillbirths, and miscarriages in pregnant women, and weakened immune systems can lead to severe illness or death in older adults.[20]

Food losses due to contamination of grains and legumes with mycotoxins are enormous. Worldwide losses of grains and legumes are estimated at 10 percent. For non-grain staples, the loss is estimated at 50 percent. Thus, one billion tons of cereals are at risk of contamination with mycotoxins annually.[21]

4.0 REPORTING FOODBORNE ILLNESSES

Every responsible consumer should find out how and where to report any suspected foodborne illness in the family. If you or a family member develop nausea, vomiting, diarrhea, abdominal cramps, and fever, it could be a case of food poisoning. Seek medical help immediately if the symptoms are severe or if the victim is an infant, young child, pregnant woman, senior, or anyone already ill or who has a pre-existing medical condition that compromises the immune system.[22]

4.1 Guide to Consumers[11,22,23]

Each nation has guidelines on how to report foodborne illnesses. Find out the procedure for your country. There may be one specific agency that handles problems for particular food products (e.g. meats, fish, drinking water, etc). If you think an illness was caused by a commercial product bought at a particular store, or by something you ate at a public picnic or large gathering, you should report it to your local or regional public health officer. Your local government officer or police department also should have a contact telephone number. By reporting the incident, you might be helping to prevent others from becoming ill.

When you make your report, try to have the following information ready:

- Your name, address, telephone number
- Where the suspected food was eaten
- Name of the product and where it was bought
- When the food was eaten; serving portions eaten
- When you started to become ill; symptoms and duration
- Names of other persons who became ill with similar symptoms and who ate the same food(s).

If you suspect a commercial product, have the container available if possible. This has important information on it, including a lot or batch number that will help public health officials trace its source, as well as the manufacturer's name and address. If you still have the suspect food, seal it in a plastic bag and write on the report or inform the investigators that you have the suspect food. They may need the specimen for laboratory tests. If not, ask for advice on how to safely dispose of it.

Cooperate in an investigation. This usually happens when public health officials suspect that a lot of people have been affected or that the contaminated food is widespread. Taking part in these investigations can help to rapidly identify an important cause of food poisoning.

4.2 Guide to Physicians

In most counties or towns, the local public health department requests physicians and clinical laboratories to notify them when certain foodborne illnesses are suspected or diagnosed. The health authorities will then investigate the outbreak. By learning how the infection was transmitted and the vehicle or food implicated, problems about food production and distribution can be further studied.

In the United States, a foodborne disease outbreak is defined as an incident in which two or more persons experience a similar illness resulting from the ingestion of a common food. Requirements for reporting foodborne diseases and conditions may be mandated by state and territorial laws and regulations. Forms and other details on reporting requirements are available electronically through the CDC.[24]

The CDC has prepared tabulated data to guide physicians for confirmation of foodborne outbreaks. The list provides information on etiologic agents, e.g. bacteria, viruses, chemical and biological toxins, and the characteristic clinical syndromes, incubation period, and confirmation by isolation, identification, and other laboratory tests.[25]

4.3 Procedures for Food Service Institutions[26]

Food service personnel should take all complaints seriously and make a report right away to their supervisor. The following steps are recommended:

- Fill out a form provided by your department (sometimes called an incident report).
- Record the exact food or beverage consumed by the customer. Note the exact time when symptoms started, including the description and duration of the symptoms.
- Ask where else and what food/drink the customer ate before or after eating in your establishment.
- Find out who else ate the food. Did they become ill with similar symptoms?
- Did the customer seek medical attention? Where and what was the diagnosis?
- What treatment was given?

IF MORE THAN ONE PERSON COMPLAINED, CALL THE LOCAL HEALTH DEPARTMENT.

- This calls for crisis management and a team is assigned to handle all questions and communicate with the media and customers. Only one spokesperson will be appointed to handle media communications.
- Outside experts for public relations and food testing may be called in by management.
- Cooperate with the investigation, express your concern, and accept responsibility.

The true incidence of foodborne diseases is difficult to estimate and evaluate because only a small number of cases are reported to the health authorities. It is believed that in developed or industrialized countries, less than 10 percent of cases are reported and in developing nations, only less than one percent.[27]

More vigorous campaigns are needed to educate consumers why reporting foodborne illnesses is crucial to the health of their families, community, and their country as a whole.

5.0 BENEFITS OF SAFE WATER AND FOOD SUPPLY

The benefits of consuming safe food and water are simply and concisely summarized by a flyer from the USDA Meat and Poultry Hotline which lists ten reasons for handling food safely.[28] The top 10 reasons are listed in the following paragraphs, supported by citing facts or cases. Statements enclosed in quotation marks were made by the USDA Meat and Poultry Hotline staff.

1. It May Save a Life

- According to the World Health Organization (WHO), an estimated 1.5 billion annual episodes of diarrhea in children under five years of age are due to foodborne diseases. Of these, an estimated three million lead to premature deaths each year.
- Listeriosis causes an estimated 2,500 serious illnesses and 500 deaths in the United States each year in persons of all ages.
- In 1992–1993, a multistate outbreak of *E. coli* food poisoning caused illness among 500 people and four of them died.
- A mouthful of food that is contaminated with a very potent toxin produced

by *Clostridium botulinum* is enough to cause death.

- A case of trichinosis led to the death of a 55-year-old woman in New York, after eating contaminated undercooked pork sausages.

2. You Will Spare Yourself and Your Family a Painful Bout of Illness

- Tables 1.2 to 1.6 from previous pages in this chapter listed the signs and symptoms of a foodborne illness, such as headache, nausea, vomiting, abdominal pains, diarrhea, fever, and weakness. Depending on the type and amount of the causative pathogenic organism and/or its toxin, the individual may recover sooner. If the illness is prolonged it may affect other parts of the body like the lungs, kidneys, pancreas, and liver. The chapter on Microbiological Hazards in Food and Water Supply gives more details on the deleterious effects of specific pathogens on organs and tissues of the body.
- Tourists who contract diarrhea by drinking contaminated water or food spoil their vacation because of the symptoms of foodborne illnesses mentioned above. Instead of enjoying the scenery and visiting tourist spots, they have to spend a few days in bed, or in worse cases, seek hospitalization.
- A working mother whose income is badly needed for family expenses encountered financial losses because she contracted a bout of food poisoning and was confined in a hospital for a month without any insurance.
- In 1999–2000, hundreds of people in the United States and Canada got sick from drinking unpasteurized orange juice contaminated with *Salmonella*. From May 3–9, 1998, another *Salmonella* outbreak occurred at a college in New Jersey. Almost 50 percent of the 188 students who ate homemade ice cream made with Grade A raw eggs that carried *Salmonella enteri* got sick. Fortunately, they all recovered and there was no fatality, but their studies were interrupted and they were less productive.

3. Save Money

- When a food company is asked to recall a contaminated product, huge losses are incurred because tons of processed foods are not sold. More serious is the damage to the company's reputation. If legal and liability costs are involved, the food company has to shoulder staggering amounts to settle the cases.
- From the standpoint of public service or the government, total costs for investigating the outbreaks, maintenance of laboratories for diagnostic and epidemiological analyses, hiring of health professionals and skilled technicians, and the cost of informing the public and education of consumers, all amount to enormous sums of money. Ultimately, the consumers (as taxpayers) shoulder the expenses.

4. Safe Food Handling is the Responsible Thing To Do

"Those for whom you prepare food deserve the best, and you expect no less from those who produce and prepare food for you. You are no less important than the manufacturer, government regulator, or grocer in assuring food safety. You are an important link in the farm-to-table chain."

5. Safe Food Handling Can Enhance Your Standing in the Community

"Food for a concession stand, bake sale or church supper must be carefully prepared. Many of those in your community are very young, elderly, or suffering from health problems that affect the immune system. These folks are at increased risk for foodborne illness. Protect their health and the reputation of your organization."

6. Safe Food Handling Inspires Confidence and Keeps Peace in the Family

"Imagine: No more family feuds because someone handled dinner in a questionable fashion. And family and friends won't call the Meat and Poultry Hotline begging to have food safety literature mailed to your address."

7. Safe Food Handling is Easy

"You are the last person to handle your food before it is eaten. You may be the last person to handle food before it is served to your family or friends. Take charge! Prevention of illness may be as simple as washing your hands–an often-neglected but VERY important act."

8. The Safest Ways to Handle Food are Usually the Most Efficient

"Don't take chances in the name of saving time. Thawing meat and poultry products at room temperature and partial cooking are examples of practices which can seem like good ideas, but that may actually encourage bacterial growth by keeping food in the "danger zone" (41°–140°F) where bacteria multiply fastest. In the case of bacteria that produce heat-resistant toxins, this becomes a problem that further cooking can't fix."

9. Safe Food Handling Lets You Enjoy to the Fullest the Nutritional Benefits of Food

"If you've taken the time to carefully select a variety of healthful foods, why not use them up, or properly preserve them for long-term storage, while nutrient levels are at their peak? Foods that must be discarded due to decay or temperature abuse nourish no one."

10. Safe Food Handling Practices are the Ones Most Likely to Preserve Food's Peak Quality

"Keeping hot food hot and cold food cold inhibits growth of the microorganisms that can spoil your food or make you ill. Storage at the proper temperature also retains the fresh appearance, pleasant aroma and agreeable texture that contribute so strongly to an enjoyable dining experience."

Examples of statistics that show the benefits of safe water were reported recently by the WHO as follows: [1]

- In the 4 billion cases of diarrhea causing 2.2 million deaths, water sanitation and hygiene interventions reduce diarrheal cases by at least a quarter.
- Intestinal worms infect about 10 percent of the population of the developing world. These can be controlled through better sanitation, hygiene, and water supply.
- Six million people are blind from trachoma and 500 million are at risk. Providing adequate quantities of water reduces median infection rate by 25 percent.

- Two hundred million people are infected with schistosomiasis. A well-designed water and sanitation interventions reduce median infection by 77 percent.

The importance of water safety and benefits derived from a safe water supply are discussed in more detail in Chapter 2.

6.0 CONCLUDING REMARKS

Food safety has to filter down to every member of the food chain, from top management to the worker and from the farmer to the consumer. Individuals can make a difference. A trained individual can prevent foodborne and waterborne illnesses. An untrained individual unaware of food safety guidelines can harm hundreds of people by lack of education and by careless food handling.

One person can make a difference! Each of us can be the catalyst to spread ways of food safety and sanitation. We can make our governments more responsive to consumers' needs for food and water safety and adequate supply. We can start in our own homes and communities. Remember that most foodborne illnesses are preventable by practicing safety guidelines in handling food and water every minute, every hour, and day to day. Sanitation is a way of life. Make it part of your culture!

REVIEW QUESTIONS

A. Define the following terms (see text or that Glossary).
   1. Epidemiology
   2. Incidence
   3. Foodborne Disease Outbreak (FBDO)
   4. Food Safety
   5. Water Safety

B Find out from your locality who is in charge of investigating any reported case of foodborne disease outbreak.

C. Narrate a case of a food company or a reputable large restaurant that was confirmed to be involved in a foodborne disease outbreak that caused serious illness to at least twenty people. What are the possible consequences of this case to the company business?

D. Mrs. Anonymous, a single parent, who is the sole source of the family income, had a bad bout of foodborne infection and was hospitalized for two months. She has no insurance of any kind and was working as a street vendor. Her young family of three other minor children went to grade school and ate in their school lunch program. A three-year-old child died from ingesting the same lunch. What do you think are the family's economic, social, and emotional losses?

REFERENCES

1. World Health Organization. *The Global Water Supply and Sanitation Assessment 2000 Report.* Geneva, WHO, 2000.
2. Khan, A. H. *The Sanitation Gap: Development's Deadly Menace. The Progress of Nations.* New York, United Nations Children's Fund, 1997.
3. World Health Organization. *Food Safety.* World Health Assembly, Eighth Plenary Meeting on May 20, 2000. Geneva, WHO, 2000.
4. World Health Organization. Fact Sheet 237: *Food Safety and Foodborne Illness.* Geneva, WHO, 2000.
5. Van de Venter, T. Emerging Foodborne Diseases: a Global Responsibility. FAO Report 2000. Available at http://www.fao.org/docrep/003/htm. Accessed June 9, 2002.

6. World Health Organization. *World Health Statistics Quarterly*. Volume 50. Geneva, WHO, October 1997.
7. Rakha, M. A. An outbreak of botulism intoxication due to salted fermented fish. Paper presented at the Expert Consultation on Fish Technology. Alexandria, Egypt, 1992.
8. Christian, J.H.B. Established bacterial and viral pathogens. Paper presented at the first Asian Conference of Food Safety–the Challenges of the 90's. Kuala Lumpur, Malaysia, September 1990.
9. Krishnamachari, K.A.V.R., Bhat, R.V., Nagarajan, V., and Tilak, T.B.G. Investigations into an outbreak of hepatitis in parts of western India, India *Journal of Medical Research, 63*:1346–1348, 1982.
10. Dawson, R. J., and Costarrica, M. L. *Emergency food control assistance for the prevention and control of cholera in Latin America Food Control, 3*(4): 209–212, 1992.
11. Scott, E., and Sockett, P. *How to Prevent Food Poisoning*. New York, John Wiley & Son, Inc., 1998.
12. Barzilay, J., Weinberg, W., and Eley, J. *The Water We Drink*. New Brunswick, N.J., Rutgers University Press, 1999.
13. Centers for Disease Control and Prevention (CDC), Diagnosis and Management of Foodborne Illnesses: A Primer for Physicians. *MMWR, 50:(RR02),* 1–69, 2001.
14. Varnam, A. H., and Evans, M. G. *Foodborne Pathogens,* St. Louis, C.V. Mosby Co., 1991.
15. Satin, M. *Food Alert*. New York, Checkmark Books, 1999.
16. Buzby, J., Roberts, T., Lin, J., and MacDonald, J. Bacterial foodborne diseases, medical costs and productivity losses. *Agricultural Economics Report, # 741*. USDA, August 1996.
17. Chapman, M. Safety and numbers. *Chain Leader 5:* (10) 8, 2000.
18. Director General, World Health Organization, Food Chain 2001–"Food Safety–a World-wide Challenge". March 14, 2001. Available at http://www.who.int/director-gen./speeches/2001/foodchain2001.upp-sala,en.html. Accessed May 5, 2002.
19. Director General, World Health Organization, Food Safety, EB105/10, December 2, 1999. Available at: http://www.who.int/fsf/eb105_10.pdf. Accessed May 5, 2002.
20. World Health Organization. *Conquering Suffering and Enriching Humanity*. World Health Report 1997. Geneva, WHO, 1997.
21. World Health Organization Fact Sheet No.237, Food Safety and Foodborne Illness. Geneva, WHO, September, 2000.
22. Matthews, D. *Food Safety Sourcebook*. Detroit, Omnigraphics, Inc. 1999.
23. Wilcox, W. *Public Health Sourcebook*. Detroit, Omnigraphics, Inc. 1998.
24. Centers for Disease Control and Prevention (CDC) Reporting Foodborne Illness: CDC, Available at: http://www.cdc.gov/ncidod/dbmd/reportfi.htm. Accessed May 5, 2002.
25. Centers for Disease Control and Prevention (CDC) Guidelines for Confirmation for Foodborne-Disease Outbreaks. *MMWR 45*(SS-5); 58–66, 1996.
26. National Restaurant Association Educational Foundation, *ServSafe® Coursebook*. 2nd ed. Chicago, NRA, 2002.
27. Director General World Health Organization, Consultation on Food Safety. November 2, 1999. Available at http://www.who.int/directorgen./speeches/1999/foodsafety/html. Accessed May 5, 2002.
28. United States Department of Agriculture (USDA). Top 10 Reasons to Handle Your Food Safely. *USDA's Meat and Poultry Hotline*. (flyer) July 1, 1994.

Chapter 2

WATER SAFETY

1.0 IMPORTANCE OF WATER SUPPLY, SAFETY, AND SANITATION

Water is worth more than gold; it is necessary for human survival above all other resources on earth. Water is our most important food and nutrient. A person may live for a while without food but not without water. It comprises 65 percent of the human body for adults and 70 percent for infants, and is responsible for the normal functioning of the different organs of the body (see Chapter 9, Figure 9.3).

A loss of 5 percent body water causes hallucinations and a loss of 15 to 20 percent can be fatal. However, death may be sooner if a person has drunk polluted water that could contain a sufficient dose of a toxic substance. Water is a known carrier of pathogenic microorganisms, contaminants that come from the erosion of natural rock formations and substances discharged from factories, applied to farmlands, or used by consumers in their homes and yards.

Over one billion people still lack access to safe water. Statistics show that more than 2.3 billion people every year suffer from water-related diseases.[1] Almost 40,000 men, women, and children die from diseases directly related to drinking polluted water daily.[2] Access to water supply and sanitation is a fundamental need and a human right. Water safety and sanitation hit on all of the main themes of development agenda: poverty alleviation, environmental sustainability, private sector-led growth, participatory development, and good governance. Because water is so essential to life, it should be ensured that everyone has access to high quality, safe, and sustainable water.

2.0 WATER SAFETY ISSUES

It is a fact that water sustains life; however, it can also endanger life. Exposure to and ingestion of contaminated water causes a number of diseases. Others may be caused by exposure to naturally found harmful chemicals or manmade pollutants in groundwater. Contaminants in water used for irrigation can also affect agricultural products, thus, the poison may enter the food chain and can also cause health problems. The World Health Organization (WHO) estimates that 80 percent of all sickness in the world is attributable to unsafe water sanitation.[3]

2.1 Water-Related Diseases

Waterborne diseases are any illnesses caused by drinking contaminated water. The contamination can be from bacteria (*Salmonella, Campylobacter*), viruses, or by small parasites (*Cryptosporidium, Giardia,* and *Toxoplasma*).[4] Outbreaks of waterborne diseases caused by the contamination of drinking water systems with the feces of infected animals or people happen from time to time. As with foodborne diseases, those most vulnerable to water contamination are infants and children, the elderly, and people whose immune systems are impaired, such as people with HIV/AIDS or those who are undergoing chemotherapy.[5]

Table 2.1
INCIDENCE RATES IN THE UNITED STATES FOR SOME COMMON WATERBORNE DISEASES

Diseases	*Diseases Rates (per annum)**
Salmonellosis	137
Shigellosis	447
Campylobacteriosis	228
Hepatitis A	36
Gastroenteritis (undefined)	11,872

*Data averaged over a 24-year period (1971–1994).

Sources: 1. Moyer, N.P.: *Microbial Risks from Sources Other than Water.* WQTC Presentation, 1995.
2. Center for Disease Control (CDC). *Water Related Disease Outbreaks. Annual Summary 1983.* CDC, Public Health Service, U.S.DHHS, Atlanta.

People infected with the more common waterborne disease agents may have no symptoms at all, and probably will not even know they have been infected. Table 2.1 is a summary of the incidence rates for some common waterborne diseases.[6, 7]

2.2 Microbial Pathogens

Microbial pathogens are the most undesirable constituents of water, because they are capable of directly affecting public health. Some pathogens that cause waterborne diseases are indigenous in water, but most come from animal and human feces that contaminate drinking water sources.

Risk of microbial contamination in water cannot be entirely eliminated. Therefore, regulation is important in ensuring water safety. Reduction of pathogenic microbial contaminants in water subsequently reduces the incidence of waterborne diseases. Table 2.2 summarizes the common microbial contaminants present in water transmitted via oral/fecal means.

2.2.1 Bacteria

A wide variety of bacterial pathogens are capable of contaminating water. Determination of every single one of these is not only time consuming, but economically impossible. To facilitate monitoring of bacterial quality in water, indicator microorganisms are used. Commonly used indicator organisms are coliforms, *E. coli,* and enterococci.

2.2.1.1 Coliform Organisms. Coliforms have long been used as indicators for ensuring water safety due to their ease of detection. Most of these gram-negative bacteria are not pathogens. They are classified as enteric bacteria that belong to the Enterobactericeae family. The presence of coliforms in water confirms suspected fecal contamination. A multiple fermentation tube method is a simple and inexpensive test employed in the determination of coliforms in water. Recommended levels of these organisms have been established to be zero, i.e., no coliforms are allowed (see Table 2.5).

2.2.1.2 *Escherichia coli.* It is the most important of the coliform bacteria and its presence in water indicates fecal contamination and the possible presence of bacteria such as *Salmonella* spp., *Shigella* spp., *Cholera* spp., and *Vibrio* spp. Drinking water should not contain any *E. coli.*

2.2.1.3 *Enterococci.* Sometimes referred to as fecal streptococci, this is a group of bacteria closely related to fecal contamination. These are gram-positive bacteria found in the

Table 2.2
COMMON MICROBIAL CONTAMINANTS PRESENT IN WATER

Contaminants	*Examples*
Bacteria	*Salmonella* spp., *Shigella* spp., *Escherichia coli, Campylobacter* spp., *Vibrio cholerae,* and *Yersinia enterocolitica*
Protozoa	*Entamoeba histolytica, Giardia intestinalis, Cryptosporidium parvum*
Viruses	Hepatitis A and E, Enteroviruses, Adenoviruses, small and round structured viruses including Norwalk virus, and Rotavirus

intestinal tract of humans and animals. They tend to be more resistant to the disinfecting process compared to fecal coliforms. Like the coliform bacteria and *E.coli,* enterococci should not be present in drinking water (see Table 2.5).

2.2.2 *Parasitic Protozoa*

Species of *Cryptosporidium* spp. and *Giardia* spp. are the most common disease-causing parasites in water. Cysts and oocysts of these intestinal parasites are exceptionally resistant to water treatments. These parasites occur in low numbers in raw untreated water supplies.[8]

Parasitic protozoa differ from other microbial water contaminants with regard to ease of detection. Disease-causing protozoa are not readily detectable in water and their behavior in water disinfection differs from that of common indicator microorganisms.

2.2.3 *Viruses*

Viruses are among the wide variety of pathogens in water. Improperly disposed excreta from infected individuals are the major source of viral water contamination. Unfavorable environmental conditions, as well as improper disinfection processes, further promote this.

Ideally, to ensure water quality and safety, viral testing should be administered for drinking water. Detection of viral contamination is administered in raw water, not in drinking water. Testing for the presence of viral contamination in drinking water is relatively expensive, complicated, time consuming, and requires sophisticated techniques and equipment. This is the major reason why a viral test in drinking water is not a required test for ensuring drinking water quality. Viruses present in water are removed or decreased in number during the purification and disinfection step of the water treatment process. The US EPA (1994) does not allow the presence of any virus in drinking water.

2.3 Chemical Contaminants

Chemical contaminants that may be present in source water include organic and inorganic compounds.

2.3.1 *Organic Compounds*

Organic compounds are either inherent in nature or are added from various resources. Some of these compounds are combustible and have lower melting and boiling points compared to inorganic chemicals. These chemicals can be health risks not only because of their toxicity, but also as sources of nourishment for bacteria, thus promoting their growth. Organic compounds found in drinking water can be subdivided into four categories: Synthetic Organic Chemicals (SOCs), Volatile Compounds (VOCs), Phenols, and Trihalomethanes (THMs).

2.3.1.1 SYNTHETIC ORGANIC CHEMICALS (SOCS). The most common organic chemicals found in water are surfactants. Popularly known as detergents, surfactants are synthetic chemical compounds used in cleaning materials such as soaps. In testing for drinking water quality, the presence of surfactants is an indication of water pollution. The presence of 0.5 mg/l of surfactants in the water is considered a maximum level.

2.3.1.2 VOLATILE ORGANIC COMPOUNDS (VOCS). VOCs are lightweight compounds that are easily evaporated. Phenols and halogenated chloro-organic compounds are common VOCs found in water and detection is of primary importance.

2.3.1.3 PHENOLS. Phenols are colorless, crystalline substances. Phenolic substances are naturally present in the tar of wood and coal. Phenols are used in manufacturing medicines, dyes, resins, and other commercial products.

Phenolic substances are slightly water-soluble. They may contaminate the water supply by means of industrial pollution. Ingestion of phenols in high concentrations has been known to cause acute toxicity. Ingestion of high doses in drinking water is rare. High levels of phenols in water have an off odor, which is detectable by humans.

2.3.1.4 TRIHALOMETHANES (THMS). The cause of concern for these compounds is their possible carcinogenic effects on humans. Formation of chloro-organic halogens is promoted by the chlorination treatment in water disinfection. Increasing levels of pollution would mean increasing levels of water disinfection, consequently increasing the formation of THMs.

2.3.2 Inorganic Compounds

Table 2.3 is a summary of some inorganic chemicals, their source and health risks. These contaminants are either inherently present in water in small amounts or added from pollution, disinfection and other natural processes. Chemical contaminants can pose a health risk when they are consumed in high doses. Toxic effects are exhibited after prolonged exposure.

2.4 RADIOACTIVE CONTAMINANTS[11, 27, 29]

Radionucleotides are naturally occurring radioactive materials. Whenever uranium and radium are present in the ground, there is a risk of these elements or their decay products (radon) contaminating water. There are about 20 isotopes of radon, but the type of most concern in water safety is Radon-222, which can pollute well water. Some areas may have geologic formation and soil that is more likely to release radon into the groundwater than other areas. The best guideline for consumers is to find out from local authorities in charge of water safety about the level of radioactive contaminants in their water supply. Know about the location of any nuclear testing grounds or nuclear waste disposal. (See also Chapter 7 about radon and its effects on health, especially in relation to cancer.)

3.0 ENSURING WATER SAFETY

Water is essential to sustain life. It accounts for approximately 65 percent of the total body weight. It carries nutrients in the body, helps lubricate the joints, regulate tempera-

Table 2.3
COMMON INORGANIC CHEMICAL CONTAMINANTS IN WATER

Metal Contaminants	*Sources*	*Health Risks*
Antimony	Waste of petroleum refineries	Increases blood cholesterol, decreases blood sugar
Arsenic	Natural deposits in soil, industrial waste, pesticides	Skin damage, carcinogenic
Asbestos	Decaying asbestos, erosion of natural deposits	High risk of fibrosis, cancer
Beryllium	Industrial wastes of metal refineries, coal refineries, electrical plants	Intestinal lesions, nerves
Barium	WaWaste from refineries, natural deposits	Gastrointestinal sickness, cardiovascular disease
Cadmium	Waste from metal refineries, from pipes	Kidney disease
Chromium	Industrial steel plants, erosion of natural deposits	Allergic reaction
Copper	Corrosion of plumbing systems, erosion of natural deposits	Gastrointestinal illness, liver or kidney damage
Cyanide	Industrial waste of steel, metal and plastic mills and fertilizers	Thyroid problems, nerve damage
Fluoride	From water treatments, from fertilizers, factories	Bone disease and may cause mottled teeth
Lead	Household pipes, natural deposits	High blood pressure, delay in mental and physical development of children, kidney problems
Mercury	From refineries, runoff from landfills, erosion of natural deposits	Kidney damage
Nitrate	From fertilizers, leaching from septic tanks, sewage, erosion of natural deposits	Causes breathing problems for infants if ingested at high levels
Selenium	Discharge from petroleum factories, mine waste, erosion of natural deposits	Hair and fingernail loss, circulatory problems
Thallium	Leaching in ore processing sites, discharge from electronic, glass and drug factories	Hair loss, kidney, intestine or liver problems

ture, and aids in digestion and metabolism. Thus, a satisfactory water supply must be made available to consumers.[9] It is also essential for economic productivity and poverty alleviation.[10]

The provision of drinking water that is not only safe but also pleasing in appearance, taste, and odor is a matter of high priority. The supply of water that is unsatisfactory in this respect will undermine the confidence of consumers, leading to complaints and possibly the use of water from less safe sources. It can also result in the use of bottled water, which is expensive, and home treatment devices, some of which can have adverse effects on water quality.[9]

3.1 Selection and Protection of Water Sources

Proper selection and protection of water sources are of prime importance in the provision of safe drinking water. It is always better to protect water from contamination than to treat it after it has been contaminated.

Before a new source of drinking water supply is selected, it is important to ensure that the quality of the water is satisfactory or treatable for drinking, and that the quantity available is sufficient to meet continuing water demands. The daily and seasonal variations, and projected growth in the size of the community being served, should also be taken into account.

The watershed should be protected from human activities. This could include isolation of the watershed and/or control of polluting activities in the area, such as dumping of hazardous wastes, mining and quarrying, agricultural use of fertilizers and pesticides, and the limitation and regulation of recreational activities.

Sources of groundwater such as springs and wells should be sited and constructed in order to be protected from surface draining and flooding. Zones of groundwater subtraction should be fenced to prevent public access, kept clean of rubbish and sloped to prevent the collection of pools in wet weather. Animal husbandry should be adequately controlled in such zones.[9]

3.2 Treatment Process

Water treatment processes used in any instance must take into account the quality and nature of the water supply source. The intensity of treatment depends on the degree of contamination of the source water. For contaminated water sources, multiple treatment barriers to the spread of pathogenic organisms are particularly important and should be used to give a high degree of protection and to reduce the reliance on any individual treatment step.

The fundamental goal for water is to protect the consumer from pathogens and impurities in the water that may be offensive or injurious to human health. Urban treatment of water from lowland sources usually consists of 1) a reservoir of storage or pre-disinfection; 2) coagulation, flocculation, and sedimentation (or flotation); 3) filtration; and 4) disinfection. (See Figure 2.1 for a chart on water treatment processes.) A multiple-barrier concept can be adopted for treating surface waters in rural and remote regions. A typical series of processes would include 1) storage, 2) sedimentation or screening, 3) gravel pre-filtration and slow-sand filtration, and 4) disinfection.

3.2.1 Pre-Treatment

Surface waters may be either stored in reservoirs or disinfected before treatment. Impoundment in lakes and or reservoirs improves microbial quality due to sedimentation, lethal effects of UV from sunlight in surface water or starvation and predation. Reductions of fecal indicator bacteria, Salmonella, and enteroviruses are about 99 percent in most modern facilities today.

Pre-disinfection is usual when water is abstracted and treated without storage. It destroys animal life and reduces the numbers of fecal bacteria and pathogens, assists in the removal of algae during coagulation and filtration, as well as removal of ammonia.

Microstraining through very fine screens (~30 micrometer pore diameter) is an effec-

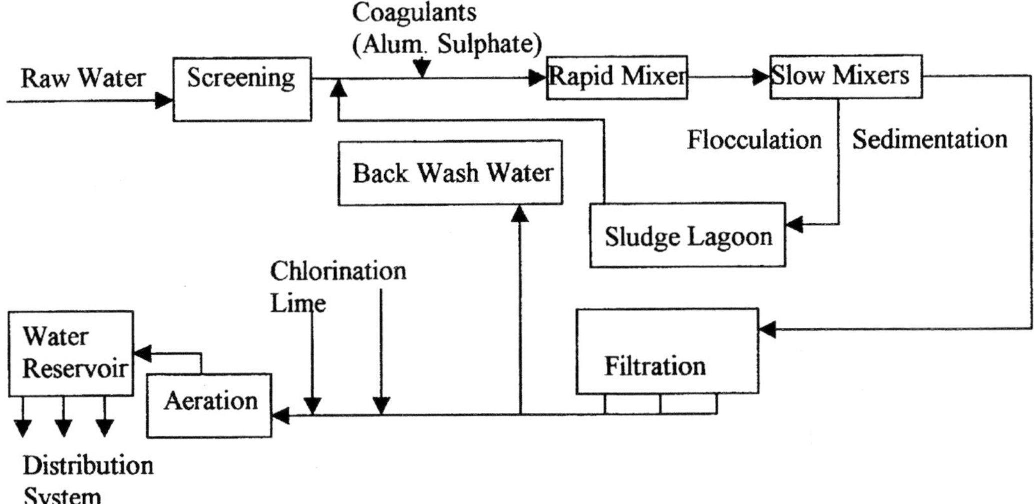

Figure 2.1. Water Treatment Process

tive way of removing many microalgae and zooplanktons that may otherwise clog or even penetrate filters.

Infiltration of raw or partly treated surface water into riverbanks or sand dunes is practiced where water of very high quality is required. This serves as a buffer in case raw river water cannot be used, due to incidences of industrial pollution. However, abstracted water usually needs additional treatment to remove iron or manganese compounds. Detention periods need to be as long as possible to attain the quality approaching that of groundwater. Removal of fecal bacteria and viruses exceeds 99 percent through this method.

3.2.2 Coagulation, Flocculation, and Sedimentation

Coagulation involves the addition of chemicals (e.g. aluminum sulfate, ferrous or ferric sulfate and ferric chloride) to neutralize the charges on particles and facilitate their agglomeration during the slow mixing provided in the flocculation step. Flocs thus formed co-precipitate, absorb, and entrap natural color and mineral particles, and can bring about major reductions in turbidity and in counts of protozoa, bacteria, and viruses. The purpose of sedimentation is to permit submersible floc to be deposited and thus reduce the concentration of suspended solids that must be removed by filters. Among the factors that influence sedimentation are: size, shape, and weight of the floc, viscosity and hence the temperature of water, detention time, number, depth, and areas of the basin, surface overflow rate, velocity of flow, and inlet and outlet design.

3.2.3 Rapid and Slow Sand Filtration

When rapid filtration follows coagulation, its performance in removing microorganisms and turbidity varies through the duration of the run between backwashing. Immediately after backwashing, performance is poor until the bed has compacted. Performance will also deteriorate progressively at the stage when backwashing is needed, as floc may escape through the bed into the treated water. Slow sand filtration is simpler to operate than rapid filtration, as frequent backwashing is not required. It is therefore particularly suitable for developing countries and small rural systems, but is applicable only if sufficient land is available.

3.2.4 Disinfection

Terminal disinfection of piped drinking water supplies serves as the final barrier to the transmission of waterborne bacterial and viral diseases. Disinfectants include chlorine (hypochlorite, chloramines, chlorine dioxide), ozone, and ultraviolet radiation.[9] Drinking water from different sources may contain elements that are detrimental to consumers' health, such as organic or inorganic (e.g., metals) elements. This led to the development in water purification techniques and/or treatments to assure consumers of water safety from the home to the industrial level.

The process of removing water contaminants through the use of water purifiers depends on the purpose of filtration. If the desire is to purify the water of infectious agents such as bacteria and parasites, certain types of mechanical filters are appropriate. On the other hand, if one desires to remove metals (e.g., lead) or minerals (e.g., calcium), resins may be needed for chemical purification of water. If excessive levels of one or more contaminants are found, or one has a compromised immune system that puts him or her at risk for parasitic infections, a water treatment device should be considered.[11] Sedimentation is so far the oldest method of water purification. In sedimentation, water is allowed to stand in protected pools to allow contaminants to settle out. Other methods for water purification are mechanical filtration, ion exchange water purification, distillation, reverse osmosis, aeration filtration, chemical disinfection, coagulation/flocculation, and ozonation.[12] Advanced water purification techniques include membrane purification techniques built with high-tech artificial filters and reverse osmosis systems.

3.3 Water Safety Testing[11,28,29]

People should be concerned with the quality of their drinking water, especially if it comes from a private source. The requirements for a public water supply are summarized as follows:

Public water supplies should:

- not contain organisms that cause disease.
- be sparkling clear and colorless.
- be good tasting, free from odors, and preferably cool.
- be reasonably soft.
- not be corrosive, or capable of forming scales.
- be free from objectionable gases, like hydrogen sulfide.
- be free from objectionable minerals, like lead, iron, manganese.
- be low in cost, plentiful and accessible.

To be assured of the above qualities, water testing is done. The suggested kinds and frequency of common test procedures are given in Table 2.4 (Sample Monitoring Schedule for Water Testing).

Safe levels of drinking water contaminants are regulated by law. Check with your community about what governmental agency has the jurisdiction of enforcing such laws. Table 2.5 is a partial list of contaminants showing the maximum contaminant level goals (MCLGs) and the maximum contaminant

Table 2.4
SAMPLE MONITORING SCHEDULE FOR WATER TESTING

Contaminant	*Minimum Monitoring Frequency*
Acute Contaminants	
Bacteria	Monthly or quarterly, depending on system size and type
Protozoa and Viruses	Continuous monitoring for turbidity, monthly for total coliforms as indicators
Nitrate	Annually
Chronic Contaminants	
Volatile Organics (e.g. benzene)	Ground water systems, annually for 2 consecutive years; surface water systems, annually
Synthetic Organics (e.g. pesticides)	Larger systems, twice in 3 years; smaller systems, once in 3 years
Inorganic/Metals	Groundwater systems, once every 3 years; surface water systems annually
Lead and Copper	Annually
Radionuclides	Once every 4 years
General requirements may differ slightly based on the size or type of drinking water system.	

Source: US Environmental Protection Agency, *Water on Tap: A Consumer's Guide to the Nation's Drinking Water,* EPA 815-K-97. July 1997. Available at http://www.epa.gov/safewater/wot/introtap.html. Accessed April 30, 2002.

levels (MCLs). The values are taken from the US-EPA Form 810-F-94-001, February 1994.

It should be noted that water tests have limitations and water conditions could change as affected by the weather, accidental spills, floods, draughts, and other environmental factors. Therefore, consumers should consult the proper authorities for how often tests should be done at home if they have a private water supply

3.4 Water Safety in Homes[19,21]

The information discussed above is also applicable to households. From a practical viewpoint, house dwellers will find the checklist in Table 2.6 useful in evaluating overall quality of their water supply as they open their faucets daily.

As a concerned consumer getting drinking water from a private source, have your water tested periodically. Get professional help to collect samples and test them. Find out if your local health agency can do the tests free of charge.

Common home water treatments to clean and purify your water supply include: 1) use of activated charcoal media and other media like crystalline quartz, electrokinetic, aluminum titanium silicate (ATS), ion-exchange media; 2) use of filters like micro-pore material filters, sediment trap filters, fluoride-removing filters, and ceramic filters; 3) reverse-osmosis units; and 4) water distillers.

Table 2.5
DRINKING WATER CONTAMINANT LEVELS REGULATED BY THE US FEDERAL GOVERNMENT

	MCLG[1]	*MCL*[2]	*Potential Health Effect From Ingestion of Contaminated Water*	*Source of Water Contamination*
Contaminant	*(mg/1)*[3]	*(mg/1)*	*Contaminated Water*	*Contamination*
A. Coliforms and Infectious Agents				
Total coliform	0/L	0	Gastroenteric disease	Human/animal fecal waste
Viruses	0/L	0	Gastroenteric disease	Human/animal fecal waste
Giardia lambia	0/L	0	Gastroenteric disease	Human/animal fecal waste
B. Inorganic Agents				
Asbestos	7	7	Cancer	Asbestos cement in water pipes
Cadmium	0.005	0.005	Kidney disease	Corrosion of galvanized pipes
Chromium	0.1	0.1	Liver and kidney disease	Mining, natural deposits
Mercury	0.002	0.002	Kidney and nervous system disorders	Crop runoff, natural deposits
Nitrites	1	1	Methemoglobulinemia	Fertilizers, animal waste, natural deposits
Nitrates	10	10	Methemoglobulinemia	Animal waste, septic systems, fertilizers
Fluoride	4	4	Skeletal and tooth fluorosis	Natural deposits, treatment of water
Lead	0	0	Nerve and kidney disease	Soldering, corroded plumbing
Copper	1.3	–	Gastrointestinal disease	Corroded plumbing, natural deposits
Nickel	0.1	0.1	Heart damage	Metal alloys, batteries, chemicals
Cyanide	0.2	0.2	Nerve damage	Mining, fertilizers, electroplating
C. Volatile Organic Agents				
Benzene	0	0.005	Cancer	Pesticides, paints, plastics
Carbon tetrachloride	0	0.005	Cancer	Solvents, industrial by-products
Vinyl chloride	0	0.002	Cancer	Solvents
D. Organic Agents				
Aldicarb	0.001	0	Nervous system injury	Insecticides
Carbofuran	0.04	0.04	Nervous and reproductive system injury	Soil fumigants
Chlordane	0	0.002	Cancer	Termite insecticides
Heptachlor	0	0.004	Cancer	Termite insecticides
Lindane	0.0002	0.0002	Liver, kidney, and immune system injury	Garden and lumber insecticides
PCBs	0	0.0005	Cancer	Coolant oils; plasticizers

Continued on next page

Table 2.5–*Continued*

Contaminant	*(mg/1)*[3]	*(mg/1)*	*Contaminated Water*	*Contamination*
Toluene	1	1	Liver, kidney and nerve disease	Gasoline additives
Xylenes	10	10	Liver, kidney and nerve disease	Gasoline by-products

1. MCLG, Maximum Contaminant Level Goal
2. MCL, are Maximum Contaminant Level
3. All units are mg/1 (milligrams per liter) unless otherwise indicated

*Asbestos levels are measured in units of millions of fibers per liter.

Source: Barzilay, J. I., Weinberg, W. G., and Eley, W. J.: *The Water We Drink,* Piscataway, N.J., Rutgers University Press, 1999.

Before investing in any method, consult the health authority that is recommended as a result of your water tests. None of the methods will remove all contaminants. There are advantages and disadvantages of each. For example, a good filter of the correct pores is needed to remove Cryptosporidium. However, chlorination of water does not destroy this parasite. Hardness of water has to be treated according to the amount of the minerals, and turbidity removal methods will depend on how polluted and cloudy the water is. Activated carbon filters remove most of the chlorine taste and heavy metals.

4.0 WATER SAFETY SYSTEMS IN INDUSTRY AND INSTITUTIONS

4.1 Agrifood Production

The agriculture industry is one of the biggest users of water. For that reason it is important to ensure the safety, security, and sustainability of water supplies.

4.2 Food Processing/ Manufacturing

Water is one of the most important factors in food processing operations. It is a major component of most foods; it serves as the vehicle for transfer of power and heat; and for conveying materials throughout the plant and in other food processing operations. Its use stems from the preparation of raw materials and equipment to its use as an ingredient in the food product, and finally in the final stages of the operation. Cleaning and sanitation in food plants also requires the generation of enough water, as well as that used by personnel for drinking, washing, and flushing of toilets.

In the food industry, water quality is a primary concern. There are certain criteria and guidelines to serve as the basis for quality assessment in food manufacturing. For instance, water hardness must be controlled when used in food preparation and in the processing of many commodities. Hard water causes many problems in food operations. Most important is the scale formation in

Table 2.6
PROBLEMS WITH WATER QUALITY AND SUGGESTED REMEDIES

Problems with Water Quality	*Test for*
Well too near a landfill	Total dissolved solids, pH, volatile organic compounds, heavy metals
Well too near a septic system	Total coliform bacteria, nitrate, total dissolved solids, chloride, sodium, sulfates, detergents
Corroded plumbing	Corrosiveness, pH, lead, iron, zinc
Lead pipes or solder	Lead, copper, zinc, pH
Infant in household	Nitrates
Illness from drinking water	Total coliform bacteria, nitrates, sulfates
Gasoline smell or taste to the water	Hydrocarbon scan, aromatic organic chemicals
Musty, earthy smell or taste to the water	Total coliform bacteria, iron
Rotten-egg smell to water	Hydrogen sulfide, sulfur bacteria
Salty-tasting water	Total dissolved chlorides, sodium
Bitter-tasting water	Nitrates, sulfates
Dirty appearing water	Turbidity, sediment, organic matter
White scale on fixtures, or soap scum	Water hardness, iron
Greenish-blue stains on laundry and/or fixtures	Copper
Brownish-black stains on laundry or fixtures and/or black flakes in the water	Manganese
Reddish stains on laundry and/or fixtures	Iron

Source: Bower, L. M. *Creating a Healthy Household.* Bloomington, The Healthy House Institute, 2000.

pipelines and boiler tubes, and as deposits on equipment.[15]

Water for cleaning the equipment and the factory must also be accounted for, and the most important quality factor for water is the microbial load that may be present.

4.3 Food Service Establishments

Provision for ensuring sanitary water supply in food establishments has been formulated to safeguard public health. Food establishments such as restaurants, fast food chains, cafeteria, canteens and diners, must comply with sanitary guidelines set by local authorities. Guidelines set may differ from country to country. The difference in some aspects of the guidelines is brought about by factors such as socioeconomic differences, water supply, and cultural differences of countries.

General provisions with regard to ensuring water safety and quality of food establishments are the following:

- Water supply shall be adequate and must be potable. To ensure potability, all sources of water should be certified by a local health agency.
- Hot and cold running water must be provided in all areas where food is prepared or equipment or utensils are washed.
- In the advent of a shortage or lack of drinking water, the water to be used should be transported from an approved source and must be handled and dispensed in a sanitary manner. It may be stored in a separate tank, reservoir or containers approved by local health agencies.
- Bottled or packaged drinking water should be handled, stored, and protect-

ed from contamination. It should come from an approved source and should be dispensed from the original container filled by the supplier.

- Bottled water should be served to consumers in bottles directly and not already dispensed in glass.
- Ice, used for any purpose, should be made from water from an approved source and should be transported, distributed, and packed in a sanitary manner.

5.0 RECREATIONAL WATER FACILITIES

The World Health Organization has been concerned with the safety of recreational water facilities due to the increase in outbreaks in the decade, 1988 to 1998, as observed in Table 2.7. While the data are for cryptosporidiosis only, it gives the reader an idea of the extent of the problem, considering that the number is often a low estimate of actual cases, most of which are unreported. Other microorganisms are involved in contaminating recreational waters, such as *Giardia lamblia, E. coli, Shigella* spp. and *Cyclospora.*

Since water in swimming pools and spas involves sharing water with many people, it may contain various body fluids, dirt, soil, fecal matter, etc. Fecal matter is introduced when someone has accidentally released stool or residual fecal matter is washed into the pool. This is likely to occur when there are diaper-aged and toddler-aged children. Accidental swallowing of infected feces is the primary mode of transmitting enteric pathogens. Even with adequate chlorination, not all pathogens get killed. *Cryptosporidium* is highly resistant to normal chlorine concentrations.

In rivers, streams, beaches, and lakes, contaminated sewage, soils and human and animal feces that contain harmful pathogens flow into these bodies of water. Surface water is generally more at risk than ground water. The oocysts of *Cryptosporidium* are very resistant to adverse conditions of the environment and can stay dormant for months.

Use of ozone instead of chlorine as a disinfectant, followed by filtration, will help prevent the outbreak of cryptosporidiosis. Radiation and ultraviolet rays are also effective.

With regard to other enteric pathogens, adjusting the dose of chlorination, frequent, regular changes of water and adding fresh disinfectants will be adequate.

Prevention is in the hands of the individuals and their families. It is best to avoid crowded recreational facilities, especially when outbreaks are more prevalent in warm weather. Pregnant women and individuals with suppressed immune systems should avoid such places.

Since transmission is by oral-fecal route, or by person to person, or from animal to person contact, personal hygiene and general sanitation, practices such as proper disposal of excreta, and the like, should be religiously observed by everyone.

6.0 WATER SAFETY DURING TRAVEL

Water safety is also an issue during travel. Contaminated food and drink are the major sources of stomach and intestinal illness while traveling. Travelers' diarrhea (TD) is the most common illness during travel. It is acquired through ingestion of fecal contaminated food or water, or both. No data have been presented to support noninfectious causes of TD, such as changes in diet, jet lag, altitude, and

Table 2.7
OUTBREAKS OF CRYPTOSPORIDIOSIS IN RECREATIONAL WATER FACILITIES

Facility	*Location*	*Year*	*Disinfectant Used*	*No. of Cases Estimated/Confirmed*
Pool	Doncaster UK	1998	Chl	[a]/79*
Pool	Los Angeles County	1988	Chl	44/5
Pool	British Columbia	1990	Chl	66/23
Pool	Gloucestershire, UK	1992	O/Chl	[a]/13
Water slide	Idaho	1992	Chl	500/[a]
Pool (wave)	Oregon	1992	Chl	[a]/52
Pool (motel)	Wisconsin	1993	Chl	51/22
Pool (motel)	Missouri	1994	Chl	101/26
Lake	New Jersey	1994	None	2,070/46
Pool	New South Wales	1994	Chl	[a]/70
Pool	Kansas	1995	[a]	101/26
Water park	Georgia	1995	Chl	2,470/62
Water park	California	1996	Chl	3,000/29
Pool	Andover, UK	1996	Chl	8/[a]
Lake	Indiana	1996	None	3/[a]
River	NW England and Wales	1997	None	27/7
Pool	SW England and Wales	1997	Chl & O	[a]/9
Fountain	Minnesota	1997	Sand filter	369/73
Three pools	Canberra, Australia	1998	[a]	[a]/210
Pool	Oregon	1998	[a]	51/8
Pools	Queensland	1997	[a]	129/[a]
Pools	New South Wales	1998	[a]	370/[a]
Pools	Hutt Valley, New Zealand	1998	[a]	[a]/171

[a] No data available. Chl, chlorine; O, ozone.
Source: CDC. Cryptosporidium parvum. *Emerging Infectious Diseases.* Available at http://www.cdc.gov/ncidod/EID/vol5no.4/carpenter. Accessed July 1, 2002.

fatigue. Existing evidence indicates that in all but a few instances, such as drug-induced or pre-existing gastrointestinal disorders, an infectious agent or agents can cause diarrhea in travelers. However, even with the application of the best existing methods for detecting bacteria, viruses, and parasites, 20 to 50 percent of cases of TD remain without recognized etiologies.[16] TD is slightly more common in young adults than in older people. The typical symptoms of travelers' diarrhea are diarrhea, nausea, bloating, urgency and malaise. TD usually lasts from 3 to 7 days. It is rarely life threatening.[16]

There are four possible approaches to prevention of TD: 1) instruction regarding food and beverage consumption, 2) immunization, 3) use of non-antimicrobial medications, and 4) use of prophylactic antimicrobial drugs, but the best way to prevent TD is by paying meticulous attention to choice of food and beverage.[16]

7.0 GUIDELINES FOR DRINKING WATER

The World Health Organization (WHO) estimates that 80 percent of all sickness in the world is attributable to unsafe water and sanitation.[3] Each year more than ten million people die from water-related diseases.[7] More people die each year from unsafe water than from all forms of violence, including war.[18] No single type of intervention has greater overall impact upon the national development and public health than the provision of safe drinking water and the proper disposal of human excreta.[7] About a third of the population of the developing world is infected with intestinal worms that can be controlled through better water hygiene and sanitation. These parasites can lead to malnutrition, anemia, and retarded growth.[8] Of the thirty-seven major diseases in developing countries, twenty-one are water and sanitation related.[9]

The levels of contaminants in drinking water are seldom high enough to cause acute (immediate) health effects. In 1974, the US Congress passed the Safe Drinking Water Act that requires the US Environmental Protection Agency (EPA) to determine the safe levels of chemicals in drinking water, which do, or may, cause health problems. These non-enforceable levels, based solely on possible health risk and exposure, are called Maximum Contaminant Level Goals (MCLGs). For carbofuran, a possible water contaminant, the MCLG, has been set at 0.04.[18] According to the EPA, a short period of exposure to acrylamide at levels above the MCLG can cause damage to the nervous system, weakness, and incoordination in the legs. Furthermore, lifetime exposure at levels above the MCLG can cause further damage to the nervous system and paralysis and cancer.[19]

Contaminants are more likely to cause chronic health effects that occur long after repeated exposure to small amounts of a chemical. Evidence relating chronic health effects to specific drinking water contaminants is limited. In the absence of exact scientific information, scientists predict the likely adverse effects of chemicals in drinking water using human data from clinical reports, epidemiological studies, and laboratory animal studies.[20]

There are several factors that contribute to the contamination of water. Among these are contamination of distribution pipelines which may arise from intermittent water supply, low water pressure in the distribution network, leaking pipes, inadequate wastewater collection systems, cross-contamination due to unsanitary design practices, incorrect disinfection methods or misuse of disinfectants, and others. Another possible source of water contamination is the residual acrylamide after water treatment. Acrylamide is an organic solid of white, odorless, flake-like crystals. It is used as a clarifier during water treatment. When added to water, acrylamide coagulates and traps suspended solids for easier removal, but some acrylamide does not coagulate and thus remains in the water.[19]

7.1 Standards for Drinking Water

7.1.1 Standards for Natural Mineral Water

The standards for drinking water include physical, chemical, and microbiological parameters. Physical parameters of water that are regularly tested and of prime importance include color, taste, odor, turbidity, pH, hardness, and amount of solids present. Aesthetic parameters such as color, taste, and odor are not considered immediate health threats, however, consumers have established them to be a primary basis for water acceptability. Furthermore, some parameters serve as warning devices for potential hazards and determine the potability (drinkability) of water.

7.1.1.1 COLOR. Water should be clear and colorless for it to be acceptable for the general public. Presence of even the slightest discoloration is considered an objectionable characteristic that would make water psychologically unacceptable. Discoloration in water can be attributed to the presence of iron and magnesium, or to the presence of humus, peat molecules, and plankton, and the pH level of the water.

Color values of water are measured and expressed as True Color Units (TCUs). It is established that colors above 15 TCU are detectable by the naked eye. Acceptable limits of color values may vary according to local circumstances. The WHO has established that color levels below 15 TCU are acceptable for most consumers. At present, no health-based guideline value for color has been proposed.

7.1.1.2 TASTE. Sensory evaluation is used in determining the acceptability of water. It has no scientific value; nevertheless it plays an important role in the acceptability of drinking water. Objectionable taste is likely to be found in raw untreated water. This is attributed to the natural biological processes such as degradation of waste and algae. Contaminants that bring about objectionable taste are classified as either organic or inorganic. Common inorganic substances that affect the taste and odor are agricultural and industrial wastes.

Offensive taste of water from streams and lakes (surface water) is attributed to biological processes mentioned earlier. Offensive taste of water coming from underground basins or groundwater is attributed to human activities such as landfill and septic tank leaching, as well as sewage treatment.

There is no established health-based guideline for taste. However, it is generally recognized that offensive taste should not be present in water for it to be acceptable to consumers.

A common consumer complaint about water is the "chlorine taste." The water disinfecting treatment brings this about. In order to eliminate this problem, strict watershed supervision must be implemented during treatment. This will ensure that the amount of chlorine added in treating water will be of lower threshold and undetectable to consumers.

7.1.1.3 ODOR. Detectable odors in water are an indication of pollution or improper water treatment. Offensive odors in water are attributed to natural, biological, and chemical contaminants and processes.

A common odor in water is described as the "rotten egg smell." This phenomenon is attributed to the formation of hydrogen sulfide gas by the action of anaerobic bacteria on organic sulfur compounds.

Odor is measured through organoleptic means. Like any aesthetic parameter, there is no established health guideline for it. Acceptable levels of odors present in water differ from country to country and individual tolerances.

7.1.1.4 TURBIDITY. Defined as a measure of fine suspended colloidal matter in water, turbidity in drinking water is attributed to the presence of clay, silt non-living particles, planktons, and other microorganisms. The presence of turbidity is an indication of inadequate treatment or from suspension of sediments in the distribution process.

Turbidity in water does not only decrease consumer acceptability but also poses a health risk. High levels of turbidity can protect disease-causing microorganisms during water disinfection. Coagulation, sedimentation, and filtration remove particles that cause turbidity in water.

The level of turbidity in water is determined using the nephelometric method. It has been established that turbidity values less than 5 nephelometric turbidity units are usually acceptable for consumers, although levels may vary with local circumstances. Due to its protective ability of colloidal particles to harmful microorganisms, it is recommended that turbidity levels be kept as low as possible.

7.1.1.5 Hardness. Water hardness is defined as the sum of polyvalent ions, such as calcium and magnesium concentration expressed in $CaCO_3$. The harder the water, the more polyvalent ions present. Public acceptability of the degree of water hardness differs from one community to another. Taste thresholds for calcium and magnesium differ in range. Calcium has a range of 100 to 300 mg/L $CaCO_3$, while magnesium has a higher threshold level compared to calcium. Hard water is simply water that contains two minerals–calcium and magnesium. They make the water hard to develop a sudsy lather. Water is considered "hard" if it measures more than 120 parts per million or 7.0 grains per gallon. Although hardness does not affect the safety of the water, some customers may find it to be inconvenient. Hard water causes scale deposition in distribution systems, excessive soap consumption, and "scum" formation. On the other hand, soft water which contains 100mg/L $CaCO_3$ may have low buffering capacity and may be more corrosive to pipes.[9]

7.1.1.6 Dissolved Solids. Dissolved solids present in water are classified as organic salts and organic matter, which come from rocks and soil. The amount of dissolved solids in drinking water has an important effect on water quality and taste. The presence of high levels of dissolved solids is objectionable to consumers because it causes scaling in pipes and other water facilities, while low levels of dissolved solids may be unacceptable to some consumers because of its flat and insipid taste. A range of 600 mg/L to 1200 mg/L is considered acceptable to consumers.

7.1.1.7 pH. pH is defined as the logarithmic base 10 of the reciprocal of hydrogen ion concentration activity expressed in moles per liter. Although pH has no direct impact on the health of consumers, it is one of the necessary parameters that need to be analyzed to ensure water quality. Control of pH in drinking water is necessary in ensuring satisfactory water disinfection and clarification. A pH reading of less than 7.0 facilitates the optimum action of chlorine during the disinfection process. The pH of the water entering the distribution system is controlled in order to minimize corrosion and scale formation in pipes.

The WHO has established that a pH range of 6.5 to 9.5 is the optimum pH range of water. An extremely acidic and basic pH reading in water is an indication of faulty treatment or accidental spills. Determination of pH readings is done with a pH meter.

7.2 Standards of Quality for Commercially Bottled Drinking Water

There is a growing concern for the safety and quality of drinking water because of several major outbreaks involving water. At present, many people are increasingly looking toward bottled water as a means of meeting some or all of their daily water needs. Water is classified as bottled if it is sealed in a sanitary container, sold for human consumption, and meets all applicable standards. Bottled water must be calorie-free and sugar-free, and it cannot contain artificial sweeteners or additives.[21] Consumers have several reasons for buying bottled drinking water, such as taste, convenience, or fashion, but for many, safety and potential health benefits are important considerations.

The World Health Organization (WHO) publishes *Guidelines for Drinking Water Quali-*

ty which many countries use as the basis to establish their own national standards.[22]

8.0 WATER SAFETY IN EMERGENCIES

Consumers have grown understandably concerned about the safety of drinking water supplies. We have witnessed contaminations due to natural disasters, catastrophes that disrupt electricity, and terrorist activities. They are just a few circumstances that may lead to the contamination of drinking water, thus leading to limited supply of safe drinking water (see also Chapter 13).[23]

Unless absolutely certain that the water is not contaminated, one should purify all water before using it for drinking, preparing food, brushing teeth, or washing dishes. When emergency disinfection is necessary, examine the physical condition of the water. Disinfectants are less effective in cloudy water. There are two general methods by which small quantities of water during emergencies can be effectively disinfected. One method is boiling. It is the most positive method by which water can be made bacterially safe to drink. However, boiling water containing certain contaminants, such as lead or nitrate, will increase the concentration and the potential risk. Another method is chemical treatment. The two chemicals commonly used are chlorine and iodine. Chlorine and iodine are somewhat effective in protecting against exposure to *Giardia,* but may not be effective in controlling *Cryptosporidium.*[23]

9.0 ENSURING WATER AVAILABILITY AND SAFETY IN THE FUTURE

Water is unevenly distributed. While people in some parts of the world pile up sandbags to control seasonal floods or struggle to dry out after severe storms, others either shrivel and die like their crops and their livestock before them, or move on as environmental refugees. In Canada, which has about the same amount of water as China but less than 2.5 percent of its population, the resource has been labeled "blue gold." In parched Botswana, dominated by the Kalahari Desert, water is so precious that the national currency is called *pula*–"rain" in the Setswana language.[24]

According to *Time* Magazine, 2001[2], distribution of the world's water is as follows: Canada (7%), Russia (11%), China (7%), Brazil (17%), Indonesia (6%), Bangladesh (6%), US (6%), India (5%), and others (35%).

In Africa, although the proportion of people who have access to a flush toilet connected to a sewer system increased slightly from 11 to 13 percent, there has been no progress in terms of the percentage of the population with access to sewer connections over the 1990s, which represents only 20 percent of the new African population (169 people).[25]

In Asia, the proportion of people with access to a household sewer connection increased from 13 percent in 1990 to 18 percent in 2000, and there has also been a considerable increase in the total number of people with access to improved sanitation. However, of the 502 million new inhabitants of this region, only 241 million (or 48 percent) gained access to a sewer connection.[25]

Latin America and the Caribbean have the highest rates of sanitation coverage among the developing regions. Of the 79 million new inhabitants in this region, 68 million (or 68 percent) gained access to a sewer connection.

Managing our water is a twenty-first century challenge. Ensuring water safety in the future means reducing the onset of waterborne diseases and, in turn, fueling the economy, however, there are things that need to be addressed to attain such objectives. Among these are to encourage government, non-governmental organizations, the private sector, and donors to review their sanitation policies, and the effective implementation of sanitary programs in local communities and at the international level (better treatment and delivery systems). This means setting effective and feasible guidelines to water quality, which is as much as possible, accessible to manufacturers and consumers (cost-effective drinking water standards). There should also be strict monitoring of the standards set which means a regular checking of public water processing facilities. Industries should also be responsible to provide safe water by adhering to the standards set and making sure they are efficiently implemented in the facility. If at all possible, the government or any active organization should provide training programs or orientations to small-scale industries to ensure water safety.

In the home, water safety can best be applied by attaining inputs from schools. Schools could provide information dissemination campaigns for such purposes. Other programs include: improved source-water protection by integrating local economic development and land use with environmental and drinking water protection efforts; address infrastructure needs and the cost of replacement to ensure that water systems have the capacity to meet the challenges of public health protection; increased research, i.e. engage in public-private partnership on research that will answer the most pressing public health issues and prepare for emerging contaminant threats; to develop better, cheaper, and faster analytical methods to improve their ability to identify health threats; and create more effective and flexible water treatment methods.

10.0 POLICIES AND GUIDELINES FOR WATER SAFETY

The World Health Organization is a specialized agency of the United Nations that is dedicated to upgrading public health. The agency has established sets of guidelines and standards that are internationally recognized which promote the improvement of public health. One of these is the International Guidelines for Water Quality.

Establishment of these standards was made possible by the consolidated efforts of countries such as Belgium, Canada, Denmark, Finland, France, Germany, Italy, Japan, The Netherlands, Norway, Poland, Sweden, United Kingdom, and the United States of America, as well as organizations such as the Danish Agency for Development Assistance (DANIDA), the Norwegian Agency for Development Cooperation (NORAD), the Swedish International Development Cooperation Agency (SIDA), and Japan's Official Development Assistance (ODA). In 1984, the WHO published the *Guidelines for Drinking Water.* With the change in technology and science, new information on potential health risks of contamination in drinking water became available. The WHO then revised the *Guidelines* and published the revised edition in 1993.

This document gives the global perspective of the state of drinking water quality. It summarizes the common water problems encountered, and recommends solutions. Recommended levels of physical, microbial, and chemical contaminants established by the WHO are also contained in this document. The recommended values concerning

Table 2.8
EUROPEAN UNION COUNTRIES

Australia	Belgium	Denmark
France	Finland	Germany
Ireland	Italy	Luxembourg
Netherlands	Northern Ireland	Portugal
Spain	Sweden	United Kingdom (UK)

water quality are expressed as Guideline Values (GVs).

WHO emphasizes that these GVs are not considered as formal standards or strict regulatory limits. They are 1) to be used as a conceptual framework for the establishment of local drinking water standards; and 2) to assist in developing alternative control procedures where implementation of drinking water standards is not feasible.

In developing national drinking standards based on these guideline values, it is necessary to take into account the differences in geographical, socioeconomic, dietary, and other conditions prevailing in a specific locality or nation. Therefore, national standards for locality or country differ appreciably from the guideline values set by WHO.

11.0 SOURCES OF INFORMATION ON WATER SAFETY

11.1 European Union

The European Union, or EU, formerly known as the European Community, or EC, is considered to be the Health Authority in Europe. It is composed of fifteen countries (Table 2.8) and was established to promote and enhance the economic and social cooperation between member countries.

Unlike the WHO, the EU issues drinking water standards that are applicable directly to each member nation and should be strictly enforced by all fifteen countries. The standards set are relatively the same as that of WHO standards.

11.2 The Americas

In North America, the agency responsible for establishing rules and guidelines for drinking water quality and distribution is the Environmental Protection Agency (EPA). Unlike the EU, the EPA alone cannot enforce the standards, but it is a joint effort. This is due to the differences in the economic and environmental conditions, as well as the water supply, available in every state. Enforced standards in one state may not be applicable to another state due to differences in available resources and other factors mentioned previously.[26]

REVIEW QUESTIONS

1. Define important terms (see text or the Glossary):
   a. Radioactive contaminants
   b. Microstraining
   c. Acrylamide
   d. Disinfection
   e. Coliforms
   f. Maximum Contaminant Level Goals (MCLGs)
2. Which agencies set the water safety guidelines in your country?

3. What are usual microbial contaminants in water? Chemical contaminants in water?
4. How can one be sure of the microbial and chemical safety of water?
5. What are the precautions one must take to be assured of water safety during travel?
6. What are the possible dangers of water safety in recreational facilities?
7. What are the standards for bottled water?
8. What are the steps one must take to be ensured of water safety during emergencies?
9. Which agencies safeguard water safety in your community?
10. What are the steps a family can take to be assured of water safety in their home?

REFERENCES

1. United Nations Department for Policy Coordination and Sustainable Development: *Critical Trends–Global Change and Sustainable Development,* pp. 43–56, New York, UN, 1997.
2. Bird, M. Dried Out, *Time Magazine,* pp. 50–53, May 14, 2001
3. Water and Sanitation for Health Project, sponsored by the US Agency for International Development, 1993: Lessons Health in Water, Sanitation and Health". Battling Waterborne Illnesses in the Sea of 950 Million, *The Washington Post,* February 17, 1997.
4. From the Health Files, *Waterborne Diseases in British Columbia, Health File # 49a,* February 2000. Available at http://www.hlth.gov.bc.ca/hlthfile/file_49a.html. Accessed May 23, 2002.
5. National Environmental Education and Training Foundation: *NEETF's Guide to Consumer Confidence Reports on Drinking Water Quality.* Available at http://www.waterqualityreports.org/safety.html. Accessed May 23, 2002.
6. Moyer, N.P.: *Microbial Risks from Sources Other than Water,* WQTC Presentation, 1995.
7. Moyer, N.P. *Microbial Risks Presentation,* 1995.
8. Chan, M.S. The global burden of intestinal nematode infections fifty years on. *Parasitology Today, 13* (11): 438–443, 1997.
9. WHO. *Guidelines for Drinking Water Quality,* 2nd ed. Vol. 1–Recommendations: 8–29, Geneva, WHO, 1993. Available at http://www.who.int/water_sanitation_health. Accessed May 23, 2001.
10. WHO. *Report of the Regional Director on the Work of WHO in the Western Pacific Region: July 1, 2000–June 30, 2001,* Philippines, WHO, June 2001.
11. Barzilay, J. I., Weinberg, W. G., and Eley, W. J. *The Water We Drink,* Piscataway, N.J., Rutgers University Press, 1999.
12. Lewis, S. *The Sierra Club Guide to Safe Drinking Water,* San Francisco, Sierra Club, 1996.
13. U.S. Environmental Protection Agency. *Water on Tap: A Consumer's Guide to the Nation's Drinking Water, EPA 815-K-97.* July 1997. Available at http://www.epa.gov/safewater/wot/introtap.html. Accessed April 30, 2002.
14. Federal Emergency Management Agency. *Locating Safe Drinking Water.* Available at http://www.fema.gov./rwr/water.htm. Accessed April 30, 2002.
15. Gould, W.A. *CGMP's Food Plant Sanitation.* 2nd ed. 180, Baltimore, CTI, 1994.
16. National Center for Infectious Diseases. *Food and Water Precautions and Travelers' Diarrhea Prevention,* December 18, 2000. Available at http://www.cdc.gov/travel/foodwater.htm. Accessed June 23, 2002.
17. WHO. *Fact Sheet: Water and Sanitation,* WHO, Geneva, November 1996. Available at http://www.who.int. Accessed April 13, 2002.
18. *USA Today* Snapshots, June 7, 2001.
19. US EPA. *Consumer Fact Sheet on Acrylamide,* May 22, 2002. Available at http://www.epa.gov/safewater/dwh/c-voc/acrylami.html. Accessed May 23, 2002.
20. Zaslow, S. and Herman, G. *Fact Sheet: Disease Statistics for Various Activities.* North Carolina Cooperative Extension Service, 1992.
21. Mehta, A. R., Lemley, A. T., and Schwartz, J. J. *Drinking Water Alternative: Bottled Water,* Fact

Sheet No. 11, New York, Cornell University, 1999. Available at http://www.cce.cornell.edu/factsheets/. Accessed May 23, 2002.
22. WHO. *Fact Sheet No. 256: Bottled Drinking Water,* Geneva, WHO, October 2000. Available at http://www.who.int. Accessed May 23, 2002.
23. US EPA. *Groundwater and Drinking Water. Emergency Disinfections of Drinking Water,* 810-F-93-002, July 1993. Available at http://www.epa.gov/ogwdw000/faq/emerg.html. Accessed April 13, 2002.
24. Centers for Disease Control (CDC). *Water Related Disease Outbreaks. Annual Summary 1983.* CDC, Public Health Service, US DHHS, Atlanta, 1983.
25. WHO. *Global Water Supply and Sanitation Assessment 2000 Report,* Geneva, WHO, October 23, 2001. Available at http://www.int. Accessed January 30, 2002.
26. Environmental Protection Agency (EPA). *The Safe Drinking Water Act: 25 Years of Progress.* US EPA, 1999.
27. Bower, L. M. *Creating a Healthy Household.* Bloomington, The Healthy House Institute. 2000.
28. Longree, C., and Armbruster, G. *Quantity Food Sanitation,* 5th ed. New York, John Wiley & Sons. 1996.
29. Ritchie, I., and Martin S. J. *The Healthy Home Kit.* Chicago, Real Estate Education Co., 1995.

Chapter 3

FOOD SAFETY SYSTEMS

1.0 INTRODUCTION

Many successful companies have succeeded in promoting food safety for their companies and for their suppliers. This chapter highlights a training method of going step-by-step from the 5 S Good Housekeeping System (sort, systemize, sweep, standardize, and self-discipline), to Good Agricultural Practices (GAP)/Good Hygienic Practices (GHP)/and Good Manufacturing Practices (GMP) before attempting to introduce Hazard Analysis Critical Control Point (HACCP) as shown in Figure 3.1. This method has proven very helpful in that the workers go from a relatively simple 5S program before attempting to go to the other more complex food safety systems. Through this gradual method, the workers do not develop an aversion for food safety systems, but rather they identify with them and make important contributions. By the time HACCP is introduced to the factories, even the casual employees should have first been made aware of 5S, GAP/GMP/GHP if the system is expected to succeed. After all, food safety has to be considered by all members of the organization from the managers to the workers, not just a set of rules and regulations, but also more a culture, a habit, and a way of life.

2.0 THE NEED FOR FOOD SAFETY SYSTEMS

2.1 Key Factors that Influence Food Safety Policy

The rate a company adapts to a food safety system is usually influenced by the country's food safety policies. Food safety policies, in turn, may be influenced by several key factors including the increasing cost of foodborne illness, the increase in public interest in food safety, the changing nature of foodborne illness, and the current complexity of the food supply, and the increase in volume and value of world trade.

2.1.1 Increasing Cost of Foodborne Illness

Foodborne illness is a significant public health burden worldwide. The United States estimates that approximately 76 million illnesses, 325,000 hospitalizations, and 5,000 deaths cost this most powerful nation an approximate total of $8.3 billion, annually.[1]

Most developing countries do not have such statistics, but food poisoning cases involving hundreds per reported case involving children are quite common. The World Health Organization has estimated that in 1999, 1.8 million children under five years of age died of diarrheal diseases traceable to food and water.

2.1.2 Increase in Public Interest in Food Safety

People worldwide are now more knowledgeable and demand national food safety policies. Industry and government therefore are pressured to respond to such public concerns. Consequently, developments in analytical technology now make possible the detection of minute amounts of contaminants, and advances in information technology contribute to broader communication worldwide about foodborne illnesses.

2.1.3 The Changing Nature of Foodborne Illness

New emerging pathogens have surfaced in the United States, Canada, Europe, and

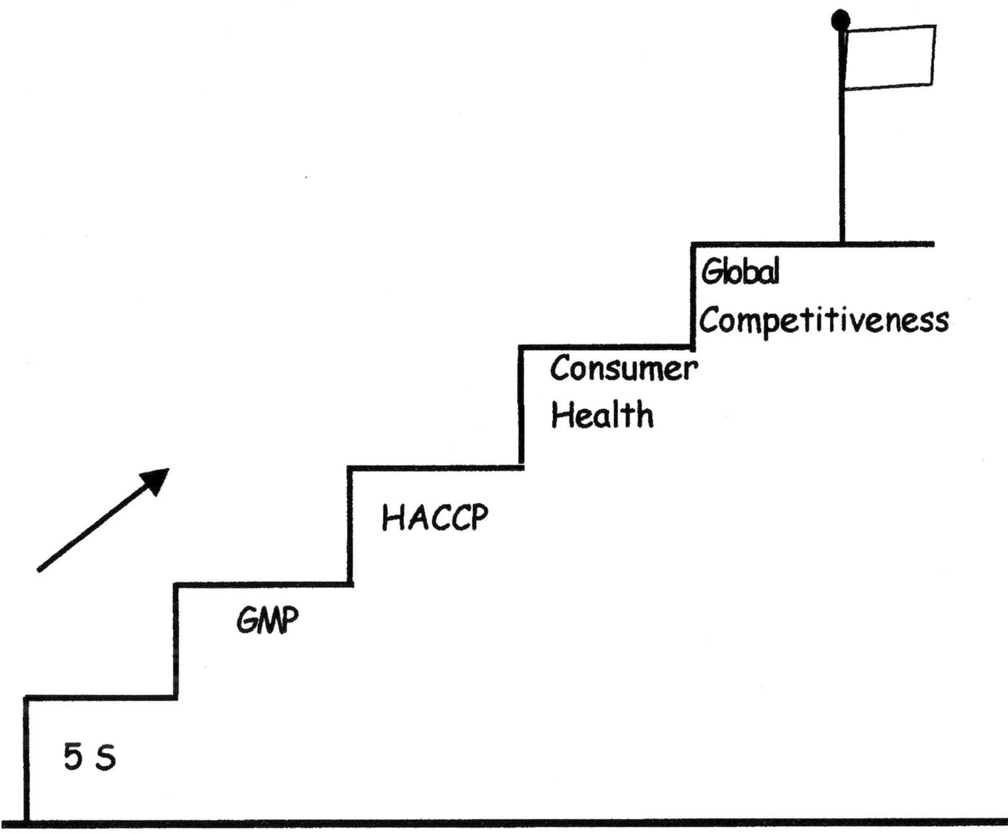

Figure 3.1. Global Competitiveness Through Different Levels of Food Safety Systems

Japan. Three decades ago we had not heard of *Escherichia coli* O157:H7. In fact, we used to consider *E. coli* not as a pathogen in its own right but as an indicator microorganism. Today, *E. coli* has come to the fore as a significant pathogen that is changing the course of the dairy and meat industries, as well as formerly "safe" products such as fruit juices and fresh cut fruits.

We are also made aware by current studies[2] that foodborne illness is responsible not just for acute illness (diarrhea, nausea, vomiting, and abdominal pain), but for chronic illness as well. *Campylobacter* infections are being linked with Guillain-Barre Syndrome, an ascending paralysis; Salmonella with endocarditis (infection of heart valve), endoarteritis (infection of large blood vessels), and osteomyelitis (infection of the bone). These and other emerging pathogens are discussed in greater detail in Chapter 5.

The use of antibiotics and hormones in animal husbandry has led to the development of resistant strains such as the multiple drug resistance of *Salmonella Typhimurium* DT 104 and the flouroquinolone resistance of *Campylobacter*.[3]

Also, as mentioned earlier, another factor is the increase in susceptible individuals such as immune-compromised people, the young, the elderly, and allergic individuals.

2.1.4 The Current Complexity of the Food Supply

The demand for fresher foods includes minimally processed, or just refrigerated but convenient food, organic food without any preservatives, and the popularity of eating away from home.

2.1.5 Increase in International Trade

International trade now makes available food produced halfway around the world. What used to be prepared for smaller communities is now marketed worldwide.

3.0 5S GOOD HOUSEKEEPING SYSTEM[4,5,6]

5S traces its name to the first letters of the five elements of this system. Table 3.1 gives the elements in Japanese, English. As shown in the table, in Japanese these are *Seiri, Seiton, Seiso, Seiketsu,* and *Shitsuke.* In English the five elements are *Sort, Systematize, Sweep, Standardize,* and *Self-discipline.* The system has been successfully applied to many manufacturing establishments resulting in a clean and organized workplace contributing to the improvement in productivity and overall quality of goods and services. The 5S System is also based on the idea of *kaizen,* the Japanese term for continuous improvement. It is therefore easy to see how useful this basic housekeeping system is to the practice of Good Agricultural Practices (GAP), Good Manufacturing Practices (GMP), and/or Good Hygienic Practices (GHP).

The elements of the 5S System are as follows:

3.1 *Seiri*/Sort

Remove unnecessary items in the workplace. Before starting work, only those needed for the task should be on the workbench. This principle is applicable to a workbench, a room, or the entire processing plant.

3.2 *Seiton*/Systematize

Arrange in a systematic manner items necessary for the job to be done so that when an item is needed, it is easily retrieved without losing time to locate it. Principles for this phase are as follows:

- Follow the First-In-First-Out (FIFO) rule.
- Assign each item a dedicated location.
- All things should be in a proper place and with proper labeling.
- Place all items in a visible area in order to minimize searching.
- Place all items in a systematic location so that they can easily be reached and handled safely.
- Separate exclusive tools from those for common use.
- Place frequently used tools near the user.

3.3 Seiso/Sweep

Clean the workplace. The task includes checking all machines, equipment, and tools

Table 3.1
5S TRANSLATION

Japanese	*English*	*Your Language*
Seiri	Sort	
Seiton	Systematize	
Seiso	Sweep	
Seiketsu	Standardize	
Shitsuke	Self-discipline	

to make sure they are in good order and working condition. Guidelines for implementing this step are as follows:

1. Practice cleaning the workplace daily for 5 to 10 minutes before and after work. Each person must be responsible for his or her own work area.
2. Assign a person to a machine; the person must not be a user of the machine assigned to him or her.
3. Combine cleaning with inspection.
4. Repeat sweep-wipe-polish-check-fix.
5. Organize a "Big Cleaning Day" once or twice a year or as needed.

3.4 *Seiketsu*/Standardize

Standardize the protocol of sorting, arranging, and cleaning every time a job is done. Cleaning should be done in an organized fashion, so that it is done in the same way each time.

3.5 *Shitsuke*/Self-discipline

Make a habit of the first four S's so that the system becomes second nature to each worker. Many activities can be devised so that the work teams can participate actively in the program. Contests can be planned to encourage workers to make songs or even dances showing the value of cleanliness in the workplace. The workers can also be asked to draw and make suggestions for the improvement of the workplace. Thus, they can feel empowered and participate actively in the programs on food safety throughout the year. Newsletters and house bulletins can cite examples of improvement in the surroundings and in the work area.

To be useful in a food safety system, the specifics have to be focused on the principles of Good Manufacturing Practices and Hazard Analysis Critical Control Point.

4.0 FOOD SAFETY SYSTEMS

4.1 Good Agricultural Practices (GAP)

GAP refers to the practices of primary food producers, such as farmers and fishermen, necessary to assure production of quality food products conforming to food laws and regulations.[7] In the farm-to-plate continuum, primary food producers are at the forefront of the "battlefield." They are the ones involved in the production of raw materials supplied to food industries, including the marketing, processing, food service sectors, and consumers.

Figure 3.2. The 5S Good Housekeeping Guide

4.2 Good Manufacturing Practices (GMP)

GMP refers to the practices of food industries that are necessary to produce safe and quality food products conforming to food laws and regulations.[7] Different countries have different versions of GMP, but the common emphasis is the prevention of product contamination from direct and indirect sources. Generally, GMP is concerned with the basic aspects of food manufacturing, namely the site for building and facilities, grounds, building and facilities design and construction, plant layout, sanitary facilities, equipment and utensils, and personnel.[8]

4.2.1 Site for Building and Facilities

The factors to consider are as follows:[8, 9]

- Water Supply–There is an adequate supply of potable water.
- Waste Disposal–There is a system for proper waste disposal.
- Pest Control–The surroundings are not suitable for breeding and harboring of pests and other disease carriers.
- Plant Surroundings–The site is far from potential sources of pollution such as streams and other bodies of water, drainage, refuse dumps, equipment, and storage yards.
- Plant Area–It meets the required plant area and allows the possibility for future expansion.

4.2.2 Grounds

Having selected the most ideal site, it is important to install the necessary structures to guard the site from possible contamination from the environment. Grounds are harbingers of pests and diseases that could invade the food processing premises. Methods for proper maintenance of grounds include:[8]

- Provide adequate draining areas.
- Install a system for proper waste disposal and treatment.
- Maintain proper equipment storage.
- Maintain roads, yards, and parking space.
- Cut weeds or grasses.

4.2.3 Building and Facilities Design and Construction

To begin with, a processing plant should be of the right size, construction, and design to allow hygienic handling of food and effective cleaning and sanitation, prevent entry of pests, assure the safety of personnel, and provide a good working environment.

The criteria for the proper design and construction of building and facilities are as follows:[8, 9]

- Sufficient areas for receiving, inspecting, dry raw material storage, refrigerated and frozen raw material storage, preparation, cooking/ processing, packing, and finished product storage
- Sufficient space for placement of equipment and storage of tools
- Adequate lighting. Light bulbs located above food preparation and processing areas should be shielded, coated, or be shatter-resistant to prevent glass fragments, in case of breakage, from getting into the food and onto food contact surfaces and equipment.[10]
- Adequate ventilation
- Screens over windows and other openings that will prevent entry of pests and airborne contaminants (i.e., dust)
- Work spaces between equipment and walls

- Measures that will reduce the potential for contamination of food, food contact surfaces and packaging materials with microorganisms, filth, chemicals, and other extraneous materials, i.e., air flow, and delineation of operations
- Control areas over and around vessels to eliminate harborage of pests
- Floor is made of durable and water-resistant materials. It is smoothly constructed; cracks, crevices, and depressions tend to allow accumulation of water and dirt.[9]
- The interior walls are smooth, flat, light-colored, impermeable to moisture and do not easily crack.[9]

4.2.4 Plant Layout

The plant layout is another important component of GMP. It should allow the smooth flow of the different food preparation and food processing operations without compromising hygienic food handling and have a good working environment.[8]

- A single-story layout is preferred for simplified material handling.
- A straight-line process flow of materials from receiving, production, packaging, and storage to distribution is the most efficient for food processing plants. The same principle applies to food service.
- The food preparation and processing areas should be separate from eating, recreational, and toilet facilities.
- Partition walls can be installed in areas where there is a possibility of cross-contamination between the raw material receiving area and the food preparation/processing area. Otherwise keep partition walls to a minimum to allow good ventilation.

4.2.5 Sanitary Facilities

The most important requirement in sanitation operations is the availability of adequate potable water, which aside from being used in food preparation and processing operations is necessary in cleaning operations. Water is used for cleaning floors of processing areas, equipment, and utensils. Other pointers for having an ideal sanitary facility are as follows:[8]

- Adequate size and design of the plumbing system that will carry water to the required locations and will convey sewage and disposable liquid waste from the plant. The system has features that will prevent cross-connection and backflow, which can contaminate the potable water system.[10]
- Proper location of floor drains and gutters. The floor should have the right slope to allow wash water to flow into the drain and gutter.
- Toilet facilities that are located away from the food preparation and processing areas, with handwashing facilities, self-closing doors, and waste receptacles that do not require manual opening.

4.2.6 Equipment and Utensils

The important points to consider when buying equipment and utensils for food use are the design and type of material(s) they are made of. The design should allow for hygienic handling of food and proper care of the equipment and utensils. They should also be safe and easy to operate.[8]

- There are no pockets where food can accumulate.

- Seams on food contact surfaces are smoothly bonded so as to prevent accumulation of food particles, dirt, and other organic matter.
- Fuel and lubricants do not come in contact with food.
- The lowest horizontal parts are at least six inches above the floor.
- Vertical and horizontal supports are round.
- The equipment is easy to clean and repair.
- All surfaces and areas are readily accessible.
- The parts can be easily dismantled and reassembled.
- It is self-draining.
- It must not have sharp edges and unsecured parts.
- It is electrically safe.
- It is easy to handle.
- It has adjustable legs.
- It is not excessively noisy.

Considering that food processing equipment and food preparation utensils come in direct contact with food, they should be made of materials that will not pose any risks of contamination. The properties of safe equipment or utensils are as follows:[8, 9,10]

- It is made of stainless steel.
- Food contact surfaces are not made of aluminum. An aluminum sheet easily warps and is susceptible to oxidation. It is soft and therefore it is also susceptible to pitting and scratching.
- Food contact surfaces are not made with galvanized finish. A galvanized finish is not resistant to corrosion caused by foods, non-neutral cleaning materials, and brine solutions.
- No parts are made from wood. Wood is porous, which allows absorption of moisture and liquid food materials.
- All materials are non-toxic, therefore metals such as lead, cadmium, copper and antimony are not to be used.
- Parts do not disintegrate into metal fragments.
- For freezer or cold storage compartments, there should be a device for measuring the temperature.

4.2.7 Personnel Hygiene

Probably the most immediate consideration in personnel hygiene is the health of workers. A sick worker should not go to work, especially if he or she has a respiratory or intestinal illness, skin infection, or fresh open wound, which can be sources of contamination of food and food contact surfaces and utensils. However, a worker who has a cut or abrasion can still work provided that the wound is adequately covered or he or she can be assigned a different task that does not involve handling of food, such as administrative work. Illnesses aside, healthy workers should observe the following rules on cleanliness:[8,9,10]

- Maintain adequate personal cleanliness, which includes taking baths daily, wearing clean clothes, and keeping nails trimmed. Women should also maintain natural and unpolished nails as polish may chip-off during food handling.
- Wear outer garments suitable to the operation such as working gowns or aprons. Outer garments are meant to protect food from risk of contamination and to keep one's clothes clean.
- Wear hair restraints such as hairnets and beard covers.
- Remove jewelry.
- Wash hands adequately before and after handling food and food utensils.

Also, wash hands every time a different food is handled to prevent cross-contamination.

Handwashing is the most important factor in personal cleanliness. Hands are common carriers of germs. Germs get on hands through bad personal habits such as touching the nose, mouth, ears, hair, and pimples. The nose, mouth, and ears harbor *Staphylococci.* Coughs and sneezes can carry droplet infection. Habits, like picking and scratching the nose, are not acceptable.

Most bacteria are removed from your hands by careful washing with soap and water. Wash hands only in handwashing sinks and never in food preparation sinks. Use a clean towel or hand dryer to dry your hands.

This is the proper way to wash your hands:

- Wear gloves when necessary such as when handling food. Gloves should be clean and made of plastic or other impermeable material.
- Store clothing and other personal belongings in a locker room or area other than where the food is exposed or where equipment and utensils are washed.
- Eat food, chew gum, drink beverages, or smoke only in areas other than where food is prepared or utensils are washed.

See Chapter 5 for more details about personal hygiene. Appendix H is a sample form of the FDA Sanitary Inspection Form to check on the compliance of a food establishment or food plant.

4.3 Sanitation Standard Operating Procedures (SSOP)

SSOP is a step-by-step sanitation procedure at the pre-operational and operational stages of food processing or handling. It is designed to prevent direct product contamination. While GMP encompasses all aspects of food processing and handling, SSOP only pertains to sanitation, however, it is prepared using GMP guidelines and is really a part of GMP.[11]

4.4 Hazard Analysis Critical Control Point System (HACCP)

4.4.1 Overview

According to WHO, the HACCP system is a "scientific, rational and systematic approach to identification, assessment, and control of hazards during production, processing, manufacturing, preparation, and use of food to ensure that food is safe when consumed."[12] The concept behind HACCP is explained by two sets of words that form its acronym–*Hazard Analysis Critical Control Point.* The Hazard Analysis component of HACCP is involved in identifying biological, chemical, and physical hazards in food that have the potential to cause harm to a person consuming the product. The Critical Control Point component is involved in determining critical control points (CCPs) or specific food operations where loss of control may result in an unacceptable health risk.[13]

HACCP is designed to monitor the whole food chain in contrast to other systems where only the end products are tested for the presence of hazards. With HACCP, the objective is to avoid or minimize opportunities for contamination, reduce the amount of contamination, or delay further changes in food as a result of contamination, thus there is greater assurance that food is safe.[14]

The immediate benefits of implementing HACCP are the reduced incidence of foodborne illnesses, and the assurance that a safe food supply is available to consumers. Other

Figure 3.3. Proper Handwashing. *Source:* http://www.images/google/handwashing/frithart.com.

benefits of HACCP are that it can aid regulatory authorities in their inspection duties and it can promote international trade as a result of increased confidence in food safety.[13]

4.4.2 History

Having witnessed the first man landing on the moon propelled scientists at the National Aeronautics and Space Administration (NASA) to put their efforts into space travel research that will send more manned spacecraft into outer space. One of the major concerns of the scientists was the need for a system that will ensure the microbial safety of food for the astronauts. The result was a food safety system developed by The Pillsbury Company, together with NASA and the U.S. Army Laboratories at Natick, Massachusetts. That very system is what we have come to know as HACCP in all commercial and food operations.[12]

In 1971 HACCP made its first "public appearance" at the first American National Conference for Food Protection. Since then, various regulatory agencies have integrated HACCP into their food control system (i.e. USFDA's Low Acid Canned Foods Regulations, USDA's meat and poultry inspection). The WHO and the International Commission on Microbiological Specifications for Foods (ICMSF) have also recommended its use.[15]

HACCP has evolved from a system that initially focused only on biological hazards to a system that also includes the chemical and physical hazards. Food companies in the US that have the HACCP system already in place have found it to be a preventative and cost-effective approach to food safety. Other countries that have adopted HACCP also share the same experience.[12]

In 1993 the Codex Alimentarius Commission (CAC) recognized and accepted the HACCP system as the most cost-effective approach for ensuring food safety because of the reported decrease in foodborne illnesses. Since CAC is an international body setting the standards for food safety, many countries have integrated HACCP into their food control system.[12]

4.4.3 The Seven Principles of HACCP

The HACCP system is comprised of seven principles. These principles were developed in a logical manner. As a whole, it serves as a step-by-step guide in implementing the HACCP system:

1. Conduct hazard analysis
2. Identify critical control points (CCPs)
3. Establish critical limits (CLs)
4. Establish monitoring procedures
5. Establish corrective action procedures
6. Establish verification procedures
7. Establish recordkeeping system

4.4.4 Preliminary Steps

Implementing HACCP is not a simple task because concern does not start or end with the finished product. It involves understanding the farm-to-plate continuum–from production, postharvest, storage, transportation and distribution of raw materials to preparation, processing, packaging, storage, transportation, distribution, finished products including preparation prior to final consumption. Such is the natural order of things that makes HACCP implementation a multidisciplinary task.

What sets HACCP apart from other food safety systems is its specificity. While GMP is concerned with the overall management and process system, HACCP is concerned with product safety. However, this does not mean that HACCP can stand alone. It needs other systems to be able to function well. One system that was made a prerequisite of HACCP is the GMP accompanied by its SSOPs. Continuous adherence to GMP, especially those pertaining to personnel hygiene, and sanitary and maintenance operations of plant, grounds, equipment, and utensils, helps reduce the risks that would likely affect product safety.

To start the ball rolling, a company must form a HACCP team. Since HACCP involves all the steps to ensure food safety, the team must be composed of people who understand the entire process, like the plant supervisor and those who are experts in epidemiology, food technology, microbiology, chemistry, process engineering, quality assurance, and management. If all the necessary HACCP players are not available within the company, a private consultant may be hired.

Once the prerequisites of HACCP are in place, and the HACCP team members have understood and pledged their commitment to this endeavor, and have gained support from the entire workforce, the company is now ready for HACCP.

4.4.5 The HACCP Plan

The implementation of the HACCP system makes use of the HACCP plan, which is a complete documentation of how the system works for the intended food product. The plan indicates all the details of the seven HACCP principles in action.[16, 17]

1. *Conduct Hazard Analysis.* This involves the identification of biological, chemical, and physical hazards in food. Something is considered a hazard when it has the potential to cause an adverse health effect. Hazard analysis is done in 5 steps:
   a. Review incoming material
   b. Review processing steps
   c. Review operations
   d. Take measurements
   e. Analyze measurements
2. *Identify Critical Control Points* (CCPs). A critical control point is any process or procedure in a food system where loss of control may result in an unacceptable health risk. It is at this point where the identified hazards that present the greater risk are controlled. A decision tree (Figure 3.4) is used to identify CCPs.[13]

   A decision tree is made up of a series of questions arranged in a logical manner. Each question is answerable by a yes or no. An answer leads to either the next question or a decision, which is whether a step or operation is a CCP or not. A step is considered a CCP if it is designed to 1) eliminate or reduce the likely occurrence of a hazard to an acceptable level, or 2) if a subsequent step will not be able to eliminate identified hazard(s) or reduce the likely occurrence to an acceptable level in case contamination with the identified hazard could occur in excess of acceptable level(s), or increase to unacceptable level.[12]
3. *Establish Critical Limits.* A critical limit is a value that delineates what is acceptable and what is unacceptable in terms of safety. It is set at a minimum, which if not reached will likely result in a potential health hazard.
4. *Establish Monitoring Procedures.* These are scheduled observations and/or measurements of control parameters to assess whether a CCP is under control.
5. *Establish Corrective Action Procedures.* These are actions specific for each critical control point. Once a deviation from the critical limit is detected, such actions must be implemented in order to eliminate the hazard that may result from the deviation.
6. *Establish Verification Procedures.* These are methods, procedures, or tests used to ensure that hazards are controlled. Examples of these are audits, laboratory tests, and records verification.
7. *Establish Recordkeeping Systems.* This consists of all records of monitoring done, and corrective actions, preventative actions, and verifications made. A record is a tool that helps ensure that all CCPs are continuously under control. It also tracks repetitive deviations that a company can use as basis for designing preventative actions. A record also serves as a legal document in cases where there are customer complaints, for example, if there is an outbreak of foodborne illness and a company manufactured the implicated foods. That company can use their

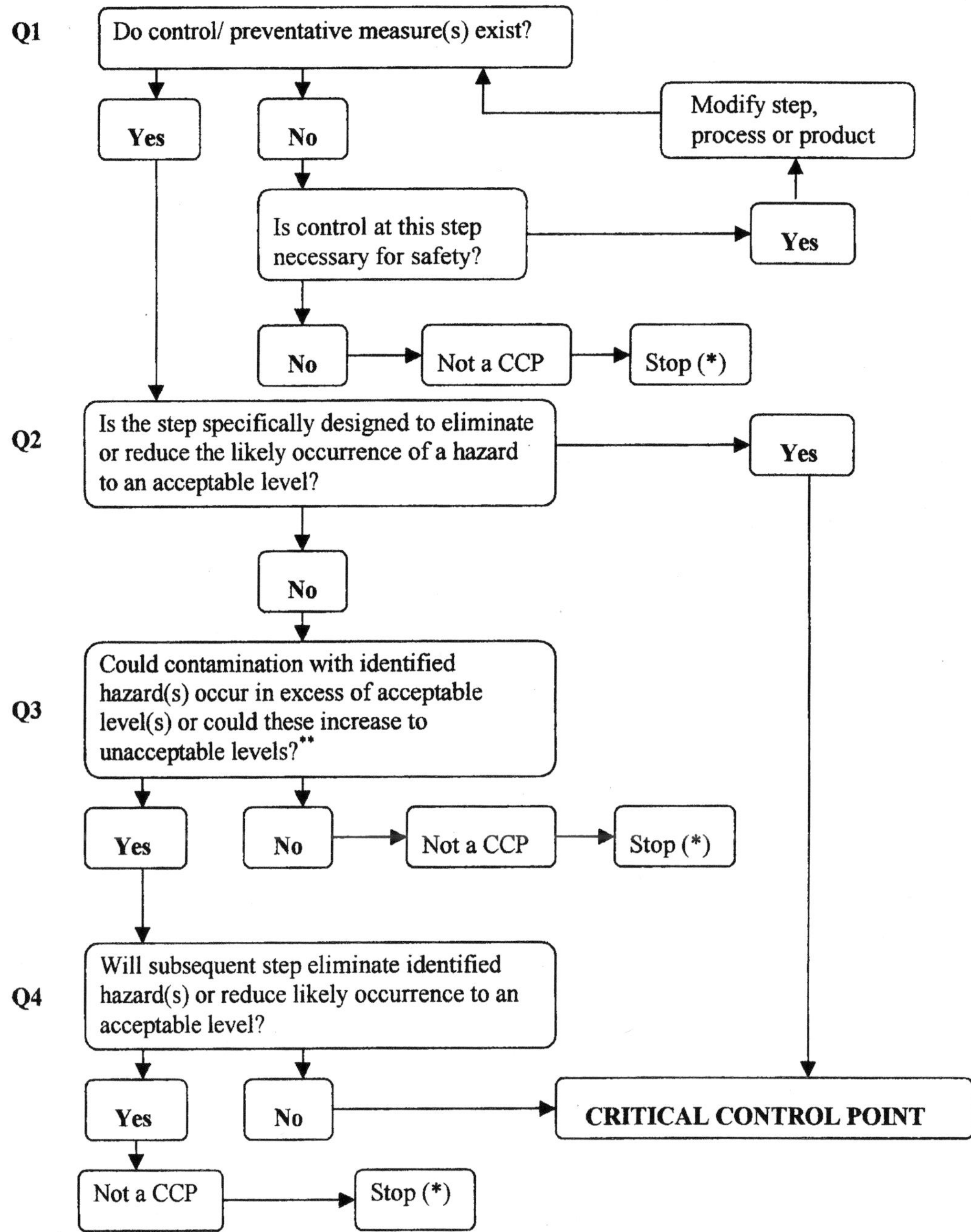

Figure 3.4. Example of Decision Tree to Identify CCPs. Answer the questions in sequence. * Proceed to the next identified hazard in the described process. ** Acceptable and unacceptable levels need to be defined within the overall objectives in identifying the CCPs of the HACCP plan.

A Little Story

This is a story about four people
Named Everybody, Somebody,
Anybody, and Nobody.

There was an important job to
be done and Everybody was sure
that Somebody would do it.

Anybody could have done it,
but Nobody did it.

Somebody got angry about that
because it was Everybody's job.

Everybody thought Anybody could
do it, but Nobody realized that
Everybody wouldn't do it.

It ended up that Everybody blamed
Somebody when Nobody did what
Anybody could have done.

Figure 3.5. "A Little Story"

record to prove that their HACCP system was able to control hazards and that the end product is guaranteed safe.

5.0 CONCLUSION

Food safety is everyone's concern and responsibility–the managers, the food handlers, and the consumers. Managers are responsible for implementing the appropriate food safety system(s) that will ensure production of safe food and food products. Food handlers are responsible for meeting the specifications for product safety as guided by food safety systems. Consumers are responsible for reporting their complaints about a product and in the first place they are responsible for demanding safe and quality food. As end-product users, consumers are also responsible for the preparation of food in their own homes. Ensuring food safety is a concerted effort. It does not start or end with one or two persons. Rather it is the concern of everyone as depicted in "A Little Story" by an unknown author (Figure 3.5).

REVIEW QUESTIONS

1. Define important terms: (see text or the Glossary)
   a. Critical Control Point (CCP)
   b. Food Safety
   c. Food Safety Systems
   d. Good Agricultural Practices (GAP)
   e. Good Manufacturing Practices (GMP)
   f. Hazard Analysis Critical Control Point (HACCP) system
   g. Hazard
   h. Personnel Hygiene
   i. Risk
   j. Sanitation Standard Operating Procedures (SSOP)
2. Why are food safety systems important?
3. Why is 5S important in achieving food safety in a company?
4. What are the key elements in Good Manufacturing Practices?
5. What are the main points regarding personnel hygiene?
6. Why is HACCP important worldwide? Why should HACCP be considered an investment and not a cost?
7. How can we increase the awareness for HACCP?
8. What are the advantages of applying HACCP? What are the disadvantages?
9. What are some of the companies that you know which are applying HACCP?
10. How can consumers be more aware of food safety systems?

REFERENCES

1. Billy, T. J. Factors driving food safety policy and their implications in the harmonization of food standards. *Proceedings of the 7th ASEAN Food Conference.* Manila, 2000.
2. Acheson, D. Long-term consequences of foodborne disease. *Food Quality* 7:7, 2000.
3. Garcia, M. Emerging foodborne pathogens. *Proceedings of the 7th ASEAN Food Conference.* Manila, 2000.
4. Foundation for the Advancement of Food Science and Technology. *Application of 5S in the Workplace.* Quezon City, FAFST, 1998.
5. Ishiwara, A. *An Introduction to 5S: Productivity and Quality Improvement Step by Step.* Development Academy of the Philippines Productivity and Development Center, Quezon City, 1992.
6. Chavez, L. L. *5S of Good Housekeeping Training Module.* Quezon City, FAFST, 2002.
7. World Health Organization. *Guidelines for Strengthening a National Food Safety Programme.* WHO/FNU/FOS/96.2, 1996.
8. Foundation for the Advancement of Food Science and Technology. *Application of GMP in the Workplace.* Quezon City, FAFST, 2001.
9. Chavez, L. L. (ed.). *HACCP for Consumer Safety and Global Competitiveness.* Quezon City, FAFST, 1997.
10. McSwane, D., Rue, N., and Linton, R. *Food Safety and Sanitation,* 3rd ed, Upper Saddle River, N.J., 2003.
11. Marriott, Norman G. *Principles of Food Sanitation,* 4th ed. New York, Kluwer Academic, 1999.
12. World Health Organization. *Introducing the Hazard Analysis and Critical Control Point System.* WHO/FSF/FOS/97.2, 1997.
13. Codex Alimentarius Commission. *General Requirements (Food Hygiene),* 2nd ed. FAO-WHO, Rome, 1997.
14. Bryan, F. L. Current controversies in the application of HACCP systems, Part I. *Food Safety Magazine, 8*:28–35, 2002.
15. Leaper, S. (ed.). *HACCP: A Practical Guide.* Technical Manual No. 38. The Campden Food and Drink Research Association, UK, 1992.
16. World Health Organization. *Hazard Analysis Critical Control Point System Concept and Application.* WHO/FNU/FOS/95.7, 1995.
17. WHO. *Strategies for Implementing HACCP in Small and/or Less Developed Businesses.* Report of a WHO Consultation, The Netherlands, 1999.

Chapter 4

FOOD CONTROL

1.0 INTRODUCTION

Consumers play a very important role in food safety. Through the proper appreciation of the workings of the food control system, an active and effective consumer group can make recommendations and in fact assist in improving a country's food control system. This chapter seeks to explain the need for food control; to give examples of food control as applied to selected commodities, namely meat, fish, and fruits and vegetables; to explain the criteria for a national food control system; and to elucidate the role of the Sanitary and Phytosanitary Standards agreement and the World Trade Organization in the present global trade scenario.

2.0 FOOD CONTROL SYSTEMS IN GENERAL

The government protects consumers through laws and regulations to ensure food safety from farm to fork. It has to have regulatory personnel to monitor the whole food chain from the agricultural production through processing and distribution. It is necessary to strengthen the inspections systems to ensure regulatory compliance and safety.

An effective food control system requires the commitment of the government in terms of firm budgetary allocations for human and other resources. The number of inspectors required to actually monitor the whole food chain may be difficult for some countries to support. It is therefore necessary to have the private and the public sector, the government and the food industry working together for food safety and consumer health.

The Food and Agriculture Organization (FAO) classifies the main food commodity groups, by origin, as follows:

- *Plant:* cereals, roots and tubers, pulses, nuts and oilseeds, vegetables, fruits, spices, stimulants, and alcoholic beverages
- *Animal:* meat and offals, eggs, fish and seafood, milk
- *Plant and animal:* sugars and honey, oils and fats

The food control of meat and poultry, fish and seafood, and fruits and vegetables are briefly discussed in the following sections to give an overview of the systems involved. References are given for further reading.

3.0 FOOD CONTROL OF MEAT AND POULTRY[1]

Some foods of animal origin are considered to have a high potential to be vehicles of foodborne pathogens because of their high susceptibility to microbial contamination; considerable opportunity for survival of the contaminants; high likelihood that growth of the contaminants will occur at some point before serving; and reasonable likelihood that the food may be subjected to mistreatment just before serving.

It is necessary to protect consumers from possible harm by proper regulation and control of meat and meat products from the farm to the fork.

3.1 Inspection

The major purposes of meat and poultry inspection are to eliminate diseased meat, to prevent the sale of objectionable meat, to maintain strict hygiene, and to secure proper labeling. If effectively done, meat inspection can result in the following benefits: control of animal disease, information regarding causes of condemnation, prevention of foodborne disease, increased marketability of products, consumer confidence, and improved production efficiency.

3.2 Antemortem Inspection

The inspection of animals before death is important to remove animals with conditions that cannot be detected at postmortem inspection. It prevents unscrupulous farmers from sending ill or injured animals to slaughter. Further, it prevents unnecessary contamination of personnel and equipment inside the abattoir by diseased animals.

3.3 Postmortem Inspection

Animals that "pass" on antemorton and are found upon postmortem inspection to have no evidence of generalized disease or recent medication with the potential for producing foodborne disease are then passed. The problem begins when the veterinarian finds evidence of recent medication, localized disease condition, or generalized disease with the potential for producing foodborne disease. In the latter case, for example, if the foodborne disease threat cannot be removed by special procedures, then the meat is condemned.

4.0 FOOD CONTROL OF FISH AND SHELLFISH PRODUCTS[3,5]

All phases of production and processing are taken into consideration in fish inspection systems. These include the microbial and chemical quality of harvest waters, the cleanliness of fishing vessels and processing plants, and the marketing of the final product. "Food Safety Issues Associated with Products from Aquaculture" is a report of a joint FAO/NACA/WHO study group done in 1999. The study group reviewed the biological and chemical hazards inherent in aquaculture products, along with their associated risks, proposed strategies for food safety assurance applicable to the aquaculture sector, and identified research needs.

5.0 FOOD CONTROL OF FRUITS AND VEGETABLES[4,6]

National laws are existent in different countries pertinent to the establishment of a tolerance or maximum residue limit (MRL), which defines the maximum amount of a pesticide residue that may legally remain in or on a food commodity after the pesticide is used according to its Good Agricultural Practices (GAP). Disputes may arise between importing and exporting countries in the case of pesticides. The Codex Committee on Pesticide Residues (CCR) has the responsibility for the development of Codex standards for pesticide residues on food. Use of Codex MRLs by member countries is meant to preempt divergent MRLs from constituting nontariff barriers to international trade in food.

6.0 NATIONAL FOOD CONTROL

It has often been stated that food control programs "based on well-established food standards and other regulations are more necessary now than ever before to improve nutritional status, control food quality and safety, prevent food losses and protect the consumer."[9]

6.1 Major Constraints

The major constraints of national food control include

1. insufficient funding for food control activities such as inspection, testing, and analysis,
2. inadequate human resources for inspection and analysis, especially in government departments; often this has given rise to poor enforcement of legislation, particularly in rural areas and an influx of substandard imported foods,
3. poor participation and representation at international/national food stands conferences, workshops, and seminars

by developing countries. It is noteworthy that there is now a conscious effort on the part of Codex to hold some of the major meetings in developing countries,

4. absence of appropriate in-service training, especially in areas of food legislation and inspection,
5. inadequate facilities and infrastructure for food analysis, and
6. consumer ignorance on issues of food quality and food handling, as well as the absence of consumer education programs.[9]

6.2 History of National Food Control

Many books have dealt with the history of the evolution of food laws and regulations in the different countries. Hubbert et al., for example, traced the evolution of meat inspection in the United Kingdom, Canada, and Australia, and federal meat inspection in the United States.

6.3 Food Regulations in Selected Countries

6.3.1 South East Asian Counties

Various participants in a consultative workshop on food safety held in Bangkok, Thailand, in 2001 presented their food safety country situation. Mr. Halim Hababan of the National Agency of Drug and Food Control presented the Indonesian Food Control System; Ms. Zahara Merican of the Malaysian Agricultural Research and Development (MARDI) presented Food Safety in Malaysia. One of the senior authors of this book (S. de Leon) from the University of the Philippines, Diliman, presented the Philippine Country paper on Food Safety. Dr. Supranee Changbumrung of the Department of Tropical Nutrition and Food Science of Mahido University presented Food Safety in Thailand; and Ms. Phan Thi Kim and Dao Thi Mai Phuong of the Vietnam Food Administration presented the current situation, challenges, and solutions for assurance of food quality, hygiene, and safety of Vietnam.

The issues raised during the discussion included the following:[12]

- Mandates are generally in place, but there are overlaps and conflicts between implementing agencies, and the implementation tends to favor large exporters.
- Surveillance is inadequate since foodborne infections caused by emerging pathogens are not reportable.
- Consumer education is wanting in the larger parts of the countries represented.
- Promotion of basic food sanitation and hygiene practices must be more aggressive.
- There is a need to integrate food safety courses in university curricula.
- Codex-based Hazard Analysis Critical Control Point (HACCP) must be based on sound science, particularly consumption data.
- Food safety awareness and training must begin at the grassroots, such as retail food services and consumers.
- There is need for regional collaboration in risk assessment to resolve uncertainties to protect human health and the environment.
- The approach to food safety must be holistic.

There is indeed a need for developing countries to improve their national infrastructure to contribute to the international standards. As discussed in Chapter 12, the benefits of enforcing adoption of national standards are many.

6.3.2 *African Countries*

The Codex Coordinating Committees for Africa have prepared these guidelines regarding national food control:

- National food laws and regulations for import and export inspection and certification should be harmonized with existing Codex standards and guidelines, and in consideration of the Application of Sanitary and Phytosanitary Measures and the Agreement on Technical Barriers to Trade.
- Government should give the utmost priority and support to the strengthening of national food control activities by providing increased resources including support to allow the participation of government representatives at Codex committee sessions.
- National intra-agency, intergovernmental coordination and harmonization should be rationalized to allow for maximum efficiency, utilization of resources, and exchange and dissemination of information to the public and private sectors.
- International bodies and governments should be encouraged to provide assistance to developing countries in any way possible.

7.0 REGIONAL FOOD CONTROL

7.1 European Community

The Commission of the European Communities issued the "White Paper on Food Safety" on January 12, 2000.[11] The White Paper makes proposals "that will transform European Union food policy into a proactive, dynamic, coherent, and comprehensive instrument to ensure a high level of human health and consumer protection. Chapter 2 sets forth the principles of food safety, among which are such basic concepts as

- Food safety policy must be based on a comprehensive, integrated approach. The pillars of food safety namely scientific advice, data collection and analysis, regulatory and control aspects as well as consumer information, must form a seamless whole to achieve this integrated approach. It also means that throughout the food chain, which covers the whole of the feed and the food chain across all food sectors between the member states, at the EU external frontier and within the EU, in international and EU decision-making for and at all stages of the policy-making cycle, food policy is integrated.
- A successful food policy demands the traceability of feed and food and their ingredients.
- The comprehensive, integrated approach will lead to a more coherent, effective and dynamic food policy.
- Risk analysis must form the foundation on which food safety policy is based.

7.2 South American Countries

Toledo wrote a comprehensive review of Southern common market standards in 2000.[7] In the review, she describes the historical background, the objectives of MERCOSUR institutional structure, the Food Commission, and FAO Technical assistance. The Southern Common Market (MERCO-

SUR) covers four Latin American countries: Argentina, Brazil, Paraguay, and Uruguay that signed the Treaty of Asuncion. The objectives of MERCOSUR include:

- Free transit of goods, services and production factors between member countries; establishment of a common external tariff; and the adoption of a common trade policy with regard to nonmember countries.
- Coordination of macroeconomic and sectoral policies of member countries in order to ensure free competition.
- Commitment by the member countries to harmonize their laws to allow for the strengthening of the integration process.

The issues addressed in MERCOSUR legislation are similar to those faced by other countries that are attempting to harmonize standards. Countries have "different legislations, habits, traditions, and national sovereignty," so harmonizing of standards can indeed be very challenging!

8.0 RISK ANALYSIS

It is necessary first to define the terms being used in international deliberations on food safety. The WHO / FAO definitions of the terms are as follows:

Risk: an estimate of the probability and severity in exposed populations of the adverse health effects resulting from hazard/s in food.

Risk Analysis: a process consisting of three components: risk assessment, risk management and risk communication.[2]

Risk Assessment: the scientific evaluation of known or potential adverse health effects resulting from human exposure to foodborne hazards. The process consists of the following steps: 1) hazard identification, 2) hazard characterization, 3) exposure assessment, and 4) risk characterization. The definition includes quantitative risk assessment, which emphasizes reliance on numerical expressions of risk, and also qualitative expressions or risk, as well as an indication of the attendant uncertainties.

Risk Management: the process of weighing policy alternatives to accept, minimize or reduce assessed risks and to select and implement appropriate options.[2]

Risk Communication: An interactive process of exchange of information and opinion on risk among risk assessors, risk managers and other interested parties.[2]

Risk analysis is a formal process adopted by governments to help evaluate food safety programs and formulate public policy. In the field of food safety, application of risk analysis may result in the following benefits: 1) help government programs be more efficient by allocating economic resources to areas of greatest need, 2) utilize current scientific data about risks of foodborne diseases, 3) formalize the decision-making process about specific steps in food production, processing, packaging, distribution, and inspection, and 4) help communication among major stakeholders including the consumers. In establishing maximum levels of additives and contaminants for example, risk assessment plays a very important part.[8]

Hazard is defined as a biological, chemical, or physical agent in food or a condition of food, with the potential to cause harm.

Hazard Analysis Critical Control Point (HACCP) is an important aspect of the risk analysis system of a country. HACCP is discussed in detail in Chapter 3. As the industry slowly accepts increasing responsibility for control of its own products by gradual adaptation of HACCP, then the consuming public is more and more assured of greater protection against foodborne diseases.

9.0 THE WORLD TRADE ORGANIZATION

With the signing of the General Agreement on Tariffs and Trade (GATT), Codex standards have become reference texts used by the World Trade Organization for international trade and food safety, thus Codex standards form a basis for international standards. There was very little at stake in Codex in terms of world trade obligations, prior to January 1, 1995. However, with the Agreement on Sanitary and Phytosanitary Standards (SPS Agreement) under the World Trade Organization, many changes occurred. Now, the SPS agreement is binding on all WTO members. Decision making and the setting of Codex standards have become even more controversial.

The members of the World Trade Organization may participate in the governing General Council. All members are also automatically members of the distinct committees that oversee the implementation of the various agreements, i.e. the SPS Agreement on Agriculture, and the revised 1995 Technical Barriers to Trade (TBT) agreement.

10.0 SANITARY AND PHYTOSANITARY STANDARDS (SPS) AGREEMENT

The SPS agreement requires the SPS Committee to develop a procedure to monitor the use of international standards by WTO members. The SPS agreement provides as follows in Article 5: 1) Members shall ensure that their sanitary or phytosanitary measures are based on an assessment, as appropriate to the circumstances, of the risks to human, animal or plant life or health, taking into account risk assessment techniques developed by the relevant international organizations; 2) in the assessment of risks, Members shall take into account available scientific evidence; relevant processes and production methods; relevant inspection, sampling and testing methods; prevalence of specific diseases or pest; existence of pest- or disease-free areas; relevant ecological and environmental conditions; and quarantine or other treatment; 3) in assessing the risk to plant or animal life or health and determining the ease to be applied for achieving the appropriate level of sanitary or phytosanitary protection from such risk. Members shall take into account as relevant economic factors: the potential damage in terms of loss of production or sales in the event of the entry, establishment or spread of a pest or disease; the costs of control or eradication in the territory of the importing Member; and the relative cost effectiveness of alternative approaches to limiting risks.[10]

The SPS agreement requires adherence to certain disciplines including transparency, consistency, and nondiscriminatory application.

11.0 CONSUMERS' CONCERNS IN FOOD CONTROL

It is necessary to consider consumers' concerns in the whole system of food control. This will only come about if there is effective consumer participation at the national and international level. This remains a challenge for the future. Consumers need to know and they need to be assured that their interests are given priority and not overshadowed by commercial interests. Consumers must be clear as to what they need and they must set up mechanisms to ensure that all members of the food chain always address their needs for food safety and health.

12.0 CONSUMERS NEED TO BE INFORMED THROUGH FOOD SAFETY WEB SITES

Intelligent advocacy is possible only if the consumers are well informed. They should avail themselves of information from all sources, from television, from radio, from print whether from books, newspapers, technical publications, and lay publications. There are many food safety web sites that can be used to access current information (see Appendix J).

REVIEW QUESTIONS

1. Define important terms:
   a. Risk analysis
   b. Risk assessment
   c. Risk management
   d. Risk communication
   e. Hazard
   f. Functional foods
   g. Organic foods
   h. Food Code (US)
   i. Allergies
2. Why should governments allocate funds for food control?
3. What are the effects of European White Paper on Food Safety to world trade?
4. What are some of the sanitary and phytosanitary measures that concern the industry of your country today?
5. Give some examples of technical barriers to trade affecting the exporters of your country today.
6. What are some of the factors that are taken into consideration in a risk assessment study?
7. Who are responsible for risk management in your country? Who takes care of risk communication in your country?
8. How can consumers affect the food control system prevailing in their country?
9. Why should consumers try to be informed of food safety issues?
10. What are the means by which consumers can be informed of food safety matters?

REFERENCES

1. Hubbert, William T., Hagstad, Harry V., Spangler, Elizabeth, Hinton, Michael H., and Hughes, Keith L. *Food Safety and Quality Assurance.* 2nd ed. Ames, University Press, 1996.
2. WHO and FAO. *Application of Risk Analysis to Food Standards Issues.* Report of the Joint FAO/WHO Expert Consultation. Geneva, 1995.
3. Joint FAO/NACA/WHO Study Group. *Food Safety Issues Associated with Products from Aquaculture.* WHO Technical Report Series. World Health Organization. Geneva, 1999.
4. Claudio, V.S., Leocadio, C.G., de Leon, S.Y., and Serraon-Joves, L. *Food Safety and Sanitation for Philippine Consumers.* Manila, Merriam and Webster Bookstore, 2002.
5. MAFF/DH joint Food Safety and Standards Group. *Surveillance and Short-term R&D: Requirements Document 2000–2001.* United Kingdom Department of Health and Ministry of Agriculture, Fisheries and Food. July 1999.

6. The Educational Foundation, National Research Association. *Serving Safe Food Certification Coursebook.* Chapter on Regulatory Agencies and Inspection. (160–169). 1995.
7. Toledo, Maria Cecilia de Figueiredo. Southern Common Market Standards, *International Standards for Food Safety* by Rees, N. and Watson, D. (79–85). New York, Kluwer, 2000.
8. Lustre, A. *Meeting Standards of the World Food Market.* (42–53) Proceedings of The Philippine Association of Food Technologists 35th Annual Convention, Lexicon, Philippines.
9. Rees, N. and Watson, D. *International Standards for Food Safety.* New York, Kluwer Academic, 2000.
10. General Agreement on Tariffs and Trade, 1994. Agreement on the Application of Sanitary and Phytosanitary Measures. The Results of the Uruguay Round of Multilateral Trade Negotiations: The Legal Texts. *General Agreement on Tariffs and Trade.* Geneva, pp. 69–84, 1994.
11. Commission of the European Communities. *White Paper on Food Safety.* Brussels, January, 2000.
12. SEAMEO Regional Center for Graduate Study and Research in Agriculture in cooperation with SEAMEO Tropical Medicine and Public Health Network (TROPMED) and University of California. Regional Consultative Workshop on Food Safety Research and Development Proceedings, May 10–11, 2001. Bangkok, Thailand. SEAMEO SEARCA College, Los Banos, Laguna, Philippines.

Chapter 5

CONTROL OF MICROBIOLOGICAL HAZARDS

1.0. Introduction
2.0 Classification of Microorganisms and Relative Sizes
3.0 Foodborne and Waterborne Pathogenic Bacteria
  3.1 *Bacillus cereus*
  3.2 *Clostridium botulinum*
  3.3 *Clostridium perfringens*
  3.4 *Campylobacter jejuni*
  3.5 *Escherichia coli*
  3.6 *Listeria monocytogenes*
  3.7 *Salmonella* spp.
  3.8 *Shigella* spp.
  3.9 *Staphylococcus auereus*
  3.10 *Vibrio* spp.
  3.11 *Yersinia* spp.
4.0 Foodborne and Waterborne Viruses
  4.1 Hepatitis A virus
  4.2 Norwalk virus
  4.3 Rotavirus
5.0 Foodborne and Waterborne Parasites
  5.1 *Anisakis* spp.
  5.2 *Ascaris lumbricoides*
  5.3 *Cryptosporidium parvum*
  5.4 *Cyclospora cayetanensis*
  5.5 *Diphyllobotrium latum*
  5.6 *Giardia lamblia*
  5.7 *Entamoeba histolytica*
  5.8 *Taenia* spp.
  5.9 *Toxoplasma gondii*
  5.10 *Trichinella spiralis*
6.0 Harmful Fungi
  6.1 Molds
  6.2 Yeasts
  6.3 Mushrooms

1.0 INTRODUCTION

Microorganisms belong to the biological world. Because most of the foodborne and waterborne illnesses transmitted to humans are caused by bacteria, the subject of microorganisms is discussed separately from the other biological hazards. Many of these pathogenic microorganisms seriously affect the health of an individual and some may even cause death, unless safety measures are taken to prevent their growth. This chapter is focused on the four groups of microorganisms, as etiologic agents for specific diseases. Knowing the signs and symptoms to recognize a specific foodborne disease, its onset, duration of the illness, and foods implicated with its occurrence, will help the consumer and food handler understand the rationale for preventive measures. Additionally, ways and means of controlling these microbiological hazards are better implemented if consumers are familiar with the conditions for microbial growth or their multiplication.

2.0 CLASSIFICATION OF MICROORGANISMS AND RELATIVE SIZES

The five major groups of microorganisms significant to food and water safety are bacteria, viruses, parasites, fungi, and prions. They are found almost everywhere. Bacteria are especially ubiquitous, and many can survive very hot temperatures or very cold conditions; e.g., under the Antarctic ice. As one scientist said, we live in a microbial world. Fortunately, most bacteria are either useful or are important to the maintenance of an ecological balance on earth. To cite a few beneficial bacteria: the human intestines contain millions of bacteria that resist the action of pathogenic microorganisms.

Some microorganisms are used to produce foods (e.g., pickles, soy sauce, certain cheeses, and yogurt) and chemicals or drugs (e.g., antibiotics, alcohols, enzymes, etc).

Of the thousands of microbial species known to date, about 200 are pathogenic. The disease-producing microbes (microorganisms) are commonly called germs, although this term is often used to refer to all microorganisms. The relative sizes of the general groups of microorganisms are shown in Table 5.1.[1]

Bacteria and yeast can be seen under a regular light microscope. Viruses can be viewed by the use of an electron microscope that magnifies an object 50,000 times. Molds are visible with the naked eye as they form colonies, which are sometimes colored. The distinctive characteristics of the major groups of microorganisms are presented in the coming sections.

3.0 FOODBORNE AND WATERBORNE PATHOGENIC BACTERIA[2-12]

Bacteria are one-celled microorganisms that do not have a distinct nucleus. For this reason, bacteria are called procaryotes, from the Greek word, meaning pronucleus. Bacterial cells appear in one of these shapes: bacillus (rod-like), coccus (spherical or oval), spiral (curved or corkscrew) (Figure 5.1). Some may be square or star-shaped. They are often in a vegetative stage, although some are spore-formers. They form colonies in pairs, clusters, or chains and other such formation, which is characteristic of a particular genus or species. Many have flagella allowing them to swim in a liquid medium, but they cannot move from one place to another. Bacteria have to be transmitted by human hands, animals, birds, insects, by air or water to a host or another nonliving place. An example of the latter happens in cross-contamination.

The five sources of bacteria that cause foodborne illness are:[13]

- Infections on body surfaces (hands, arms, skin) of food handlers
- Nasal and throat discharges of sick individuals or asymptomatic carriers
- Fecal matter and urine of infected humans or animals
- Contaminated soil, dust, mud, or water
- Sea water, marine life, and marine materials
- Food and water usually serve as the final link in transmitting the disease.

3.1. *Bacillus cereus*

Bacillus cereus is a bacterium that produces toxins and forms spores. It is found in soil and dust, which are carried by air and could settle on food. It is also normally present in

Table 5.1
MICROORGANISMS: RELATIVE SIZES

Microorganisms	*Average Sizes in Micrometers**	*Number on a Pinhead***
Viruses	0.01 to 0.3	One billion
Bacteria	2 to 7	One million
Yeasts	5 to 50	200,000
Molds	Highly variable	

* 1 micrometer (μm) = 1/10,000 of a centimeter; 1 millimicron = 1/1000 of a micron
** Estimated population
Sources: Satin, M. *Food Alert: Facts for Life Book.* New York, Checkmark Books, 1999.
Jay, J.M. Personal communications. University of Nevada, Las Vegas. August 6, 2002.

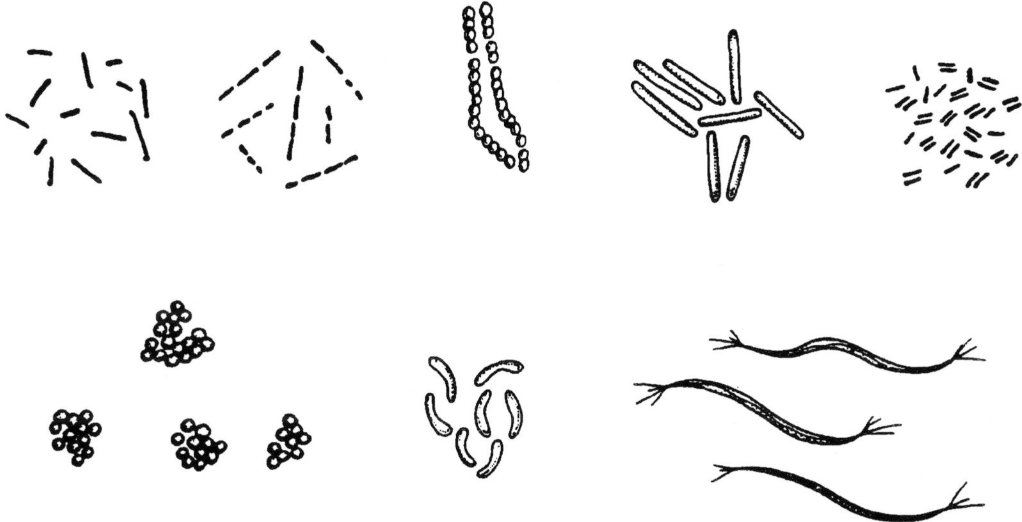

Figure 5.1. Different Shapes of Bacteria. Top row from left to right: *Salmonella, Shigella, Streptococci,* Anthrax bacilli, and *Perfringens* group. Bottom rows from left to right: *Staphylococcus aureus, Cholera vibrio, Spirilla.*

water. Fortunately, it is not transmitted person-to-person and the death-to-case ratio is zero in the United States.

It produces two types of toxins. One is a heat-stable peptide that causes nausea and vomiting (emetic type) within 0.5 to 6 hours after consuming the contaminated food. The other type of toxin is a large molecular weight protein, which causes watery diarrhea and abdominal cramps (diarrheal type) within 6 to 15 hours after eating the contaminated food. The emetic type is more severe and acute than the diarrheal type. The latter is mild and of shorter duration, lasting from 6 to 16 hours. The emetic type could last up to 24 hours.

See Table 1.2 for signs and symptoms and Table 5.2 for implicated foods and preventive measures. For a case of documented food-borne outbreak due to *Bacillus cereus,* see FBDO Report # 5, page 246.

Table 5.2
COMMON FOODBORNE PATHOGENIC BACTERIA: IMPLICATED FOODS AND PREVENTIVE MEASURES

Etiologic Agent	*Implicated Foods*	*Preventive Measures*
Bacillus cereus (diarrheal toxin)	Wide variety of foods: vegetables, meat, milk, fish, if left uncovered because of soil and dust contaminates. Spores survive milk pasteurization.	Does not grow at recommended refrigerator temperature (below 41°F/5°C), but it can grow at slightly higher temperatures. Therefore, cook food thoroughly. Cool rapidly and separate cooked foods from the environment by covering them to reduce their contamination by airborne spores.
Campylobacter jejuni	Raw poultry, beef, lamb, unpasteurized milk (foods of animal origin eaten raw or undercooked or recontaminated after cooking.	Cook foods thoroughly; use pasteurized milk; use safe food-handling methods.
Clostridium botulinum (children and adults)	Anaerobic environment of low acidity (canned corn, peppers, green beans, soups, beets, asparagus, mushrooms, ripe olives, spinach, tuna, chicken, chicken liver, luncheon meats, ham, sausage, garlic in oil, lobster); smoked and salted fish.	Use proper canning methods for low-acid foods; pressure cooker. Refrigerate homemade garlic and herb oils; avoid commercially prepared foods with leaky seals or with bent, bulging, or broken cans.
Clostridium botulinum (infants)	Honey. This is the one dietary vehicle of *C. botulinum* spores linked to infant botulism.	Do not feed honey to infants. Do not prepare infant formulas with honey or dip pacifiers in honey.
Clostridium perfringens	Leftover meats and meat products stored at between 120 and 130°F.	Use safe food-handling methods; cook foods thoroughly; use pasteurized milk.
E. coli (ETEC)	Undercooked ground beef, unpasteurized milk and milk products, contaminated water, and person-to-person contact.	Cook ground beef thoroughly (160°F); avoid raw milk and milk products; use safe food handling methods; use treated, boiled, or bottled water.
Listeria monocytogenes	Raw meat and seafood, processed meats, raw milk, and soft cheeses.	Use safe food handling methods; cook foods thoroughly; use pasteurized milk.

Continued on next page

Table 5.2–*Continued*

Etiologic Agent	*Implicated Foods*	*Preventive Measures*
Salmonella spp.	Raw or undercooked eggs, meats, poultry, milk and other dairy products, shrimp, frog legs, yeast, coconut, pasta, and chocolate.	Use safe food handling methods; use pasteurized milk; cook foods thoroughly; refrigerate foods promptly and properly.
Shigella spp.	Person-to-person contact, raw foods, salads, dairy products, and contaminated water.	Use safe food handling methods; cook foods thoroughly; proper refrigeration.
Staphylococcus aureus	Toxin produced in meats, poultry, egg products, tuna, potato and macaroni salads, and cream-filled pastries.	Use safe food handling methods; cook food thoroughly; refrigerate foods promptly and properly.
Vibrio cholerae	Raw seafood and contaminated water.	Use safe food handling methods; cook foods thoroughly.
Yersinia enterocolitica	Undercooked pork, unpasteurized milk, contaminated water.	Use only pasteurized milk and other dairy products. treated water for drinking and for food preparation. Cook foods thoroughly. Separate cooked foods from raw foods. After handling raw foods, wash your hands properly.

Source: Compiled from Chapter 5 References 2, 3, 5, 9-12, 22.

3.2 *Clostridium botulinum*

Clostridium botulinum is an anaerobic, spore-forming bacterium that produces any one of seven potent toxins, but only four (types A, B, E, and F) cause botulism in humans. Their spores are found in the soil, water, and in the intestinal tract of animals and humans. They are airborne, waterborne, and foodborne. When preformed, adults consume botulinum toxin, it causes weakness, tiredness, and dizziness within 18 to 36 hours after ingestion. Sometimes, onset of early symptoms occurs after 8 days. Later symptoms are double vision, difficulty in breathing, speaking, and swallowing. This neurotoxin can cause paralysis of motor nerve terminals and when the diaphragm and chest muscles are fully affected, death from asphyxia occurs. An average death-to-case ratio in the USA from 1993 to 1997 is 18 per 1,000 cases. The duration of the intoxication can be as long as one year. Fortunately, the toxin is heat labile and is destroyed at 176°F (80°C). Boiling the food and water for 20 to 30 minutes will destroy the toxin.

Infant botulism is different from the adult type, because it is a noninvasive infection. When the bacteria spores are ingested, they produce the toxin in the gastrointestinal tract. Symptoms include constipation, weakness and lethargy, an altered cry, and loss of head control. Infants over 12 months tend not to be affected due to the establishment of a more normal intestinal biota.

See also Table 1.2 for signs and symptoms and Table 5.2 for foods associated with botulism outbreaks and preventive measures. For selected cases of foodborne disease outbreaks due to *C. botulinum,* see FBDO Reports # 6 and 7, page 246. Read also about the issue of *C. botulinum* and bioterrorism in Chapter 14.

3.3 *Clostridium perfringens*

Clostridium perfringens needs very little oxygen and forms spores. It causes a toxin-mediated infection that results in severe diarrhea and abdominal cramps within 8 to 22 hours after ingesting the contaminated food. The illness usually lasts one day in healthy adults, but longer in the elderly or individuals with other illnesses. Its spores are found in the soil and in the intestines of humans and other animals.

All persons are susceptible to *C. perfringens* poisoning, especially in institutional feeding where large quantities of foods are prepared and proper holding time and temperature before serving are not observed. Fortunately, this bacterium does not grow in the refrigerator at temperatures below 41°F (5°C). No deaths have occurred in reported cases (total =2,772) in the USA from 1993 to 1997.

See Table 1.2 for details on symptoms of *C. perfringens* illness and Table 5.2 for implicated foods and preventive measures.

3.4 *Campylobacter jejuni*

Campylobacter jejuni is unique as a microaerophile, i.e. it can grow in a very strict air with only 3 to 6 percent oxygen. It is found in the intestinal tract of cats, dogs, cattle, poultry, swine, monkeys, rodents, wild birds, and some humans. It is also found in untreated water that has been contaminated with infected feces. Raw poultry is the most common source. Campylobacteriosis is one of the major causes of bacterial infection in people, with onset of symptoms (mainly diarrhea) within two to five days. The illness usually lasts seven to ten days. This microorganism is non-spore-forming, but produces a heat-stable toxin and could result in complications involving the urinary tract (hemolytic uremic syndrome, colitis, meningitis, and Guillain-Barre syndrome. Fortunately, these sequelae or complications are rare and are seen with a person whose immune system is compromised. The estimated death-to-case ratio in the USA is one per 1,000 cases.

The bacteria can be destroyed through cooking and regular water treatment systems. CDC estimates that consuming as low as 500 bacterial cells may cause campylobacteriosis in humans.

See Table 1.2 for more details in symptoms and Table 5.2 for foods associated with campylobacteriosis and how to prevent its occurrence.

3.5 *Escherichia coli*

There are many strains of *E. coli*. Most of them are harmless inhabitants of the end part of human intestinal flora. They are aerobic, non-spore-forming bacteria. The foodborne pathogens referred to collectively as the Enterovirulent *E. coli* Group (EEC Group), are presented below:

1. Enterotoxigenic *E. coli* (ETEC) causes gastroenteritis, prevalent among infants and travelers in developing countries that consumed contaminated food and water. It is noninvasive with symptoms of watery diarrhea, abdominal cramps, nausea, and low-grade fever. It is highly infectious in infants, but in adults, an infective dose can be as many as 10^6 or more cells.
2. Enteroinvasive *E. coli* (EIEC) produces an invasive infection more commonly known as bacillary dysentery. Symptoms occur within 12 to 72 hours after ingesting contaminated food or

drink. See Table 1.2 for details on symptoms. Chronic sequelae may include hemolytic uremic syndrome (HUS), reactive arthritis, or Crohn's disease. As little as 10 bacterial cells can initiate the illness.

3. Enterohemorrhagic *E. coli* (EHEC) is best known by the strain 0157:H7. It produces a verotoxin that is a threat to children and the elderly, because it produces severe symptoms like bloody diarrhea, intense abdominal pain, HUS, and when prolonged, could lead to kidney failure and sometimes death.
4. Enteropathogenic *E. coli* (EPEC) is often observed among bottle-fed infants in developing countries. It is suspected that contaminated water used for formula preparation is the source of EPEC. Infantile diarrhea, which is either watery or bloody, is the main consequence. It is highly infectious and the infective dose required is low. First characterized in 1955, EPEC strains generally affect infants under one year of age. Interestingly, a report of an EPEC outbreak (1961) in Romania was a result of drinking a substitute coffee.[4]

For other foods implicated with *E. coli* cases and preventive measures, see Table 5.2. There are many reports of foodborne disease outbreaks from *E. coli* group. Only a few are given in FBDO Reports #10 to #13, pages 247–248.

3.6 *Listeria monocytogenes*

L. monocytogenes was first detected in humans in 1929. This bacterium can cause a serious disease called listeriosis. Healthy people do not develop the symptoms readily, but it can cause grave illness to newborns, pregnant women, the elderly and persons with weakened immune systems. It could lead to spontaneous abortions, stillbirths, meningitis, septicemia and even death. See Table 1.2 for other signs and symptoms of listeriosis. The Incubation period is from 1 to 6 weeks. For some individuals, early symptoms are flu-like and could appear within twelve hours after ingesting the pathogen.

These bacteria have been isolated from soil, dried leaves, sewage, silage, dust and water. Besides humans, carriers of this pathogen include many domestic as well as wild animals, birds, and fish. *Listeria* group is widely present in the environment. Care in food handling from the farm throughout the food chain is the best way to keep food safe from *L. monocytogenes*. For foods associated with the disease and preventive measures, see Table 5.2

3.7 *Salmonella* spp.

Salmonella spp. are facultative non-spore-forming bacteria that are widespread in animals, particularly in poultry and swine. Other carriers are birds, insects, and wild animals. They are found in feces, which are cycled in the environment via soil, sewage, and polluted water, such as ponds and rivers. There are many serotyped *Salmonella* isolates, which are pathogenic to humans. The common ones are *S. Typhimurium, S. Enteriditis, S. Newport,* and *S. Muenchen*. Current data from FoodNet (a foodborne surveillance network in the United States) reported about fifteen laboratory-confirmed cases of salmonellosis per 100,000 cases of foodborne diseases annually.

As few as 15 ingested cells may cause salmonellosis. The dose varies with the health and age of the person and the serotype of *Salmonella* spp. See Table 1.2 for signs and symptoms of salmonella infection. The incubation period is from twelve to seventy-two hours and the duration of the illness is four to seven days. *S. typhi* and *S. paratyphi* A, B, and C produce typhoid and typhoid-like fevers in humans, causing lesions to some organs. The fatality rate of most salmonellosis is one percent, compared to 10 percent for typhoid fever. Salmonellosis can affect anyone, but occurs more frequently among persons with immuno-compromised disorders, young children, and the elderly.

See Table 5.2 for foods associated with outbreaks and preventive measures for salmonellosis. Read the reports involving salmonellosis in FBDO # 17 to 22, pp. 249–250.

3.8 *Shigella* spp.

The classic bacillary dysentery is a common invasive infection caused by a gram-negative bacillus called *Shigella dysenteriae.* There are three other species (*S. flexneri, S. boydii,* and *S. sonnei*). *S. sonnei* is the mildest and is commonly found in developed countries. *S. dysenteriae* is the most virulent, and usually occurs in the developing nations where as high as 25 percent of infants die from it. Poor personal hygiene is the main factor for the transmission of the disease via fecal-oral route. Infected food handlers are considered the primary vehicles of transmission.

Table 1.2 describes the signs and symptoms of shigellosis, which start to appear within a week after consuming infected food or water. The duration of the illness depends on the kind of treatment received by the sick individual. Gastroenteritis may subside after a week.

Table 5.2 lists the foods associated with shigellosis and guidelines on how to prevent its occurrence. For selected outbreaks involving *Shigellae,* see FBDO Report #23, page 250.

3.9 *Staphylococcus aureus*

Staphylococcus aureus is a facultative anaerobic bacterium that does not form spores, but can survive high acidity. It produces heat-stable enterotoxins and requires a dose as low as less than one microgram in contaminated food to produce staphylococcal intoxication. It has a sudden onset, usually within six hours and the duration is short, about two days. Recovery is often complete and death is rare among healthy individuals, but may occur in chronically ill adults, infants, children, or elderly.

This bacterium is found in the nose, throat, hair, skin, and hands of humans. About 50 percent of humans are asymptomatic carriers. Since people are the primary reservoir of *Staphylococcus* aureus, personal hygiene and sanitary practices in the food flow are the main preventive measures. The bacterium can survive very high salt and sugar concentrations and is resistant to drying and freezing. There are other species that produce enterotoxins, but the most prevalent is *Staphylococcus aureus.*

See Table 5.2 for details on implicated foods. Read FBDO Report #24, page 251, for an outbreak involving *Staphylococci.*

3.10 *Vibrio* spp.

Vibrio cholerae 01 is a non-invasive pathogen responsible for endemic cholera in Asia. The other two species are *Vibrio parahaemolyticus* and *Vibrio vulnificus.* They all produce gastroenteritis within 2 to 48 hours after ingesting the contaminated food or drink. Fortunately, recoveries from *Vibrio* infections are complete, usually after a week, without known sequelae or complications. Death is rare, but can occur in individuals who are immuno-suppressed. See Table 1.2 for signs and symptoms of the disease process and

Table 5.2 for implicated foods and preventive measures to avoid its occurrence. All species are highly resistant to salt and are common in seafood, especially those harvested from warmer waters.

One report of an outbreak from *Vibrio* spp. is narrated in FBDO Report #25, page 251.

3.11 *Yersinia* spp.

Yersiniosis is an invasive infection that causes gastroenteritis within 1 to 2 days after ingestion and usually lasts 3 days, but can be weeks in the very young, elderly and those with weakened immune system. There are several kinds, depending on the geographic location: *Y. enterocolitica* is predominant in the United States and *Y. pseudotuberculosis* occurs in Japan. Humans transmit the Yersinia bacteria and cross-contamination is not uncommon.

Table 5.2 summarizes the foods associated with major foodborne pathogenic bacteria and preventive measures for consumers to control them. Read FBDO Report #26, page 251, about an outbreak of *Y. enterocolitica.*

4.0 FOODBORNE AND WATERBORNE VIRUSES[1,2,3,5,7,10,14]

The term *virus* means, "poison" in Latin. Viruses were first discovered in 1892 when a Russian microbiologist, Dimitri Ivanosky, observed tiny microscopic particles that caused mosaic disease in tobacco plants. After forty years, W. M. Stanley, an American biochemist, demonstrated that viruses consisted only of the genetic material, ribonucleic acid (RNA), and an outer protein covering. Viruses cannot live by themselves and need a living host to inhabit before they can multiply. They cannot reproduce in food.[1]

Viruses are the smallest infectious microorganisms affecting humans. They can be seen only with an electron microscope and they exist in different shapes (spherical, rod-like, polyhedral, etc.). They can pass through the smallest filters since the size of a virus can be as small as 15 nanometers (billionths of a meter).[14]

Viruses can survive freezing. They are transmitted from person-to-person, or from person-to-food, or by cross-contamination. They can contaminate both food and water supplies.

The most common viral diseases of humans are given in the next section.

4.1 Hepatitis A[3,10,12,15]

Infection by Hepatitis A or hepatovirus has a long incubation period, from ten to fifty days. It usually lasts one to two weeks, but it can be months for severe cases. Sources of the virus are human feces. Eating raw shellfish harvested from contaminated harvest beds and swallowing ice or water contaminated with the virus are sources of the illness.

See Table 1.3 for signs and symptoms of Hepatitis A. Food handlers who are sick with hepatitis A are contagious a week before the onset of the symptoms and two weeks after. Some food establishments offer free vaccines for their employees. The best medicine for prevention is to stay healthy. See Table 5.3 for foods associated with the transmission of Hepatitis A and preventive measures.

4.2 Norwalk Virus (SRSVs)[2–5,9–11]

Norwalk virus belongs to a class of tiny viruses known collectively as SRSVs (small round structured viruses). They are prevalent among school age children and adults, and result in diarrhea, gastroenteritis and low-grade fever. See Table 1.4 for more signs and symptoms. Symptoms of SRSVs are usually mild. Onset of symptoms is about one to two days after ingestion of the virus and the illness lasts about three days.

Sewage-contaminated water is the most common vehicle of Norwalk viruses. See Table 5.3 for foods associated with the illness and recommended preventive measures. A recent case of Norwalk virus infection among British military personnel in Afghanistan is narrated in FBDO Report #32, page 253.

4.3 Rotavirus[14]

This viral infection is more serious than Norwalk viral cases, because the diarrhea is more severe. An estimated 75 to 125 deaths occurs each year in the United States. Worldwide, there are nearly one million deaths from an estimated 140 million cases. Sources of contamination are marine foods from polluted water and drinking infected water supplies from wells, lakes, streams, and untreated municipal waters. For more details on implicated foods and means of preventing outbreaks of this viral disease, see Table 5.3.

An emerging disease that is not known yet to be foodborne is Hantavirus. Research developments about this virus are of interest to food industries, food establishments, and consumers, because rodents (rats and mice) are primary reservoir hosts, although other small mammals could be infected also (e.g. brush mice, chipmunks). The infected rodents shed the virus in their saliva, urine, and feces. People can get infected from rodent bites or transmission of contaminated excreta inhaled as aerosols. The chance of exposure is greater if humans work or live in closed spaces where there is active rodent infestation. Although the possibility of getting Hantavirus Pulmonary Syndrome (HPS) is very low, its consequences are very serious. The affected person usually requires intensive care treatment when fever, muscle aches, and coughing rapidly progresses to severe lung disease.

5.0 FOODBORNE AND WATERBORNE PARASITES[1–3,9–12,14,15]

Protozoan parasites are unicellular microorganisms that belong to the kingdom *Protista*. Although they are larger than bacteria, a light microscope is still needed to view them. They are ubiquitous in moist places, especially in water.

A protozoan cannot replicate in food, but the cyst form harbored in foods remains infectious. In general, a very low number may be infectious.

Compromised health is a direct result of parasitical infestation in humans. The loss of nourishment because the parasites live off the body's ingested food, cellular damage, and reduced immune system creates havoc especially in growing children. Fortunately, medical intervention, such as deworming and other medical means are ways to get rid of the intestinal parasites. However, the most important preventive measures are personal hygiene, general sanitary practices, and proper disposal of excreta. Consumer education on frequent handwashing and observing safety tips in handling foods is endless. The role of public health authorities in treating water supplies and sewage cannot be overemphasized.

5.1 *Anisakis* spp.

Anisakis simplex is a roundworm that is transmitted from infected marine fish, like herring, haddock, cod, and salmon that are eaten raw or undercooked. See Table 1.3 for signs and symptoms for this disease. Onset of

Table 5.3
FOODBORNE VIRUSES: IMPLICATED FOODS AND PREVENTIVE MEASURES

Etiology Agent	*Implicated Foods*	*Preventive Measures*
Hepatitis A	Water and ice, shellfish, salads, deli meats and sandwiches, fruits and fruit juices, raw milk and milk products, vegetables, any food that will not receive a further heat treatment.	Obtain shellfish from approved sources, prevent cross-contamination from hands, ensure food handlers practice good personal hygiene, clean and sanitize food contact surfaces, use sanitary water sources.
Norwalk-like viruses	Water, shellfish (especially raw or insufficiently steamed clams and oysters), raw vegetables, fresh fruit and salads, contaminated water.	Obtain shellfish from approved sources, prevent cross-contamination from hands, ensure food handlers practice good personal hygiene, thoroughly cook food to required minimum internal temperatures, use sanitary, chlorinated water.
Rotavirus	Water and ice, raw and ready-to-eat food (salads, fruits, and hors d'oeuvres), contaminated water.	Ensure food handlers practice good personal hygiene, thoroughly cook food to required minimum internal temperatures, use chlorinated water. Person-to-person spread through contaminated hands is probably the most important means by which rotaviruses are transmitted in close communities such as hospitals, day care centers, and family homes.

Source: Compiled from Chapter 5 References 2, 3, 5, 9-12, 22.

symptoms is only a few hours to a week and can last up to three weeks. For other foods associated with this roundworm infection and how to prevent its occurrence, see Table 5.4.

5.2 *Ascaris lumbricoides*[23,24]

The WHO estimated that annually, 1.3 billion persons around the world contract ascariasis infections with about 1,550 deaths per year. Fatalities are due mostly to intestinal obstruction because the number of adult worms that stay in the lumen of the small intestines can be numerous. An adult female roundworm is about 20 to 35 cm long and an adult male, 15 to 30 cm.

Known as the most common human helminthic infection, it is highly prevalent in tropical and subtropical regions, and in areas with poor hygienic and sanitary practices. Proper handwashing, disposal of excreta, and safe consumption of water and food are key to prevention. Public health water treatment reduces risk of ascariasis.[4] See also Table 5.4 for preventive measures of intestinal parasites.

Table 5.4
COMMON FOODBORNE PARASITES:
IMPLICATED FOODS AND PREVENTIVE MEASURES

Etiology Agent	*Implicated Foods*	*Preventive Measures*
Anisakis spp.	Raw, undercooked, or improperly frozen fish, especially cod, haddock, fluke, Pacific salmon, herring, flounder, monkfish, and fish used for sashimi and sushi.	Obtain seafood only from certified sources, when serving raw or undercooked fish, only use sashimi grade fish that has been properly frozen; avoid eating raw or partly cooked fish and shellfish unless it has been properly treated to eliminate parasites; fish intended to be eaten raw should be frozen at –4°F (-20°C) or lower for 7 days in freezer, or at –31°F (-35°C) or lower for 15 hours in a blast chiller. Sanitary disposal of feces; cook food thoroughly.
Ascaris lumbricoides	Contaminated food and water. Person-to-person contact.	Ensure that food handlers practice good personal hygiene; thoroughly wash produce; use potable water. Sanitary disposal of feces; cook food thoroughly.
Cryptosporidium parvum	Water, salads and raw vegetables; raw milk; raw food, such as apple cider; ready-to-eat food.	Ensure that food handlers practice good personal hygiene; thoroughly wash produce; use potable water. Sanitary disposal of feces; cook food thoroughly.
Cyclospora cayetanensis	Water, marine fish, raw milk, raw produce.	Ensure that food handlers practice good personal hygiene; thoroughly wash produce, use potable water. Sanitary disposal of feces; cook food thoroughly.
Entamoeba histolytica	Sewage contaminated water or eating fruit, vegetables and other foods contaminated with this amoeba.	This disease called amebiasis is waterborne and foodborne. Therefore, practice safe food handling and sanitary hygiene. Sanitary disposal of feces; cook food thoroughly.
Giardia lamblia	Contaminated water and ice, salads and (possibly) other raw vegetables.	Use sanitary, chlorinated water supplies; ensure that food handlers practice good personal hygiene; wash raw produce carefully.
Taenia spp.		
T. saginata (beef tapeworm)	Beef infected with tapeworm that is undercooked.	Thoroughly cook beef. Practice good personal hygiene. GENERAL SANITATION.

Continued on next page

Table 5.4—*Continued*

Etiology Agent	*Implicated Foods*	*Preventive Measures*
T. solium (pork tapeworm)	Pork infected with tapeworm that is undercooked	Thoroughly cook pork. Practice good personal hygiene. GENERAL SANITATION.
T. diphyllobothrium (fish tapeworm)	Raw and undercooked fish infected with tapeworm.	Thoroughly cook fish. Practice good personal hygiene. GENERAL SANITATION.
Toxoplasma gondii	Raw or undercooked meat contaminated with this parasite, especially pork, lamb, venison, and hamburger meat. Cross-contamination.	Avoid raw or undercooked meat; thoroughly cook meat to the minimum internal temperature, so there is no pink inside; properly wash hands that come in contact with soil, raw meat, or raw vegetables. Wash hands thoroughly after using the toilet, gardening, handling cats or their litter.
Trichinella spiralis	Undercooked pork or wild game, pork and other sausages (ground meat may be contaminated by meat grinders).	Cook pork and other meat to internal cooking temperatures; wash, rinse, and sanitize equipment, such as sausage grinders and utensils used in the preparation of raw pork and other meat.

Source: Compiled from Chapter 5 References 2, 3, 5, 9-12, 22.

5.3 *Cryptosporidium parvum*[3,5,22]

This parasite causes severe watery diarrhea within a week of ingestion. Its cysts are resistant to regular environmental conditions. It cannot be destroyed by regular chlorination for water treatment; however, the parasite can be removed by using the proper sized pores of an ultra-filtering system.

Each cyst releases four spindle-shaped motile sporozoites in the stomach that infect the intestinal walls. Fewer than ten oocysts are needed to cause cryptosporidiosis. The human infection rate is estimated to occur in one of every 100 persons with diarrhea in developed countries, and about 16 percent in less developed countries. Among AIDS patients, an average parasite infection prevalence of 3 to 4 percent is reported in the United States and 50 percent in Africa and Haiti.

Water supplies contaminated with infected feces are the main parasite transmission vehicle, whether used for drinking and cooking, or in recreational waters. Recently, there have been reports implicating unpasteurized fruit juices and milk. Infected food handlers, cross-contamination, and the consumption of contaminated raw food are other means of transmission. See Table 5.4 for preventive measures and FBDO Report # 8, page 247, for an example of outbreak of cryptosporidiosis linked to a contaminated public water supply.

5.4 *Cyclospora cayetanensis*[1,3,5]

C. cayetanensis is a tiny single-celled parasite that is about 10 microns or twice the size of *Cryptosporidium*. First observed in 1977, it is transmitted via the fecal-oral route. Infected feces contaminate groundwater, which in turn contaminates produce by irrigation.

When ingested by humans from infected produce or drinking contaminated water, it causes watery, explosive diarrhea, abdominal pain, nausea and vomiting. Onset of symptoms is within a week. See Table 1.3 for other signs and symptoms and Table 5.4 for foods implicated with this parasitic illness and how to prevent its occurrence. For outbreaks of cyclosporiasis in the United States and Canada in the year 1997 alone, see FBDO Report #14, page 248.

5.5 *Diphyllobotrium latum*[3,5,23]

Diphyllobotrium latum is the largest human tapeworm, sometimes called broad fish tapeworm. They can grow as long as three to six feet. Diphyllobotriasis is the name of the infection. Its symptoms appear about ten days after consumption of the raw or undercooked freshwater fish that contain fish tapeworms. In prolonged illness, the disease may result in pernicious anemia or vitamin B_{12} deficiency and intestinal tissue damage.

Eggs of this worm will appear in the feces five to six weeks after infection. The usual fecal-oral route is the main mode of transmission. Therefore, the general preventive measures are the same for all intestinal parasites for humans to observe (see Table 5.4). These include proper disposal of sewage and human excreta, and proper thorough cooking of fishes.

5.6 *Giardia lamblia*[5,25]

Giardia lamblia is a flagellated protozoan that can attach firmly to the human intestinal wall. Its disease, giardiasis, results in a prolonged diarrhea that could last for weeks, causing weakness, malaise, abdominal cramps, flatulence, and weight loss. Considered as one of the most common waterborne diseases, it is transmitted via contaminated water that carries the feces of infected persons, wild and domestic animals. It has been reported as the most frequently identified etiologic agent of outbreaks associated with drinking water in the United States for two decades from 1974 to 1994.

Giardiasis has an incubation period of three days to three weeks. The infectious dose is as few as ten cysts. Persons at high risk are children in day care centers, back packers and campers, travelers to disease-endemic areas, persons drinking from contaminated well water, and individuals who accidentally swallow contaminated water from recreational water facilities. See Table 1.3 for signs and symptoms and Table 5.4 for preventive measures. Read also FBDO Report No. 2, page 245.

5.7 *Entamoeba histolytica*[5,23,26]

Amebic dysentery or amebiasis is caused by the protozoan *Entamoeba histolytica,* which occurs worldwide when people consume contaminated food or water. Death from amebiasis is estimated to be 40 thousand annually and close to 40 million develop the disease, which is about one percent of the world population. The cysts are resistant to the acidity of the stomach. In the intestines, the cyst walls are digested; the vegetative cells are released and multiply rapidly. Masses of amoebae and mucus can cause intestinal obstruction.

The diarrhea caused by amebiasis contains blood and mucus. Severe infections are likely to occur when the intestinal wall is perforated.

Bacterial infection may spread and can invade other organs, particularly the liver. It is estimated that globally one person in ten is infected seriously. Amebiasis may last for some individuals for many years, unless treated with adequate and appropriate medication.

See Table 5.4 for foods implicated with *Entamoeba histolytica* and preventive measures for the disease, which include observing of hygienic practices in the use of the restroom and proper handwashing.

5.8 *Taenia* spp.[3,5,23]

Taenia spp. are parasitic tapeworms that are more harmful as mature cysts, causing the disease, cysteriosis. Pork tapeworm (*T. solium*) infestation could be very serious when the larvae penetrate the stomach wall and invade the tissues, like the muscles and brain. When the cysts begin to degenerate, the surrounding tissues become inflamed. Epileptic-like seizures may occur with visual disturbances. Death is possible.

Humans are the only definitive hosts for both beef and pork tapeworms. The eggs are passed with the feces. When humans eat raw or undercooked beef or pork, the eggs get into the intestines and are hatched. The worms can reach lengths of 5 to 10 m for *T. saginata* (beef tapeworm) and 2 to 7 m. for *T. solium.*

Both species occur worldwide, with greater prevalence in poorer and crowded communities. All persons are susceptible to taeniasis. For preventive measures, see Table 5.4.

5.9 *Toxoplasma gondii*[3,10,23]

Toxoplasmosis is a disease caused by a protozoan parasite, *Toxoplasma gondii,* which needs cats in its life cycle. Cysts of this parasite have been found in pork, lamb, and wild game. Cats acquire the parasites from eating rodents, birds, and raw meat. The disease occurs all over the world and is a serious ailment, because it affects nerve and muscle tissues. The incidence is higher in the tropics and lower in colder climates. In Europe, toxoplasmosis is observed in about five percent of newborns. In the United States, it is estimated that about 3,000 newborns annually are positive for the disease and the rates of death are high.[1]

Toxoplasmosis has serious consequences in pregnant females. It may be contracted from undercooked meats.

Cat owners should feed their pets dry, canned or boiled food, **never** undercooked meats. Wear gloves when cleaning up litter boxes or when gardening. Wash hands thoroughly before and after wearing gloves. Always cover children's outdoor sandboxes when not in use. See other details in Table 5.4.

5.10 *Trichinella spiralis*[3,5,10,11]

Ingesting undercooked pork and pork products causes trichinosis, sometimes called trichinellosis. *T. spiralis* is a nematode (roundworm) that may be harbored also in other wild animals or game. There is no person-to-person transmission. The only route is to eat the food implicated with the parasite (see Table 5.4). Table 1.3 describes the symptoms of trichinosis, which appear a few days after ingestion of the worms, which can last for months. Severe cases involve difficulty in breathing and in coordinating muscle movements.

For preventive measures, follow the three C's: COOK thoroughly, CLEAN and sanitize all surfaces and equipment, including cutting boards and meat slicers/knives; and CHILL until ready to serve. It is recommended that hog feed be cooked thoroughly before feeding to the animals. Bear in mind that curing, drying, smoking, and microwave cooking do not consistently kill the worms, but irradiation destroys *Trichinella* spp. effectively.

Several outbreaks of trichinosis are cited in FBDO Reports # 27 to 30, page 252–253.

6.0 HARMFUL FUNGI[1-3,5-12,15,18]

Fungi are eucaryotic cells that lack chlorophyll. Hence, they cannot generate energy through photosynthesis. They require an aerobic environment. They range in size from microscopic, single celled microorganisms to large multicellular organisms. They are found in nature, including air, food and water, soil, plants and animals. Harmful molds, yeasts, and poisonous mushrooms are the fungi of concern to humans in relation to food safety.

6.1 Molds

Molds are multicellular colonies that form intertwined and branching hyphae or filaments. Hyphae are threadlike cylindrical tubules that grow longitudinally. Molds produce spores for their reproduction. The fuzzy or slimy mold colonies that grow on breads, cheese, spoiled tomatoes, and rotten vegetables are visible to the naked eye. Sometimes one can recognize mold growth by their colored spots, although usually they are white. They grow best in moist warm temperatures, but can grow in a lower water activity (a_w) environment compared to bacteria and yeasts. Thus, they can be seen on the surface of salty ham or fish, jams or any sugar-concentrated food items.

Molds are responsible for food spoilage that result in the formation of odors, off-flavors and color changes. NEVER SMELL A FOOD ITEM close to your nose to avoid breathing in mold spores and other objectionable contaminants.

Most molds damage grains resulting in great economic losses. Most damage occurs during harvest time, wet seasons, and improper storage. Furthermore, farm animals often refuse to eat moldy feeds, thus lowering their immune systems.

Of greater concern about molds related to food safety is their ability to produce toxins, called mycotoxins. Hundreds of mycotoxins have been identified and are by far the most important contaminants of the food chain. In humans, mycotoxins can cause vomiting, fever, and headache. Some mycotoxins are carcinogenic.[7] See other details on the ill effects of mycotoxins in Chapter 1.

Table 5.5 is a summary of the most important mycotoxins and the foods at risk.

6.2 Yeasts[5,7,23]

Yeasts are single-celled fungi, in contrast to molds, which are multi-cellular. They differ from bacteria by their larger cell size and their shape, which may be oval, elongated, elliptical or spherical. The average cell size of yeast is from 5 to 8 micrometers in diameter. They grow in numbers by dividing (budding or fission).

Yeasts can grow over wide ranges of acid pH solutions and in ethanol solutions as high as 18 percent. Many can grow in sugar solutions that are 50–60 percent. Some can be recognized by the colors they produce (cream, pink, orange, red). Their spores are quite heat-resistant. Some can grow at very low temperatures (–20 to –34°C).

There are many genera of yeasts and some are useful for the food industry. The harmful ones cause food spoilage and undesirable taste.

The most common yeasts in foods are: *Candida* (found in beef, poultry, kefir grain, beer, ales and fruit juices), Rhodotorula (found in fresh poultry, shrimps, fish, beef, surface of butter), *Saccharomyces* (bakers' and brewers' yeasts, wine and champagne yeasts),

Figure 5.2. Examples of Molds. Left: T. roseum (causes pink rot on fruits). Center: B. fulva (spoils canned and bottled fruits). Right: C. gloseosporiodes (produces brown/black spots on some fruits).

Zygosaccharomyces (useful for shoyu and miso fermentation, but spoilers of mayonnaise and salad dressings). Genus *Torula* causes black discoloration of butter. The quality of fruit juice concentrates depends on the absence of yeast cells.

6.3 Mushrooms[2,9,11]

There is no general rule to distinguish between edible versus poisonous mushrooms. The toxins involved in mushroom poisoning are produced naturally by the toxic species of this fungus. Most of them cannot be made nontoxic by cooking, canning, freezing, or other means of processing. Therefore, the only way to avoid poisoning is to avoid eating the toxic varieties. If in doubt whether a species is poisonous or not, forget it! Do not eat wild or non-identified varieties.

Mushroom poisoning is usually acute and the severity of symptoms depends on how much was eaten and the kind or species of the toxic mushroom. There are three categories of mushroom poisoning: ***protoplasmic,*** which results in a generalized destruction of cells, followed by organ failure; ***neurologic,*** which causes hallucinations, depression, coma, convulsion; *gastrointestinal,* which include spastic colon, rapid nausea and vomiting, abdominal cramps, and diarrhea.

Amatoxins come from *Amanita* species, Autumn skullcap and its relatives. Incubation period ranges from six to forty-eight hours. Hydrazines as in false morel species are less severe than the amatoxins. Muscarine toxin is a neurotoxin caused by any number of *Inocybe* species. Green Gill, Tigertop, and Sickener are just a few of the mushroom species that are gastrointestinal irritants.

Outbreaks of mushroom poisoning are rare and sporadic. All humans are susceptible to mushroom poisoning. Serious cases may be life threatening. For an example of *Amanita phalloides* mushroom poisoning, see FBDO Report # 40, page 256.

7.0 PRIONS[3,5,16–19]

Prions refer to proteinaceous infectious particles (PrP). They are small glycosylated

Table 5.5
COMMON MYCOTOXINS: IMPLICATED FOODS AND PREVENTIVE MEASURES

Mycotoxin	*Name of Molds*	*Implicated Foods*	*Preventive Measures*
Aflatoxin	*Aspergillus flavus*	Nuts, rice, coffee, cocoa, soya, corn and corn products, milk and milk products	Inspect foods purchased carefully for any molds. Buy from reliable sources. Be sure the package is intact. Note "buy by date" on label. Store foods properly at all points of the food chain.
Citrinin	*Penicillium citrinum* *P. viridicatum*	Wheat, oats, rye, rice, cheese	Same as above.
Ochratoxins	*A. ochraceus* *P. viridicatum*	Cereal crops, nuts, citrus fruits, coffee, cocoa, soya, cheese	Same as above.
Penicillic acid	*P. cyclopium* *P. martensii*	Corn, beans, fruit	Same as above.
Sterigmatocyst	*a. versicolor*	Grains, coffee, in miscellaneous foods	Same as above.
Trichothecenes	*Fusarium graminearum* *F. tricinctum*	Corn and cereal crops	Same as above.
Zearalenone	*F. graminearum*	Corn and cereal crops	Same as above.

Source: Compiled from Chapter 5 References 2, 3, 5, 9-12, 22.

protein molecules found in brain cell membranes. The other group name for prion diseases is "transmissable spongiform encephalophathies (TSEs)," because these diseases create spongiform pathological changes in the brain, and result in encephalopathy or brain damage. Trion diseases are fatal neuro-degenerative disorders of humans and other animals.

7.1 Mad Cow Disease

The best known of the TSEs is "mad cow" disease, or "bovine spongiform encephalopathy" (BSE). The first case of an infected cow was observed to be disoriented, irritable, and unable to stand or walk properly. Most cases in Great Britain occur in dairy cows between three to six years of age. Milk production decreases and the animals show nervousness, aggression, abnormal posture, incoordination, and difficulty in rising.

BSE is a chronic, degenerative disease affecting the central nervous system of cattle. It also affects sheep and the disease is commonly called "scrapie." The incubation period takes months or years and the illness is progressively debilitating. There is no treatment and the affected animals die.

Other than the United Kingdom, countries with confirmed cases of BSE include: Austria, Belgium, Denmark, Finland, France, Germany, Greece, Ireland, Poland, Spain, and Switzerland. In the United States, there have not been any BSE cases reported, although it is considered to be a potential threat. Therefore, federal and state agencies are aggressive in enforcing related regulations to prevent TSEs from occurring.[16]

Currently, all European Union (EU) nations prohibit the feeding of certain mammalian proteins (e.g. offals) to ruminants.

7.2 Creutzfeldt-Jakob Disease (CJD)

Creutzfeldt-Jakob Disease (CJD) is a rare and fatal neuro-degenerative disease in humans. People affected are usually between 50 to 75 years old. The etiology is unknown. Typical clinical signs and symptoms include a rapidly progressive dementia. A neuropathological examination reveals cortical spongiform changes. Therefore, the term "spongiform encephalopathy" is the other name for CJD. The majority of cases are sporadic (about 85%) and between 10%–15% are familial. An inherited abnormal gene causes the latter type of CJD. In the United Kingdom with a population of about 58 million, there are only a few deaths a year due to genetic CJD.

The sporadic type occurs in the United States and worldwide at a rate of about one case per million per year. The cause of sporadic CJD remains uncertain. However, the most favored theory suggests that the normal prion protein in the brain undergoes a spontaneous change to the abnormal form that results in disease.

The first case of BSE in humans was observed in 1989, believed to have been transmitted from beef to humans when contaminated bovine offal was used as animal feed. Offal is made from the remains of butchered animals. This practice is now banned.

8.0 EMERGING FOODBORNE DISEASES[9,12,21]

The emerging foodborne and waterborne diseases have already been discussed in previous pages. This section is to explain further why there was an upsurge of interest in this group of diseases in the last two decades.

Emerging foodborne diseases are defined as those that have recently appeared in a population for the following reasons:

- changes in the pathogens themselves,
- globalization of the food supply (e.g., increased import-export trade),
- increase of populations at higher risks (e.g., street drug abuse and immunosuppressed cases)
- changes in demography (e.g., urbanization), and
- technical developments.

With regard to changes in the pathogens, microbial adaptation through natural selection is the key process in the emergence of pathogens and in some cases, the re-emergence. The increasing use of therapeutic agents like antibiotics, to farm animals and humans favor the survival of bacterial strains that become resistant to the drugs. To explain the last reason, the food chain has become more and more complex, with more opportunities for contamination. Also, with newer knowledge of identifying and analyzing pathogens, what may have existed before, have re-emerged. New food vehicles of transmission have given way to the emergence of foodborne problems. The changes in dietary behavior, a rise in risky sexual behavior, liberalization of trade, popularity of street foods, shopping for food from home, fast food dining out, etc., have contributed to the emergence of foodborne diseases.

The following list identifies the emerging foodborne and waterborne illnesses:

1.. *Campylobacter jejuni*
2. *Cryptosporidium parvum*
3. *Cyclospora cayetanensis*
4. *E. coli* 0157:H7 and other related *E. coli* strains (e.g., serotypes 0111:NM, 0104:H21)
5. Hepatitis E virus (HEV)
6. *Listeria monocytogenes*
7. Norwalk-like viruses
8. *Vibrio cholera* 01
9. *Vibrio vulnificus*
10. *Vibrio parahaemolyticus*
11. *Yersinia enterocolitica*

Note that some of the above are foodborne zoonoses, i.e., virtually all have a vertebrate animal reservoir from which humans may contract them. The animals may be apparently healthy. Currently, public health concerns now include the safety of what food animals themselves eat and drink.

9.0 CONDITIONS FOR GROWTH OF MICROORGANISMS[7,10,11]

The primary goal of food handlers and consumers is to prevent the growth of foodborne and waterborne pathogens for safe eating and drinking. To be more effective and for continued vigilance in observing guidelines on preventive measures, everyone should understand the conditions required for microbial growth. Managers and food supervisors have the responsibility to teach food employees the necessary background knowledge on this topic. A review of FAT-TOM, the acronym given for the factors of microbial growth, is presented in the succeeding sections.

9.1 Food

Microorganisms need food. Many bacteria prefer foods that are high in amino acids and simple protein, such as meat, poultry, fish, eggs, milk, and other dairy products. They also like complex carbohydrates like cereals, beans, pasta, and potatoes. Collectively, such food items are known as potentially hazardous foods (PHF). Potentially hazardous foods are foods that are natural or made by humans and are in a form capable of supporting the rapid and progressive growth of infectious microorganisms and the production of their toxins.

9.2 Acidity

Most bacteria prefer a neutral environment (pH 7.0). However, the range for optimum growth for most foodborne pathogens is between the pH of 6.0 to 8.0. Most foods humans eat (i.e., PHF items) fall within this range. A pH below 4.5 will not normally support bacterial growth, but some acid tolerant will still grow at a lower pH. Alkaline foods (pH above 7.0) include egg whites and soda crackers.

9.3 Time

Given other favorable conditions, bacteria can grow in a number at a logarithmic rate. The organism count doubles every 20 to 30 minutes on the average. A hundred cells become 10,000 after 20 minutes and after five hours there will be at least a million bacterial cells. A rule of thumb is to remember that bacteria need about four hours to reach an infective dose in ideal growth conditions.

9.4 Temperature

Most bacteria grow rapidly 60°F to 120°F (16°C to 52°C). This range is called "Temperature Danger Zone," i.e., danger signal for consumers to take extra care in food handling, but is a favorable temperature condition for microorganisms (see Figure 5.4). The

Figure 5.3. Potentially Hazardous Foods.

middle range of temperatures between 70°F and 140°F (21°C and 60°C) are best for the mesophilic bacteria. The psychotropic bacteria grow best within the range of 32°F to 80°F (0°C to 30°C). One should remember that temperature control is related with time period. Therefore, conditions of storing, preparation, serving temperatures also specify the duration or time factor.

See Appendices E, F, and G for the proper storage of foods that are refrigerated, frozen, or kept in pantry shelves for dry storage.

9.5 Oxygen

Bacteria are sometimes classified according to their requirements for oxygen:

- Aerobic bacteria MUST have free oxygen.
- Anaerobic bacteria MUST not have free oxygen because it is toxic to them. They cannot grow in the presence of oxygen.
- Facultative anaerobic bacteria can growth with or without free oxygen. Most foodborne pathogens belong to this group.
- Microaerophilic bacteria need a very limited amount of free oxygen to grow, usually three to six percent.

9.6 Moisture

Moisture is more appropriately called available water, represented as water activity (a_w), which is the amount of water not bound to food and is available for bacterial growth. **Pathogenic bacteria can grow only in foods with a water activity higher than 0.85.**

Using a scale of 0 to 1.0, examples of available water in foods are:

0.92 (raw bacon and mayonnaise)
0.94 (cheddar cheese)
0.98 (steamed rice, raw beef, chicken and fish muscles)
0.99 (raw egg white)
1.0 (distilled water).

REMEMBER THAT THE FOOD COMPOSITION TABLES FOR WATER CONTENT ARE "WATER BY VOLUME" AND NOT "AVAILABLE WATER" OR WATER ACTIVITY VALUES.

10.0 KINDS OF FOOD SPOILAGE AND FOODBORNE ILLNESSES

When microorganisms are allowed to grow or multiply, one or more of these problems will occur:

Food Spoilage. Changes in the appearance, aroma, taste, and sometimes color, occur in the food due to the chemical changes brought about by the contaminating microorganisms. For example, yeasts convert the carbohydrate in apple juice into ethyl alcohol, giving it an off-taste. Other products of microbial metabolism of carbohydrates are acids that cause food to sour, and gas resulting in the swelling of sealed cans.

The fermentation of lactose in milk by bacteria causes curdling and souring. Certain bacteria break down amino acids into foul-smelling products: tryptophan is digested by bacteria, yielding indole and skatole that give food a fecal odor. Cystine, another amino acid, when attacked by bacteria, gives off hydrogen sulfide that is responsible for the rotten egg smell in the spoiling food.

Some microorganisms produce pigments that cause color changes in the food. Capsule production by certain bacteria causes food to become slimy. An example is ropiness in milk and breads.

Some species of bacteria that produce the enzyme lipase act on fats and convert them to

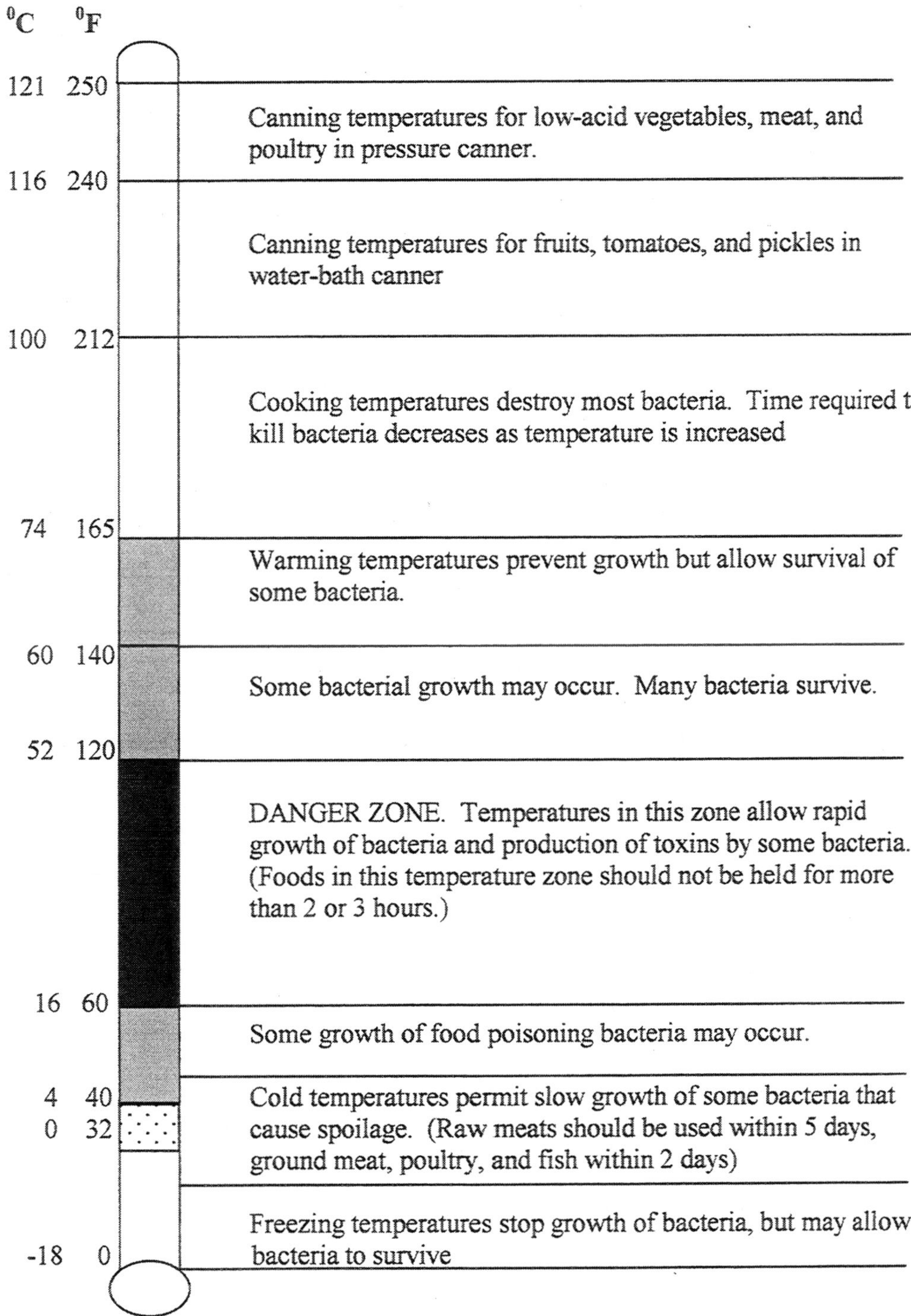

Figure 5.4. Temperature Control of Bacteria. *Source:* US Department of Agriculture. *Home and Garden Bulletin No. 162,* 1970.

glycerol and fatty acids. Rancidity of butter is an example of this type of spoilage.

The fuzzy growth of molds, along with color changes in food, is obvious to the naked eye. What cannot be smelled, tasted nor seen are the foodborne pathogens that cause illnesses, which are usually classified as foodborne infection, food intoxication, and toxin-mediated infection.

Foodborne Infection. Eating food that contains living disease-producing microorganisms causes foodborne infection. After a person ingests the contaminated food, the pathogenic organisms multiply in the linings of the victim's digestive tract and produce metabolic products that cause symptoms like nausea and vomiting, abdominal pain, and diarrhea. An example of a food infection is salmonellosis.

Food Intoxication. Sometimes called food poisoning, this is caused by the toxins produced by a living microorganism as it multiplies in food. Then, when this contaminated food is eaten along with the toxins, the person becomes ill. Examples of microorganisms in this category are: *Clostridium botulinum* and *Staphylococcus aureus.*

Toxic-mediated Infection. This occurs when the pathogenic microorganism ingested with the food produces its toxins inside the human gastrointestinal tract. An example is *Clostridium perfringens.*

Almost all food illnesses and food spoilage are preventable. One big topic for preventive measures is the control of microbial growth, which will be explained in the next sections. However, at this point, it is advisable to be reminded about other preventive measures that have been discussed in previous chapters: personal hygiene, maintaining a sanitary environment, disrupting the life cycle of the pathogenic organism as in the case of parasitic protozoan, and the use of disinfectants, etc. One factor, which is often neglected, is to maintain good health and nutrition, such that a person's immune system can resist infections.

11.0 HOW TO CONTROL MICROBIAL GROWTH

An excellent textbook for this topic is *Modern Food Microbiology* by J. M. Jay.[5]

Any method to slow down the growth of pathogenic organisms, or totally kill them, based on the application of the principles of FATTOM will prevent/reduce the incidence of foodborne illnesses. Food preservation techniques, whether traditional or newer technologies, are effective means of prolonging shelf life of foods, and improving palatability qualities in some cases, because of their effects on microbial life and growth.

11.1. Application of Heat

Adequate heat (proper temperature and period of exposure) kills microorganisms by changing the physical and chemical properties of their proteins. As structural proteins and enzymes are denatured the organism will die.

Blanching and canning are examples of applying heat. Modern commercial canning processes are complex and include a sterilization process designed to eliminate the most resistant bacterial spores, especially those of the genera *Clostridium* and *Bacillus.* Home canning should be done with a high-pressure canner (pressure cooker). For foods that are low in acid (pH higher than 4.6), lower the pH of the food by adding vinegar, lemon juice, citric acid, and the like. Consumers should follow instructions on proper canning procedures established by reliable sources, especially the full processing time required and correct temperature to attain. Use an accurate pressure gauge.

Boiling destroys non-spore-forming microorganisms rapidly. To ensure safe drinking water, bring the water to a hard boil and continue to boil for a few minutes.

In cooking meats, fish, poultry, eggs, and other foods, follow the time and temperature for doneness, and use a reliable thermometer to measure recommended internal temperatures. In hot holding of foods served, or in reheating foods safely, follow the guidelines in this chapter. The US Food Code 2001 is an excellent source of information for food and water safety (see Appendix I). Other countries may have their own agencies that recommend rules and regulations for safe food and water consumption.

The various methods of pasteurization are classic examples of applying heat to kill disease-causing microorganisms. The most traditional method is called **the holding method,** which is accomplished by heating milk in a large tank at 62.9°C or 145°F for 30 minutes. The milk is stirred constantly to ensure uniform heating, and then cooled quickly after the pasteurization process. **The flash method** heats milk through a hot cylinder at 71.6°C or 161°F for 15 to 17 seconds. A newer method is called **ultrapasteurization,** which heats milk and milk products at 82°C or 180°F for only a few seconds.

11.2 Application of Low Temperatures

This category includes refrigerating and freezing. Modern refrigeration at 40°F will stop or slow down the growth of most microorganisms, but they will still survive at refrigeration temperatures.

Listeria and *Yersinia* can grow at low temperatures. Storage periods by refrigeration for specific kinds of foods are to be observed, or food spoilage can still occur. (See Appendix E for the recommended safe periods to keep various foods under refrigeration.) It is best not to depend on the maximum storage time, but use refrigerated foods as soon as possible. Keep foods covered to avoid cross-contamination and to avoid drying. Label foods and date when first stored, especially leftovers. Defrost regularly and do not crowd the food containers in order to allow for air circulation. Monitor or check the temperature inside with an accurate refrigerator thermometer.

Freezing halts the growth of all microorganisms (see Figure 5.4 in this chapter). For recommended storage periods of a specific food commodity see Appendix F.

Frozen foods should be kept solidly frozen. Check your freezer temperature with an accurate thermometer. One practical way to detect that your home freezer is working well is to check on the ice cubes and a brick of ice cream. These should be solidly frozen, attaining a temperature of minus 18°C or 0°F throughout the product. Avoid temperatures higher than 5°F or −15°C. Be sure to date food packages. Use moisture and vapor-proof (MVP) packaging materials.

11.3 Controlling pH Conditions

Lowering the pH of a food to a level where most microorganisms cannot survive (i.e., pH values below 4.6) can be accomplished by fermentation or by acidification with acid ingredients like vinegar, lemon juice, or citric acid. Fermentation refers to the anaerobic and aerobic metabolism of carbohydrates by microorganisms (like lactic acid bacteria, acetic acid bacteria, and yeast).

Some chemical preservatives used by food manufacturers that lower the pH of foods are sorbic acid, benzoic acid, and propionic acid.

11.4 Reducing Free Oxygen

Some pathogenic microorganisms require free oxygen for growth. Partial or complete removal of available oxygen therefore will retard their growth and metabolic activities harmful to humans. Examples of such processes include: vacuum-packaging, modern canning with hermetic seals, and modified atmospheric packaging (MAP).

Another method to reduce the amount of available oxygen for bacterial growth is to coat the foods with waxes or other edible coatings, as done with fresh fruit and vegetables in the United States. Consumers should be aware that some of these coatings are regarded as food additives.

11.5 Reducing Available Water

Drying is one of the oldest traditional methods of food preservation. Modern techniques of dehydration still apply the same principle of depriving the microorganisms of free or available water for growth. The amount of free water or water activity varies among molds, yeast, and bacteria (see Section 9.6). However, molds can still grow on dried fruits and jams and jellies whereas bacteria cannot.

Most dried foods are relatively stable. They should not contain over 20 percent water. See Appendix G for recommended storage periods for a food group or commodity at 70°F (dry storage) in pantry or kitchen shelves. The kitchen shelves should not be close to a stove or source of heat.

11.6 Role of Other Chemicals

Besides the chemical additives mentioned in lowering the pH of foods, other agents that may retard microbial growth are nitrates and nitrites, salt, and sugars. There are also antioxidants and antibiotics that affect microorganisms or reduce microbial growth. The topic of pesticides, fungicides, and other agents are explained in Chapters 6 and 7. Common chemical agents used for cleansing, disinfecting and sanitizing purposes in food establishments or household kitchens include: soaps, detergents, chlorine compounds, halogens and phenolic compounds (see Chapter 7 for further details).

11.7 Role of Newer Technologies

A separate chapter discusses the more advanced methods of food preservation (see Chapter 11).

12.0 GENERAL SAFETY GUIDELINES TO CONTROL MICROBIAL GROWTH[4,7,8,10,11,22,27]

Safe steps in food handling, cooking, and storage are essential to avoid foodborne illness. Follow these food safety guidelines to keep pathogens away.

12.1 Safe Shopping

"BUY COLD FOOD LAST; GET IT HOME FAST"

- Never choose packages that are torn or leaking.
- Don't buy foods past "sell-by" or expiration dates.
- Put raw meat and poultry into a plastic bag so meat juices won't cross-contaminate cooked foods or those eaten raw, such as vegetables or fruits.
- Place refrigerated or frozen items in the shopping cart last before heading for the checkout counter.

- When loading the car in hot or warm climates, keep perishable items inside the air-conditioned car and not in the trunk or have an insulated box or cooler with ice-cubes.
- Drive immediately home from the grocery. If you live more than 30 minutes away, bring a cooler with ice from home and place perishables inside.

12.2 Safe Storage of Foods

"KEEP IT SAFE; REFRIGERATE"

- Unload perishable foods from the car first and immediately refrigerate them. Place securely wrapped packages of raw meat, poultry, or fish in the meat drawer or coldest section of your refrigerator.
- Check the temperature of your unit with an appliance thermometer. To slow bacterial growth, the refrigerator should be at 40°F, the freezer at 0°F.
- Cook or freeze fresh poultry, fish, ground meats, and variety meats within 2 days, other beef, veal, lamb, or pork, within 3 to 5 days.

12.3 Safe Food Preparation

"KEEP EVERYTHING CLEAN!"

- Wash hands before and after handling raw meat and poultry.
- Sanitize cutting boards often in a solution of 1 teaspoon chlorine bleach in 1 quart of water. Wash kitchen towels and cloths often in hot water in washing machine.
- Don't cross-contaminate. Keep raw meat, poultry, fish and their juices away from other food. After cutting raw meats, wash hands, cutting board, knife, and counter tops with hot, soapy water.
- Marinate meat and poultry in a covered dish in the refrigerator.

12.4 Thaw Food Safely

There are three safe ways of thawing foods:

1. Refrigerator: allows slow, safe thawing. Make sure thawing juices do not drip on other foods.
2. Cold water: for faster thawing place food in a leak-proof plastic bag and submerge in cold tap water.
3. Microwave: cook meat and poultry immediately after microwave thawing.

12.5 Safe Cooking

- Cook ground meats to an internal temperature of 160°F; ground poultry to 165°F.
- Beef, veal and lamb steaks, roasts, and chops may be cooked to 145°F and all cuts of fresh pork, 160°F.
- Whole poultry should reach 180°F and 170°F in the thighs and breasts.

12.6 Serving Food Safely

"NEVER LEAVE IT OUT OVER 2 HOURS"

Bacteria that cause foodborne illness grow rapidly at room temperature. Hot food should be kept hot and cold food should be kept cold.

- When serving foods at a buffet, keep hot food over a heat source (maintain temperature above 140°F) and keep cold food on ice. Maintaining the cold temperature at 40°F or below. Keep platters of food refrigerated until time to serve or reheat.

- Carry perishable picnic food in a cooler with a cold pack or ice. Set the cooler in the shade and open the lid as little as possible.

12.7 Handling Leftovers Safely

- Divide foods into shallow containers for rapid cooling. Put food directly in the refrigerator or freezer. Be sure to cover properly.
- Cut turkey or whole ham off the bone and refrigerate. Slice thick parts of the meat; legs and wings may be left whole.
- Use cooked leftovers within 3 days.

12.8 Refreezing Food

Meat and poultry defrosted in the refrigerator may be refrozen before or after cooking. If thawed by other methods, cook before refreezing.

12.9 Food Safety Advice for Expectant Mothers[28]

- Never eat raw meat, such as steak tartare (a raw hamburger dish), poultry, or seafood (especially raw oysters and clams).
- Don't eat raw or undercooked eggs and any food containing them such as Caesar salad, mousse, some custards, homemade ice cream, and homemade mayonnaise.
- Don't drink raw or unpasteurized milk or foods made from raw milk.
- Don't eat soft cheeses, such as feta, Brie, Camembert, blue, and Mexican style soft white types such as Queso Blanco and Queso Fresco.
- Avoid food from deli counters and thoroughly reheat lunch meats and hot dogs.
- Make sure food (meat, poultry, fish, seafood, etc.) is thoroughly cooked.
- Before eating stuffing cooked inside whole poultry, be sure it has reached 165°F.
- Cook thoroughly. Use a thermometer to be sure foods reach 160°F to destroy any bacteria present. Whole poultry should reach an internal temperature of 180°F.
- Eggs should be cooked solid, both yolk and white.

12.10 Cooking Safely in the Microwave Oven[29]

Microwave Oven Cooking

- Arrange food items evenly in a covered dish and add some liquid if needed. Cover the dish with a lid or wrap to let steam escape. The moist heat that is created will help destroy harmful bacteria and ensure uniform cooking. Cooking bags also provide safe, even cooking.
- Do not cook large cuts of meat on high power (100%). Large cuts of meat should be cooked on medium power (50%) for longer periods. This allows heat to reach the center without overcooking outer areas.
- Stir or rotate food midway through the microwaving time for more even cooking to eliminate cold spots where harmful bacteria can survive.
- When partially cooking food in the microwave oven to finish cooking on the grill or in a conventional oven, it is important to transfer the microwaved food to the other heat source immediately. Never partially cook food and store it for later use.
- Use a food thermometer or the oven's temperature probe to verify the food has

reached a safe temperature. Place the thermometer in the thickest area of the meat or poultry–not near fat or bone–and in the innermost part of the thigh of whole poultry. Cooking times may vary because ovens vary in power and efficiency. Check in several places to be sure red meat is 160°F, whole poultry is 180°F, and egg casseroles are 160°F. Fish should flake with a fork. Always allow standing time, which completes the cooking, before checking the internal temperature with a food thermometer. Follow instructions on the label or package; the manufacturing/processing company tests these recommendations.

- Cooking whole, stuffed poultry in a microwave oven is not recommended. The stuffing might not reach the temperature needed to destroy harmful bacteria.

Containers and Wraps

- Only use cookware that is specially manufactured for use in the microwave oven. Glass, ceramic containers, and all plastics should be labeled for microwave oven use.
- Plastic storage containers such as margarine tubs, take-out containers, whipped topping bowls, and other one-time use containers should not be used in microwave ovens. These containers can warp or melt, possibly causing harmful chemicals to migrate into the food.
- Microwave plastic wraps, wax paper, cooking bags, parchment paper, and white microwave-safe paper towels should be safe to use. Do not let plastic wrap touch foods during microwaving.
- Never use thin plastic storage bags, brown paper or plastic grocery bags, newspapers, or aluminum foil in microwave ovens.

12.11 Safe Food Handling for Picnics[30]

From the Store–Home First

- When shopping, buy cold food like meat and poultry last, right before checkout. Separate raw meat and poultry from other food in your shopping cart. To guard against cross-contamination–which can happen when raw meat or poultry juices drip on other food–put packages of raw meat and poultry into plastic bags.
- Buy only deli foods that are stored at safe temperatures and handled in a sanitary manner. Don't buy deli foods displayed at room temperature.
- Deli-sliced bologna and salami remain safe three to five days in your refrigerator; sliced turkey, chicken and roast beef, two to four days. Freeze, if not used by then.
- Store vacuum packaged cold cuts and hot dogs two weeks unopened, one week opened. For foods with a "Sell-by" date, simply use them within five days of purchase. If the product has a "Use-by" date, observe that.
- Load meat and poultry into the coolest part of the car and take the groceries straight home. In the summer, if home is more than 30 minutes away, bring a cooler with ice and place perishable food in it for the trip.
- At home, place meat and poultry in the refrigerator immediately. Freeze poultry and ground meat that will not be used in one or two days; freeze other meat within three to four days.

Defrost Safely

- Completely defrost meat and poultry before grilling so it cooks more evenly. Use the refrigerator for slow, safe thawing or thaw sealed packages in cold water. You can microwave-defrost, if the food will be placed immediately on the grill.

How to Barbecue Food Safely

- Meat and poultry can be marinated for several hours or days to tenderize or add flavor. Marinate food in the refrigerator, not on the counter. If some of the marinade is to be used as a sauce on the cooked food, reserve a portion of the marinade before putting raw meat and poultry in it. However, if the marinade used on raw meat or poultry is to be reused, make sure to let it come to a boil first to destroy any harmful bacteria.

Transporting

- When carrying food to another location, keep it cold to minimize bacterial growth. Use an insulated cooler with sufficient ice or ice packs to keep the food at 40°F or below. Pack food right from the refrigerator into the cooler immediately before leaving home. Keep the cooler in the coolest part of the car.

Keep Cold Food Cold

- Keep meat and poultry refrigerated until ready to use. Only take out the meat and poultry that will immediately be placed on the grill.
- When using a cooler, keep it out of the direct sun by placing it in the shade or shelter. Avoid opening the lid too often, which lets cold air out and warm air in. Pack beverages in one cooler and perishables in a separate cooler.
- Salads and cooked deli foods are more perishable. Use them within one or two days. Any foods with stuffing should be used on the day of purchase!

Keep Everything Clean

- Be sure there are plenty of clean utensils and platters. To prevent foodborne illness, don't use the same platter and utensils for raw and cooked meat and poultry. Harmful bacteria present in raw meat and poultry and their juices can contaminate safely cooked food. Use disposable tableware and serving utensils: plastic or paper cups and glasses, spoons and forks, etc.
- Bring a trash bag you can seal well to dispose of refuse or garbage.
- If you are eating away from home, find out if there's a source of clean water. If not, bring water for preparation and cleaning. Or pack clean cloths, and wet towelettes for cleaning surfaces and hands. Be sure to bring your own drinking water, if unsure of the water quality in the park or from outside sources.

Precooking

- Precooking food partially in the microwave, oven, or stove is a good way of reducing grilling time. Just make sure that the food goes immediately on the preheated grill to complete cooking.

Cook Thoroughly

- Cook food to a safe internal temperature to destroy harmful bacteria. Meat and poultry cooked on a grill often browns very fast on the outside. Use a food thermometer to be sure the food has reached a safe internal temperature. Whole poultry should reach 180°F. Hamburgers made of ground beef should reach 160°F; ground poultry, 165°F. Beef veal, and lamb steaks, roasts and chops can be cooked to 145°F. All cuts of pork should reach 160°F.
- NEVER partially grill meat or poultry and finish cooking later.

Reheating

- When reheating fully cooked meats like hot dogs, grill to 165°F or until steaming hot.

Keep Hot Food Hot

- After cooking meat and poultry on the grill, keep it hot until served–at 140°F or warmer.
- Keep cooked meats hot by setting them to the side of the grill rack, not directly over the coals where they could overcook. At home, the cooked meat can be kept hot in a warm oven (approximately 200°F), in a chafing dish or slow cooker, or on a warming tray.

Serving the Food

- When taking food off the grill, use a clean platter. Don't put cooked food on the same platter that held raw meat or poultry. Any harmful bacteria present in the raw meat juices could contaminate safely cooked food.
- In hot weather (90°F and above), food should never sit out for more than 1 hour. During summertime, foods can quickly reach the DANGER ZONE (temperatures between 41 to 140°F), when bacteria multiply rapidly.
- Bring food covers to protect food from insects and dust. When eating outdoors, clean table surfaces and preferably, cover with disposable tablecloths or washable linen.[11, 12]

12.12 Handling Food Safely During the Holidays[31]

Holiday parties are the best times to relish favorite meals with friends and relatives or families. Everyone loves to help in preparing special traditional recipes.

The following are tips for handling and serving festive foods safely:

- Wash your hands thoroughly before handling any food or drinks. See Figure 3.1 (Chapter 3) for proper handwashing procedures.
- Avoid cross-contamination: KEEP RAW MEATS AND READY-TO-EAT FOODS SEPARATE.
- When mixing cookie dough, cake batter or the like, do not let anyone, especially the children, lick the spoon or bowl! The raw egg in the mixture may be a potential source of harmful bacteria.
- Use ingredients that are safe to eat: like pasteurized milk, cheese, juices, etc.
- Cook to proper temperatures (see previous sections on recommended temperatures for cooking various food commodities or ingredients).
- Refrigerate promptly below 40°F. Refrigerate leftovers within two hours.
- Be sure your refrigerator is set at 40°F or below.
- Serve foods safely (see guidelines in Section 12.6).

- To store leftovers, place in shallow containers, not over 2 inches deep.
- Store stuffing and gravy separately. Use meat and stuffing within three days, and gravy within one to two days.
- Reheat leftovers to 165°F.

The message of the poem below is most appropriate for ending this section on Food Safety during the Holidays. Unfortunately, neither the origin nor the author of this poem could be traced. It was provided by a dietitian in Minnesota.

THE NIGHT AFTER CHRISTMAS

'Twas the night after Christmas and all through the kitchen
little creatures were stirring up potions bewitching.
Salmonellae were working in gravy and soup,
in the hopes they could turn it to poisonous goop!
Clostridia were nestled all snug in the ham,
while Hepatitis A viruses danced in the yam.
Little John with his Gobots and Mary in her cap,
had just settled down for a long overdue nap.
When down in their guts there arose such a clatter;
they sprung from their beds to see what was the matter.
They ran to the bathroom, threw open the door.
Wash your hands before cooking! Put your food away quick!
Or that jolly old food germ we know as Saint Sick
with his eight tiny microbes will ruin the feast.
As they make their toxins, he calls out to each beast:
"Now Hepatitis! Now Staph and Perfringens,
We'll punish those humans for holiday binges!
Oh, Botulinum! E. Coli! Shigella!
Go get'em Amoeba! Work fast, Salmonella!
If those humans cannot learn to handle food right,
A Merry Christmas they'll have, then a long, sleepless night!"

REVIEW QUESTIONS

1. Define the following key terms (see text or the Glossary).
   a. Foodborne illness
   b. Food spoilage
   c. Foodborne infection
   d. Food intoxication
   e. Foodborne toxin-mediated infections
   f. Emerging pathogens
   g. Potentially hazardous foods
   h. Incubation period
2. Differentiate between:
   a. Virus vs. parasite
   b. Aerobic vs. anaerobic microorganisms
   c. Prion vs. bacteria
   d. Vegetative cells vs. spores
   e. Molds vs. yeasts
3. Explain FATTOM for a high school sophomore class.
4. What are the parts of the human body that harbor pathogenic microorganisms associated with food and water?
5. You were invited to give a lecture on handling foods safely to a dietary department in a small community hospital. The presentation is an hour only. Prepare an outline of the main topics you want to

prioritize and what teaching aids will be most appropriate for your audience.

6. Following the food flow chart in Appendix B, list safety measures and sanitary practices to be observed by a food handler in each step or station. Some guidelines have been given in the last few pages of this chapter. Add to the list.
7. In packing lunch for work or office during summer months, what foods will be most appropriate for adults?
8. You are hosting a buffet/picnic style in your backyard at 4 to 7 P.M. for about 100 guests. Plan your menus, how to prepare, cook, and serve them that will assure quality and safety to every diner.

REFERENCES

1. Satin, M. *Food Alert! The Ultimate Sourcebook for Food Safety.* New York, Checkmark Books, 1999.
2. Bellenir, K., and Dresser, P. *Food and Animal-borne Diseases Sourcebook.* Detroit, Omnigraphics, 1995.
3. Cody, M. M., and Kunkel, E. M. *Food Safety for Professionals.* 2nd ed. Chicago, American Dietetic Association, 2001.
4. Hubbert, W. T., Hagstad, H. V., Spangler, E., Hinton, M. H., and Hughes, K. L. *Food Safety and Quality Assurance.* 2nd ed. Ames, Iowa University Press, 1996.
5. Jay, J. M. *Modern Food Microbiology.* 6th ed. New York, Kluver Academic Publishers, 2000.
6. Latta, S. L. *Food Poisoning and Foodborne Diseases.* Berkeley Heights, N.J., Enslow Publishing, 1999.
7. Longree, K., and Armsbruster, G. *Quantity Food Sanitation.* 5th ed. New York, John Wiley & Sons, 1996.
8. Marriott, N. G. *Principles of Food Sanitation.* 4th ed. New York, Kluver Academic Publishers, 1999.
9. Matthews, D. D. *Food Safety Sourcebook.* Detroit, Omnigraphics, 1999.
10. McSwane, D., Rue, N., and Linton, R. *Essentials of Food Safety and Sanitation.* 3rd ed., Upper Saddle River, N.J., Prentice-Hall, 2003.
11. National Restaurant Association Educational Foundation. *ServSafe® Essentials.* 2nd ed. Chicago, NRAEF, 2002.
12. Wilcox, W. *Public Health Sourcebook.* Vol. 34. Detroit, Omnigraphics, 1998.
13. Anon. *Report on Source of Causative Bacteria.* Available at http://www.fsb.upm.edu.my/reezal/botulism.htm. Accessed on June 22, 2002.
14. Barzilay, J. L., Weinberg, W. G., and Eley, J. W. *The Water We Drink.* New Brunswick, N.J., Rutgers University Press, 1999.
15. Varnam, A. H., and Evans, M. G. *Foodborne Pathogens: An Illustrated Text.* St. Louis, C. V. Mosby, 1991.
16. Momcilovic, D., and Dunnavan, G. Compliance with rule only way to prevent BSE. *Feedstuffs, 73,* 20, 2001.
17. Food and Agriculture Organization. *Unconventional Agents. Report 2000.* Available at http://fao.org/docrep/.htm. Accessed on June 9, 2002.
18. Gladwin, M., and Trattler, B. *Clinical Microbiology.* 3rd ed. Miami, MadMaster, 2001.
19. Anon. Cover story about mad cow disease. *Nutrition Action Health Letter,* June 2001.
20. DeSalle, R. *Epidemic! The World of Infectious Disease.* New York, New Press, 1999.
21. Tauxe, R. New approaches to surveillance and control of emerging foodborne infectious diseases. *Emerging Infectious Diseases 4* (3), 1–3, 1998.
22. Alcamo, I. E. *Fundamentals of Microbiology* 5th ed. New York, Addison Wesley Longman, 1997.
23. Markell, E. K., and John, D. T. *Markell and Voge's Modern Parasitology,* 8th ed. Philadelphia, W.B. Saunders, 1999.
24. WHO. Intestinal parasites. Available at http://www.who.int/ctd/int.para/indxhtmi. Accessed July 7, 2002.
25. CDC. Giardiasis surveillance: United States, 1992–97 *M.M.W.R. 49,* SS07, 1–13, 2000.
26. CDC. *Entamoeba Histolytica and Amebiasis.* Available at http://www.dpd.cdc.gov.dpdx/

HTML/amebiasis.htm. Accessed on July 7, 2002.

27. Food Safety and Inspection Service (FSIS). Basics for Handing Food Safely, *Consumer Information, USDA,* September 1997.
28. Food Safety and Inspection Service (FSIS), Expectant Mothers and Foodborne Illness, *Consumer Information, USDA,* May 1999.
29. Food Safety and Inspection Service (FSIS). Cooking Safely in the Microwave Oven, *Consumer Information, USDA,* November 2000.
30. Food Safety and Inspection Service (FSIS). Barbecue Food Safely, *Consumer Information, USDA,* May 2001.
31. The American Dietetic Association Foundation (ADAF). Nutrition Fact Sheet. *Unwrap the Gift of Home Food Safety This Holiday Season.* ADA, September 1999.

Chapter 6

CONTROL OF BIOLOGICAL HAZARDS

1.0 INTRODUCTION

Pathogenic microorganisms like bacteria, viruses, fungi, and parasites, are the main etiologic agents for food- and waterborne diseases. A brief profile of these harmful microorganisms and preventive measures to control their growth is presented in the previous chapter. To produce illness in human beings, they have to be ingested via food and drink in sufficient amounts, break down the defense mechanisms of the body, and multiply in the intestines.

Bacteria cannot move by themselves. They need carriers to be transferred to other places, and these could be living or nonliving habitats. The most common carriers are the food handlers. Animals, marine creatures, pests, and plants are other biologic agents that are vectors for pathogenic microorganisms.

Another means of transferring or moving pathogens is from surface to surface on nonliving things. Cross-contamination occurs frequently when contaminated water is used in washing fruits and vegetables, or by dirt, soil and air movement. Examples are discussed in Chapter 8 on the control of physical hazards.

The main objective of this chapter is to explain briefly how human beings and other biologic agents carry or transmit pathogenic microorganisms. Additionally, these biologic agents provide food and shelter for microorganisms while also harboring the pathogens. Given other favorable conditions, the microbes will then multiply and some will generate toxins that are deleterious to health or are lethal. (Review FATTOM in Chapter 5.)

2.0 BIOLOGICAL CARRIERS OF PATHOGENIC MICROORGANISMS

Some persons are carriers of a pathogenic microorganism without getting sick, but they can transmit the disease to others. The susceptible individuals then show signs and symptoms of a particular disease, after a given incubation period. The onset of symptoms depends on the species or strain and number (dose) of the etiologic agent. Animal and insect-borne diseases are transmitted to human beings by exposure to the infected animal and insect, which include: farm animals, domestic pets, marine organisms, and household pests.[1]

How each group transfers pathogenic organisms and how to control their transfer and conditions for growth are explained in the next sections.

2.1 Humans: Food Handlers

The human body is an excellent reservoir of pathogenic organisms. They are found on the skin, hair, linings of the nose, throat, respiratory tract, feet, hands, and under the fingernails. The gastrointestinal tract, especially the lower end of the small intestines, is a fertile place for potential multiplication of microorganisms. Thus, proper human excreta disposal is a very important issue to consider in preventive measures. Proper washing of the hands after using the toilet must be diligently observed.

When there are skin lesions or infection, such as infected cuts, burns, and acne, they can be sources of *Staphyloccocus aureus*. The common pathogens from the intestinal tract include: fecal salmonellae, *Clostridium perfringens,* shigellae, Hepatitis A virus, Norwalk virus, *Cryptosporidium,* and *Escherichia coli.* The respiratory tract and the skin may harbor viruses and hemolytic streptococci Group A, which is very contagious. A person with a respiratory ailment or infected skin lesions is not allowed to work.[3]

Human saliva and discharges from the nose, mouth, and throat are potential transmitters of many diseases. Thus, smoking is not permitted in areas where food is prepared or served. Some places do not follow the smoking ban regulation. Food handlers who smoke outside in designated places should wash their hands properly before returning to work.

The contaminated hands can transfer practically all foods and waterborne illnesses by the "hand habits" of a person. These are common involuntary movements of the hands, like touching the hair and face, rubbing the nose, scratching an itch, touching his or her clothes, or toying with a personal item (earrings, wrist watch, pen or pencil, utensil, etc.). Therefore, personal hygiene includes daily bathing, wearing clean clothes and shoes, and using hair restraints. Fingernails are cut short and kept clean. Wearing accessories and jewelry is limited to plain items like wedding rings. Sometimes, a mask to cover the nose and mouth may be required.

The kitchen personnel are given an orientation that includes personal hygiene, grooming, physical safety, etc. The food handler must undergo training on food preparation, storage, and service, and proper sanitizing of surfaces, kitchen tools (such as cutting boards and knives, meat slicer) and other job related sanitary practices. More details are given at the end of this chapter.

2.2 Farm Animals[3,4]

The pathogenic organisms that are common inhabitants in the intestines of livestock are: salmonellae, *Clostridium perfringens,* and coliforms. *Staphylococcus aureus* is found in the nose, mouth, throat, and skin of farm animals. An infected animal may transfer the pathogens to other animals during shipment to abattoirs, or in crowded corrals or barns. One way the pathogens from farm animals enter the food chain is via discharges, mainly fecal matter, which could happen during slaughter. Therefore, extra care must be taken to prevent fecal contamination during the slaughtering process. Chapter 4 discusses regulations on food control systems for meat and poultry for slaughtering, antemortem and postmortem inspections, labeling and shipping safely.

Brucellosis or undulant fever caused by *Brucella abortus, B. melitensis,* and *B. suis* transmitted from infected cattle, goats, and hogs, respectively, used to be a major concern. With the pasteurization of milk and cream, brucellosis and tuberculosis are no longer severe human health problems. Also, early detection and getting rid of the infected animal immediately is one way of eradicating the disease.

Beef tapeworms have been discussed in Chapter 5 under the topic of parasites.

Another disease that has ignited interest by consumers lately is foot-and-mouth disease (FMD), which occurs in infected cattle and swine. It is caused by a virus and is highly contagious, but rarely fatal. Because the cattle get sick for two to three weeks, there is loss of or decreased milk production. Fortunately, the virus is killed by heat, low humidity, or by certain disinfectants. FMD also affects sheep, goat, deer and other ruminants with cloven hooves. People do not contract this ailment readily and, to date, it has no implications in human health, but is economically important due to production losses in the livestock industry. It is not infectious for humans. However, if present in the human nasal passages, the virus can be spread to animals.[5]

Hogs are known to be a link in the *Trichinella spiralis* (roundworm) cycle that causes trichinosis in humans. Another parasitic worm that may be transmitted to people is hog tapeworm (see details in Chapter 5).

Poultry is the greatest animal reservoir for *Salmonella* and *Campylobacter.* About half of salmonellae cases that cause gastroenteritis in humans are traced to poultry products. *S. pullorum* causes many deaths of baby chicks and poults, but has not been demonstrated to be pathogenic to people. Most, if not all, of the other serotypes are infectious to humans. Eggshells that have fecal matter from infected poultry are common sources of salmonellae. When the shell is cracked, the contents (egg white and yolk) will be contaminated. Another route by which egg contents are infected is by trans-ovarian transfer by the laying hen. In this case, washing the eggshell will not remove the salmonellae. Research on the control of this second route is ongoing.

Two other emerging pathogens that can be transmitted to people from animals are *Campylobacter* and *Listeria monocytogenes.* Details about them are in Chapter 5.

Visitors to a farm should be informed that certain farm animals pose greater risk for transmitting enteric infections to humans than others. These farm animals include calves and other young ruminants, poultry, and all infected farm animals. Animal petting should be under strict supervision. Hand washing facilities are provided and signs are posted to visitors reminding them to wash their hands and arms properly after touching the animals. Hand-to-mouth activities (like eating, drinking, carrying toys and pacifiers, smoking, etc.) are not permitted in restricted areas.[6]

The best preventive measure to avoid animal-borne diseases in farm animals is to maintain a high sanitary standard in the care of livestock and poultry. Use feeds that are safe and free from pathogens. Children below age five, elderly, pregnant women and persons whose immune systems are compromised, are at high risk to these infections.[2,6]

2.3 Fish, Seafood, and Algae

Fish and marine mammals may harbor *Clostridium botulinum.* The incidence of botulism varies with the type of fish and its feeding habits. Type E is more common in fish than types A or B. The incidence is not confined to improperly canned fish. Even fermented, salted or smoked fish that are home-processed could be carriers for *Cl. botulinum.* Cases have been reported from Europe (Norwegian delicacy of fermented trout) and from the natives of Alaska and Canada.[7]

Toxins produced by certain fish have been discussed in Chapter 5. The signs and symptoms of common fish toxins are given in Table 1.6. The diseases caused by bacteria, yeast, and molds that are associated with fish are summarized in Table 6.1.

Some tropical fish are poisonous to humans and should not be eaten. These include puffers, parrotfish, surgeonfish, goatfish, and porcupine fish. They feed on poisonous marine organisms. Some fish that are usually considered safe to eat, like barracuda, mackerel, sea bass, and pompano, may sometimes be poisonous to people, because they accumulate toxins in their flesh. Ciguatera poisoning is one of the serious public health problems related to fish consumption. Paralytic shellfish poisoning (PSP) is caused by saxitoxin, an alkaloid neurotoxin known to be a potent toxin. It interferes with sensory, motor, and cerebellar functions. Ingestion of a high dose could cause paralysis and respiratory failure within an hour. Death is possible.

Scombroid poisoning is sometimes called histamine poisoning because it is caused by histamine and other vasoamines formed by the growth of certain bacteria. Their decarboxylase enzymes act on histidine and other amino acids in food, resulting in histamine. Fish associated with scombroid poisoning are spoiled fish, like tuna, mackerel, abalone, sardines, and mahi-mahi. The onset of symptoms (burning sensation in the mouth, nausea, vomiting, diarrhea, and headache) is rapid, often within 30 minutes.

Raw oysters are known to be carriers of a bacterium, *Vibrio vulnificus,* which occurs naturally in warm marine waters. Forty percent of cases are fatal.

Norwalk viruses are responsible for about one-third of viral gastroenteritis cases. Foods associated with this viral disease include raw or insufficiently cooked oysters and clams. Government agencies must regulate and inspect harvesting beds for oysters, clams and mussels.

Anisakis food poisoning, a parasitic infection due to a nematode, is associated with eating raw fish. Traditionally, people in Japan eat raw fish in sushi recipes, a delicacy gaining popularity in the Western World. Anisakiasis incidences have been increasing in the United States. Preparation of safe sushi is done by an experienced sushi chef.

Anisakis parasites are killed by normal cooking and/or freezing the raw fish at –20°C and holding it for at least a week. This low freezing temperature is not attainable in

Table 6.1
MICROORGANISMS COMMONLY FOUND ON FISH**

Bacteria	*Bacteria*	*Yeasts*	*Molds*
Acinobacter	*Listeria*	*Candida***	*Aspergillus*
*Aeromonas***	*Microbacterium*	*Cryptococcus***	*Aureobasidium (Pullularia)***
Alcaligenes	*Moraxella*	*Debaryomyces*	*Penicillium*
Bacillus	*Photobacterium*	*Hansenula*	*Scopulariopsis*
Corynebacterium	*Pseudomonas***	*Pichia*	
Enterobacter	*Psychrobacter*	*Rhodotorula***	
Enterococcus	*Shewanella***	*Sporobolomyces*	
Escherichia	*Vibrio***	*Trichosporon*	
Flavobacterium	*Weissella*		
Lactobacillus			

** More prevalent: most frequently reported. The unmarked ones are known to occur.
Source: Jay, J. M. *Modern Food Microbiology.* 6th ed. New York, Kluwer Academic, 2000.

home freezers or ordinary freezers in food service establishments. A commercial freezer has to be used.[7]

Another parasitic disease, called diphyllobotriasis, is transmitted to humans by eating infected fish. The etiologic agent is a tapeworm, known as *Diphyllobotrium latum.*[8]

An excellent reference for seafood toxins is the *Foodborne Disease Handbook* by Hui et al.[9]

The WHO has a study group on Aquaculture and their report on "Fish Food Safety" is available (read WHO Technical Report Series no. 849, dated 1995).

Clemson Extension Home and Garden Information Center has these safety tips about consuming seafoods:[10]

- Know your seafood seller.
- Buy only from approved sources.
- Purchase seafood carefully.
- Keep seafood cold.
- Keep live shellfish alive.
- Refrigerate live shellfish properly.
- Do not cross-contaminate.
- Cook seafood thoroughly.

The public should be informed about the risks taken with regard to eating seafood. When in doubt about the source of the fish, ask the seller to show the certified shipper's tag for proof.

Certain algae blooms are known to produce potent toxins. There are six distinct human clinical syndromes associated with harmful algal blooms: ciguatera fish poisoning, paralytic shellfish poisoning, neurotoxic shellfish poisoning, diarrhetic shellfish poisoning, amnestic shellfish poisoning, and *Pfiesteria* syndrome (see Chapter 5).

A recent conference on harmful algae blooms observed that they are an international phenomenon. The increase in numbers of these blooms is a result of the disruption of ecosystems, climate changes, and nutrient enrichment of waterways. Studies to develop rapid testing procedures for algae toxins are currently ongoing. Emphasis is placed on a pressing requirement to conduct regular testing of these toxins in marine produce and shellfish.[11]

2.4 Household Pests

The National Pest Control Association has developed a list of the 10 most common household pests and their living habits as follows:[12]

1. **Cockroaches** spread disease by contaminated food and create an offensive odor in large populations (see Section 2.4.1.1 for details).
2. **Mice** contaminate food with droppings, urine and hair. They are always looking for food. They nest in dark areas of sewers, flooring, garbage, and the kitchen. Mousetraps may get rid of them.
3. **Rats** nest in basements, attics, sewers, sub-flooring, open garbage cans, and piles of trash. They contaminate food with germs that can cause acute food poisoning. Caution! They will bite people.
4. **Termites** live in underground colonies and feed on wood products. In addition to destroying wood, they eat books, clothing, and anything made from pulp and paper.
5. **Ants** come in more than twenty household varieties. To get rid of these annoying indoor species that contaminate food and in rare cases bite humans and pets, find and destroy their nests and remove their source of food by practicing vigilant housekeeping methods.
6. **Carpenter ants** are frequently confused with termites because they too, destroy wood.
7. **Fleas** enter your house on pets and lay their eggs on carpeting, bedding, and upholstered furniture.
8. **Ticks:** American and Brown Dog ticks live outdoors, but can be brought in by mice and rats. These ticks are dangerous because they transmit serious diseases such as Rocky Mountain Spotted Fever and Lyme disease to humans.
9. **Spiders:** Many of the 25,000 varieties are helpful in that they trap and eat other pests. They are found in out-of-the-way spots like closets, attics, and garages. Their cobwebs gather dust, are unsightly, and are removed in good housekeeping.
10. **Silverfish** (an insect, not a fish) have not been deleterious to health, but they can do extensive damage to clothing, books, wallpaper, and important records.

Of these household pests, the most troublesome and threatening to food and water safety are cockroaches, flies, pantry insects, ants, and rodents. The next sections describe briefly their characteristics and how consumers can identify and eradicate them or avoid their entry into the building or house.

2.4.1 Insects

Insects are animals belonging to the class *Insecta,* which are small air-breathing arthropods. They usually have three bodily parts: head, thorax or abdomen with a pair of wings, and legs. Many of them are useful for ecology, but some are harmful as carriers of diseases. In food establishments and households, the most troublesome are cockroaches, flies, ants, and pantry insects. Their breeding places and eating habits are given below.

2.4.1.1 COCKROACHES.[2,13] Cockroaches are not only annoying and destructive, but are carriers of pathogens because of their eating habits. They feed on dead animals, rotten garbage, leather, wallpaper, fabrics and other materials. When they eat, they regurgitate filthy materials on the food and utensils in the kitchen. Their excrement in the form of pellets or an ink-like liquid has an obnoxious or nauseating odor. Some persons who are allergic to cockroaches get sick.

There are several kinds of cockroaches: Australian, Asian, American, German, Smoky brown, and Brown banded. They all multiply rapidly. Their eggs are deposited in a leathery case or capsule and each capsule may contain as many as forty-eight eggs. They like to hide in dark, sheltered places during the day and come out to feed during the night. Thus, they are found around the kitchen sink, cracks underneath cupboards and shelves, behind drawers, around pipes, behind windows and doorframes, or loose baseboard strips. It is not surprising to see them in radio and TV cabinets and in the bathroom. Preventive controls are coming in another section. (See Figure 6.1 for an adult cockroach and its egg.)

2.4.1.2 FLIES.[14] Fruit flies, blowflies, and houseflies are the common types found in the house or food establishments. The housefly *(Musca domestica)* is the species that can spread disease. They feed on human and animal feces, garbage, sewage, and fresh or rotten food. They carry the pathogenic organisms in their mouth parts, intestines, leg hairs, and feet. Their favorite breeding places are dumps, open garbage cans, and areas of exposed manure and feces. They multiply rapidly, especially during warm weather. Two or more generations of houseflies are produced in a year. (See Section 3.2 on Pest Control.)

2.4.1.3 ANTS.[2,15] Ants may carry pathogenic organisms in their mouth, body and feet, which can contaminate food where they pass by or feed on. Their favorite places are garbage, food pantry and kitchen shelves, or anywhere food morsels are left.

2.4.1.4 PANTRY INSECTS. There is hardly any food item in the kitchen or pantry that can escape infestation by some pests if consumers leave them long enough unprotected for pantry insects to enter and multiply. All food items are susceptible: grains, breakfast cereals, cake mixes, flours, and even spices and hot pepper.[16]

Generally, pantry insects do not carry disease-producing organisms, but their presence gives off-tastes and off-odors not fit for human consumption. Therefore, food is wasted. Weevils, moths and beetles on cereal grains are considered "foreign particles" although they are not physical hazards. In Figure 6.1 are some common pantry insects.

2.4.2 Rodents[2,14]

The common domestic rodents include: Norway rats, roof rats, and house mice. Norway rats are burrowing rats and hide in sewers, outside the buildings, or around the house yard. Their favorite foods are garbage, meat, fish and cereal. Roof rats are smaller than Norway rats, but are good climbers. They like sewers, dumps, and places of filth. The house mouse is the smallest of the domestic rodents. They feed frequently and can be found in the kitchen, garbage, or indoors where there are food crumbs, especially grains and cereals, and unprotected food.

Rodents harbor many kinds of pathogenic microorganisms that include: plague (bubonic or pneumonic types), hantavirus, and salmonellae serotypes. Hantavirus Pulmonary Syndrome (HPS) is a newly recognized disease. First discovered in the United States in 1993, about 100 cases have been identified since then in twenty states. Almost all of these cases showed evidence of close association with rodents. Human infection may occur when infected saliva or excreta are inhaled as aerosols produced directly from the infested animal.[17]

Rodents can damage property and ruin food. Their presence is easily detected from their droppings, tracks, gnawings, hairs left in their pathway, and rub marks. The latter are results of their bodies rubbing on the wall, because they like to stay close to the walls or

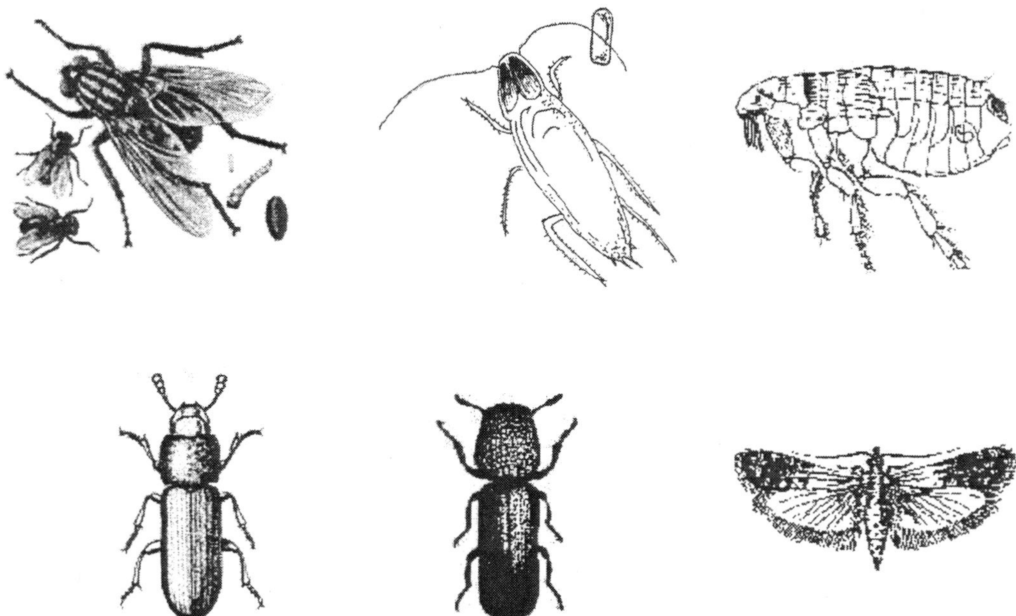

Figure 6.1. Examples of Household Pests. Top row from left to right: housefly with larva and egg; cockroach with its egg; and cat flea. Bottom row from left to right: red flour beetle, grain borer, and Indian meal moth.

baseboard. All of the three kinds of domestic rats do not travel far, but want to stay close to food and water sources.

One of the concerns of people about **plague** relates to its possible use in bioterrorism (see Chapter 13 for details).[18]

2.4.3 Birds[17,23]

Birds, like sparrows and pigeons, may enter the compound of farms, food establishments or manufacturing industries and could be carriers of diseases that are harmful to humans. Their droppings may be infected with one or more of these illnesses: mycosis, toxoplasmosis, salmonellosis, and pseudotuberculosis.

Control of these unwanted birds are similar to how rodent control measures are handled: by physical means of preventing their entry, by not providing them food and shelter, and with the use of trappings and pastes. Other methods, like the use of electric wires and some chemical means, require a professional exterminator.

2.5 Domestic Pets

There are over twenty possible kinds of animals that people enjoy around and in the house as pets. The popular ones are dogs and cats.

Dogs and cats are known to carry *Staphylococcus aureus* on their skin and nose and many serotypes *of Salmonella.* Salmonellosis in dogs has been reported and is often caused by underprocessed dog food.

Salmonella from turtles has caused gastroenteric outbreaks. In 1975, the FDA banned the shipment of turtle pets, except for scientific or educational purposes. A case of salmonellosis from turtle pets was due to contaminated turtles' water discarded in the kitchen sink. Also, children who handle their pet turtles and then handle food could be the source of transmission.[2]

Toxoplasmosis is probably one of the most common diseases transmitted from pets to humans by cat feces and undercooked meat of infected animals. The disease has very mild symptoms, but if a baby gets infected through the mother before birth, it could result in mental retardation, blindness, or death.[19]

Allergic reactions to pets are usually due to their dander or skin flakes, their saliva and urine. Animal hair by itself is not considered a significant allergen, but the contaminated dust and soil mold collected by animal hair could cause allergies.[20]

The cat flea is the most common ectoparasite from dogs and cats. It could be an intermediate host of some tapeworms. Its main immediate effect is itchiness and irritation from the bites.[21]

Psittacosis is a disease related to sick or seemingly healthy birds. Household bird pets, such as parrots and parakeets, are the frequent sources of this illness, although cats and dogs may also harbor it. Transmission may be by inhalation of the dust from dried droppings in an enclosed room. Bird droppings carry bacteria and fungi that could make some persons sick.[22]

Pets are not allowed in areas where food is prepared and served. Anyone who just handled a pet must wash hands properly and is required to change clothes when necessary.

2.6 Plants

Plants may be biological hazards to food safety due to three reasons: They may be carriers of pathogenic organisms, as sources of naturally occurring toxins, or from chemical contaminants.

1. Pathogens from plants come from the soil adhering to the plant parts, especially the roots. Depending on the moisture, pH, temperature, and organic materials present, microorganisms can thrive for a long period in the soil. Microorganisms found in soil are: *Cl. botulinum, Cl. perfringens, Listeria monocytogenes,* and most microorganisms that are waterborne. Many of the bacteria and fungi that inhabit water are also found in the soil.[2,25]

2. Certain plants naturally contain toxic substances that could cause severe illness in humans if consumed in concentrated amounts. Some could be deadly, e.g. cyanogenic glycosides found in some cassava roots, seeds of almonds, peaches and apricots. Wild onions, when eaten by a dairy cow, will cause an undesirable off-flavor to the milk. White snakeroot is another plant that has a toxic compound eaten by grazing cows. It can become concentrated in cow's milk and cause milk sickness or tremetol poisoning in humans. Some toxic plants can cause severely diseased cattle to be removed from the human food supply.[4]

Wild mushrooms contain natural toxic substances and should not be served.[23] Certain legumes may contain hemagglutinins. Fava beans and red kidney beans are not safe to eat if undercooked, but are rendered safe when properly and thoroughly cooked. Potatoes normally contain solanine in small harmless amounts, but when exposed to sunlight during storage, a deep green area underneath the skin is not desirable. This layer has to be peeled away.[24]

The best assurance of safety is to avoid wild varieties of plants or unfamiliar produce and eat the kinds that are traditionally safe from long use. Cook thoroughly varieties of plants whose toxins are easily destroyed by heat. Examples are the goitrogens in cabbage, rutabaga, cauliflower, and Brussels sprouts.[2]

3. Chemical contaminants in plants are mainly due to pesticide residues or to the kind of fertilizers used in agricultural prac-

tices. Also, some plants can serve as concentrators of environmental pollutants.

A general guideline about safe consumption of fruits and vegetables is to consider all produce to contain some chemical residues and pollutants from air and soil. Therefore, proper washing before use is very important. Use a brush or scrubber when applicable. Wash before peeling. Remove the outer leaves (as in cabbage).[4]

3.0 HOW TO CONTROL BIOLOGICAL HAZARDS

Quality assurance for food and water safety must be observed throughout the food chain starting from the source (farm/sea) to the manufacturer or processor, then to the distributor, retailer, institution, food establishment, and finally to the consumer's table. Chapters 3 and 4 elaborated on the food control systems, especially the application of HACCP principles. In this chapter, the focus is on the responsibilities of the food handler.

3.1 Responsibilities of the Food Handler

People are the major source of contamination from their hands, skin, hair, fingernails, perspiration, respiration, excreta, saliva, etc. Therefore, all food handlers have to be educated and should undergo orientation and possibly be trained on the job. But first, they have to undergo a health examination before getting hired. They should be free from pathogenic microorganisms and tuberculosis. Appendix D is an example of a form for medical clearance for a food handler. In many countries the prospective employee must have passed a test to be a certified food handler before reporting to work.

Personal hygiene is strictly enforced. This refers to the cleanliness of the body.[7] If a food handler is suffering from respiratory ailments, such as common colds, sore throat, trench mouth, pneumonia, tuberculosis, and scarlet fever, he or she should not work around food or utensils and equipment. Likewise, the food employee who has any infection on the skin, eyes, ears, infected cuts and wounds, diarrhea and gastrointestinal disorders must seek medical treatment and then get clearance to return to work from the attending physician.

The food handler may pick up microbes from dirty surfaces, contaminated equipment, towels, and his or her clothes and jewelry or watch. The use of hair restraints, sanitized linens, hot pads, aprons, and gloves are recommended. Gloves, however, should not promote complacency. Wash your hands before and after wearing gloves. Frequent hand washing is still the best safety measure for food handlers. The list below summarizes when to wash hands before or after an activity.

When to Wash Your Hands

- Before and after eating.
- After using the restroom or toilet (or changing baby's diapers).
- Before handling any food (preparing, cooking, serving, storing).
- After using your handkerchief, used hand towel, used sponge or wash cloth, or touching dirty clothes or dirty dishes.
- After touching your hair, skin, or picking up items from the floor.
- After touching household pets.
- After cleaning the litter box and food containers of pets.
- After handling money.
- After smoking and engaging in an activity that contaminated the hands, such as clearing and wiping the table, surfaces or equipment, and mopping the floor.
- After handling chemicals, such as insecticides.

- After throwing out garbage.
- After handling raw food (raw meat and fish, eggs in shell).
- Before handling and preparing cooked or ready-to-eat foods.
- Before and after wearing gloves.

Washing the hands properly is so important that periodic retraining is needed. Preferably, washing should include the arms up to the elbows. Supervisors and managers should randomly check on food handlers to ensure that they use proper hand washing techniques. (See Figure 3.3 for the steps of proper handwashing.)

3.2 Pest Control

The general rules for pest control are to practice sanitation indoors and in your surroundings. These include:

- Clean all surfaces: from ceiling, walls, floors, table, and other furniture.
- Dry, moisture free atmosphere: Maintain relative humidity at about 40 percent.
- Good ventilation and lighting.
- Food stored is well protected. No food or water is accessible to pests. This includes fresh or rotten foods. The latter refers to garbage, dumps; left over spoiled foods, pet foods in their dish. Food crumbs on the table or floor should be removed and are cleaned immediately. Fresh farm animal or pet feeds should be protected from pests.
- Discard littering and potential shelter places for pests.
- Keep pests away from entering indoors by sealing all holes, cracks, screening, and other physical means of preventing their entry. These were discussed earlier in this chapter. Double screen doors are recommended to control entry of flies.

To eradicate pests, simple non-chemical methods should be used first, such as fly glue, rat bait, and traps. If necessary, the last resort is the use of chemical means of control, such as repellents and pesticides.

Use of biological control is another method, and is usually incorporated with integrated pest management programs (IPM) (see Section 3.3 for details). The use of hormones and pheromones to sterilize male pests or growth hormones that interrupt the life cycle of insects and prevent reproduction are promising methods.

Understand the use and storage of pesticides, observing these pointers:[3]

- Bear in mind that pesticides are hazardous materials. They could be dangerous to people, directly or via food and water that have been contaminated with pesticide residues.
- Pests can develop resistance and immunity to pesticides.
- Humans should avoid prolonged exposure to pesticides.
- Do not spray directly to surfaces or areas where food is.
- Local or national laws should regulate pesticides. Be familiar with them and comply with regulations.
- Keep pesticides in their original container well sealed. Be sure that labels and dates are clearly readable. The words DANGER and WARNING should be eye-catching.
- Store in locked cabinets separate from food and away from preparation and cooking areas.
- Store in a cool place, especially aerosols. Temperatures above 120°F (49°C) may cause them to explode.
- Check proper disposal of discarded containers from your local authorities. Do not dump with the daily household garbage.

In food establishments or food industries, a file of Material Safety Data Sheets (MSDS) information should be readily accessible (see Appendix C for a sample form). Check with your Pest Control Officer (PCO).

3.3 Integrated Pest Management (IPM)

The main objective of IPM is to control pests economically through environmentally sound techniques. Many of them are biological means. Another goal of IPM is to use pesticides wisely and to research on alternatives that have economic, social, psychological, and environmental advantages. Most single methods of pest control have not been successful, because the pests develop immunity and resistance to chemical pesticides. Therefore, a combination of methods as in an IPM program is preferred.

An IPM program has two components: Prevention and Control. The five steps of IPM as recommended by the National Pest Control Association are: inspection, identification, sanitation, application of two or more pest control procedures, and follow up/evaluation.

4.0 CONCLUDING REMARKS

Continuous training and retraining of staff and food personnel should be part of management's duties. Cleaning schedules for various sanitary practices are to be posted and recorded. Maintenance of equipment and documentation of pest control activities are to be monitored and filed. Food handlers have to undergo periodic check-ups for TB and physical exams, even if they had passed them upon initial employment. Food handlers' certificates are renewed every two years for some countries or states.

In the tropics or less developed countries where parasitic diseases are prevalent, the examination of stool or fecal materials of food workers is highly recommended, if not mandatory.

For household consumers, the reminders above also apply, especially for young members of the family or for hired domestic help. It may not be as formal and rigid as for commercial settings, but train your children or everyone in your family circle to help with cleaning, hand washing, handling of garbage, use of sanitized equipment, and other basic sanitary practices.

Everyone involved with safer food handling throughout the food flow (see Appendix B) should be deeply concerned with this recent news highlight, dated October 2nd, 2000, by the Food and Agriculture Organization:

"ANIMAL DISEASES ARE SPREADING AT ALARMING RATES"

Unprecedented outbreaks of deadly livestock diseases have been reported recently in Africa, Europe, and the Middle East. Transboundary animal diseases will continue to be real threats as international trade increases.[26]

WATCHFULNESS AND IMPLEMENTATION OF PERSONAL HYGIENE AND GENERAL SANITARY PRACTICES BY EVERYONE CANNOT BE OVEREMPHASIZED.

REVIEW QUESTIONS

A. Key terms to define (see text and the Glossary).
   1. Food handler
   2. Cross-contamination
   3. Household pests
   4. Integrated Pest Management (IPM)
   5. PCO

B. Without using chemicals, what are the physical methods of pest control for:
   1. cockroaches
   2. rats
   3. flies
   4. pantry insects
C. Cite helpful hints in handling pesticides at home.
D. You are visiting a farm with your children. What precautions will you (or the owner of the farm) tell them about petting or touching the animals?
E. Give safety tips to avoid any foodborne diseases and natural toxins that could be present in marine foods.
F. How will you recognize naturally poisonous plants?

REFERENCES

1. Bellenir, K., and Dresser, P. *Food and Animal-borne Diseases Sourcebook.* Detroit, Omnigraphics, 1995.
2. Longree, K., and Armbruster, G. *Quantity Food Sanitation.* 5th ed. New York, John Wiley & Sons, 1996.
3. National Restaurant Association Educational Foundation. *ServeSafe® Coursebook.* Chicago, NRAEF, 2002.
4. Hubbert, W., Hagstad, H., Spangle, E., Hinton, H., and Hughes, K. *Food Safety and Quality Assurance.* 2nd ed. Ames, Iowa State University, 1996.
5. United States Department of Agriculture (USDA). *Foot-and-Mouth Disease Q's and A's.* Available at http://www.aphis.usda.gov.oa/pubs/qafmd301.html. Accessed May 20, 2002.
6. Centers for Disease Control and Prevention (CDC) Recommendations. *Farm Animal Contact.* September 27, 2001. Available at http://www.cdc.gov/mcidod/dbmd/farnsanimal/htm. Accessed May 20, 2002.
7. Varnam, A., and Evans, M. *Foodborne Pathogens: An Illustrated Text.* St. Louis, C.V. Mosby, 1991.
8. Food & Drug Administration (FDA). *Bad Bug Book.* Available at http://vm.cfsan.fda.gov/-mow/chap26.html. Accessed May 20, 2002.
9. Hui, Y. H., Pierson, M.D., and Gorham, J. R. *Foodborne Disease Handbook.* 2nd ed. New York, Marcel Dekker, 2000.
10. Clemson Extension Home & Garden Information Center. Foodborne Illness Related to Seafood. Available at http://hgic.clemson.edu/factsheets/HGIC3660.htm. Accessed May 25, 2002.
11. Richardson, K., and George, B. *Food Safety and Hygiene.* August 2000. Available at http://www.dfst.csiro.au/fshbull/fshbull22.htm. Accessed May 30, 2002.
12. Better Business Bureau (BBB). *Pest Control Services.* Available at http://www/buffalo.bbb.org./alerts/pest/html. Accessed May 28, 2002.
13. Koehler, P. G. *Cockroaches and Their Management.* University of Florida. Available at http://edis.ifas/ifts/ufl.edu/ig082. Accessed May 25, 2002.
14. McSwane, D., Rue, N., and Linton, R. *Essentials of Food Safety and Sanitation.* 3rd. ed., Upper Saddle River, N.J., Prentice Hall, 2003.
15. Bower, L. M. *Creating a Healthy Household.* Bloomington, Indiana, The Healthy House Institute, 2000.
16. Koehler, P.G. *Pantry and Stored Food Pests.* University of Florida. Available at http://www.edis:ifas/upd.edu/IG103. Accessed May 10, 2002.
17. Marriott, N. G. *Principles of Food Sanitation.* 4th ed. New York, Kluwer Academic, 2000.
18. American Veterinary Medical Association. *Frequently Asked Questions about Plague.* Available at http://avma.org/press/terrorism-attack/plague-faq.asp. Accessed May 20, 2002.
19. *Counseling Sheets about Pets.* Available at http://www.recheepines.org/pets/htm. Accessed May 20, 2002.
20. Health Square News. *Pets May Cause Havoc for Allergic and Asthmatic Patients.* Available at http://www.healthsquare.com/ana/pets.html. Accessed May 20.2002.
21. Hinkle, N. C., and Koehler, P. G. *Cat Flea, Ctenocephalides felis.* University of Florida,

Gainesville. Available at http://edis.ifas.ufl.edu/IG118. Accessed May 21, 2002.

22. University of Massachusetts Amherst. *Campus Pet Policy*. Environmental Health & Safety (flyer). Available at http://www.ehs.umass.edu/pet/htm. Accessed May 21, 2002.
23. National Restaurant Association Educational Foundation. *ServSafe® Essentials*. 2nd ed. Chicago, NRAEF, 2002.
24. Satin, M. *Food Alert*. New York, Checkmark Books, 1999.
25. Jay, J. M.: *Modern Food Microbiology*. 6th ed. New York, Kluwer Academic, 2000.
26. Food and Agriculture Organization (FAO). Animal diseases spreading at alarming rate. *News Highlights*. Reported on October 2, 2000. Available at http://www.fao.org.2000/oo1001-e.htm. Accessed May 24, 2002.

Chapter 7

CONTROL OF CHEMICAL HAZARDS

1.0 INTRODUCTION

Although microbial hazards still pose the greatest threat to the food supply, hazards of a chemical or physical nature, as well as other biological agents, can also compromise human health and threaten life. Chemical contaminants in foods elicit widespread concern when distributed throughout the country in all types of establishments, such as restaurants, institutions and the home. The following addresses a variety of chemical hazards that have been introduced in the food supply that have caused serious public health problems, most frequently due to acute toxic effects, but also long-term consequences associated with chronic diseases, such as cancer or lung disorders. Knowing how to detect and control chemical hazards is of utmost importance to assure the safety and wellbeing of employees in the food industry as well as consumers.

It is well known that toxicity is considered "a matter of the dose." All chemicals can be poisonous if ingested at toxic levels, with toxicity defined at many levels. Even nutrients essential to life such as sodium, iron, copper and iodine can be poisonous. Table salt (sodium chloride) becomes a poison, potentially even lethal in a healthy person, when 12 ounces are consumed at one time (see Chapter 9).[1]

Substances found as natural components of foods such as the poisons in mushrooms or fish can pose serious threats (see Chapter 6).[2] Potentially, the most devastating effects of chemical contamination are those introduced intentionally into the food or water supply. As in the case of artificial sweetener, saccharin, the long-term effects were not known for many years. After years of continuous consumer use and following the completion of laboratory animal research studies saccharin, suspected to be carcinogenic, was banned from use in the United States. Unfortunately, some substances may also be intentionally added to our food or water supply as acts of war or terrorism (see Chapter 13). Agricultural products, such as pesticides and growth hormone residues have become part of the food chain and create human health concerns. Heavy metals, cleaning supplies and airborne chemicals such as radon or radioisotopes also pose serious health risks. More recently consumers have become increasingly concerned about the potential hazards associated with herbal products and dietary supplements (see Chapter 9).

Worldwide consumer confidence in the food supply has suffered due to fears associated with chemical hazards. Increased media coverage of food and waterborne illnesses may heighten consumer awareness; it may also contribute to consumer fear and confusion regarding real and perceived risks associated with food and water safety. Thus, reports in the media are conflicting, and the public may be uncertain about the validity of such reports. In the United States, a study conducted by the Food Marketing Institute in 1995 revealed that 66 percent of Americans viewed pesticides as a serious health threat. According to a report released by the National Research Council, Americans should worry less about the risk of cancer from pesticides and food additives and more about the cancer causing effects of excessive food intake, particularly proteins, fats, and carbohydrates.[2]

Procedures for the control and regulation of these chemical substances in food and water supplies have been relatively well established in some countries. As discussed at the end of this chapter, much work is needed before all chemical hazards can consistently be detected and controlled worldwide.

1.1 Definitions[2,3]

Many different organizations or agencies have developed their own definitions for many of the terms repeatedly used in this chapter. For the purposes intended here the following definitions will be helpful:

- Food additive–any substance that is added to food, intentionally or unintentionally, and includes food colors, sweeteners, and agricultural chemicals.
- Contaminants–potentially dangerous substances, such as lead, that can accidentally get into foods.
- Organic halogens–compounds that contain one or more of a class of atoms called halogens, including fluorine, chlorine, iodine, or bromine.
- Heavy metals–any number of mineral ions, such as mercury and lead, so named because of their relatively high atomic weight. Many heavy metals are poisonous at relatively low doses.
- Toxicity–the ability of a substance to harm living organisms. All substances are toxic if present in high enough concentrations.
- Hazard–likelihood of a substance actually causing harm

2.0 CHEMICAL HAZARDS ADDED TO THE FOOD AND WATER SUPPLY

2.1 Food Additives

Food additives have traditionally been incorporated into food production to maintain or improve product quality, or nutritional quality, aid in processing or preparation or affect color and flavor. Although microbial contamination poses the most serious food safety threat, consumers are continually disproportionately concerned about the safety, in particular the potential carcinogenicity, of food additives and pesticide residues in food and water.[2]

A food additive is any substance added intentionally to food or that becomes a part of food during its production, manufacture, packing, processing, preparation, treating, packaging, transporting, or holding. In the United States there are over 3,000 food additives approved for use. Approved additives are classified as Generally Recognized As Safe (GRAS) or as regulated additives that are permitted in foods with specific concentrations and purposes. In the US, color additives, if from natural sources, may be added to foods without specific approval.[4] Table 7.1 provides a list of commonly used food additives.

Identifying food additives has become increasingly confusing due to the introduction of new products and new technologies. Now available to consumers are foods that are marketed as "nutraceutical," "functional," and "organic." New technologies produce irradiated and genetically modified foods, all of which are no longer consistent with traditional products and traditional definitions (see Chapters 9 and 14).

2.2 Pesticides

Pesticides, a term used to include herbicides, fungicides, and insecticides, emerged as the agricultural industry expanded. Agricultural practices, such as the use of pesticides during food production, have allowed for greater crop yield through greater productivity and fewer field losses. More appealing products, due to less insect damage, are also available to consumers as a result of pesticide use. However, pesticide residues may find their way into the food supply by the direct uptake of the chemical by the plant, by run off during irrigation or rainfall, and long-term exposure due to pesticides in the soil, or even inhalation by farm workers. For poorly degraded chemicals, the concentration of chemicals will be increased in products found

Table 7.1
COMMONLY USED FOOD ADDITIVES

Additives	*Common Use*
Antimicrobial agents	Preservatives to prevent spoilage due to molds and bacteria, salts (sodium chloride, sodium benzoate), sulfites (sulfur dioxide, sodium and potassium bisulfites and metabisulfites), nitrates and nitrites, sugars, spices and their oils, wood smoke, carbon dioxide, ethylene gas, nitrogen, vinegar (acetic acid), other organic acids, i.e. benzoic acid, proprionic acid, and ascorbic acid; potassium sorbate
Antioxidants	Prevent rancidity of fats and oxidative damage in foods; vitamin C (ascorbic acid), vitamin E (tocopherols), beta-carotene, BHA (butylated hydroxytoluene), BHT (butylated hydroxylanisole)
Artificial colors	Certified colors (approved by FDA) which could be natural or vegetable dyes–beta-carotene, annatto (achuete), betaine (from beets), chlorophyll, turmeric (dilaw), and caramel. Synthetic sources–orange B, citrus red 2, allura red, brilliant blue, brilliant black, and sunset yellow (no. 6), tartrazine (no. 5)
Artificial flavors	Substances that stimulate natural flavors, some are flavor enhancers sugar, fat, salt substitutes, MSG (monosodium glutamate), citrus oils, and spices, sorbitol, tartaric acid
Bleaching agents	Substances to whiten food such as flour and cheese, peroxides, chlorine bromate, and iodate
Chelating agents	To control acidity and alkalinity, citric acid, tartaric acid, malic acid, lactic acid, sodium bicarbonate
Emulsifier	Glycerides, lecithin
Humectants	Anti-caking agents–calcium silicate, magnesium carbonate, magnesium stearate, propylene glycol, and glycerine
Improve cooking	Sodium bicarbonate leavening agent
Improve health	High fiber, cholesterol lowering
Thickening and stabilizing agents	To attain and maintain desired consistency in foods, gum arabic, agar, carrageenan, guar gum, starch, gelatin, pectin

Source: Compiled from Chapter 7 References 1, 4-6, 12, 16, 19.

higher on the food chain, i.e., beef and poultry, and larger fish as compared to plants and smaller fish.[6]

Agricultural practices, such as the use of pesticides, are among the most frequently cited health concerns encountered during food production. These compounds, if eaten, consumed with beverages, or inhaled as airborne substances while at work, at home or in the garden, may cause acute adverse reactions or play a role in the development of chronic diseases such as cancer. Typical examples of chemicals used in agriculture that have shown carcinogenic effects that are now banned in most countries are DDT (pesticide) (see Ch. 15; page 254),[7] "Agent Orange" (an herbicide and war time chemical), Kepone (pesticide) (see Ch. 15; page

255),[8] and organic halogens–polychlorinated biphenyl (PCB) and polybrominated biphenyl (PBB) and dioxin–(TCDD, tetrachlorodibenzodioxin) (see Ch. 15; page 254).[9,10,11] The following situations illustrate a small sample of the many varied ways in which agricultural chemicals find their way into the food chain and impact human health.

2.3 Antibiotics and Growth Hormones

Veterinary use of antibiotics in food animals may cause problems with widespread development of microbial resistance to these drugs among human consumers. Also, people sensitive to penicillin may develop allergic symptoms after drinking milk from treated cows. Strict controls on antibiotic use now require a withdrawal period so that milk from treated cows is discarded for a given period of time until the drug has cleared the animal's bloodstream.[12]

Veterinary use of growth hormones and antibiotics may leave residues in milk, meat and eggs that may cause deleterious effects in humans. A recent report from Europe documented that persons had suffered tremors, headache, tachycardia, and dizziness 1–2 hours after eating beef liver possibly containing growth promoting drug residues.[12] One of the classic drugs creating alarm among consumers has been diethylstilesterol (DES). DES was widely used for more than 20 years beginning in the 1940s to prevent spontaneous abortions in women. In 1971, researchers showed that daughters of women who took DES had a higher rate of a rare form of cervicovaginal cancer. DES was also used by the beef cattle industry as a growth promoter until banned by the FDA in 1979.[5]

Today, endocrine disrupting chemicals (EDC) have become the focus of the popular press, regulatory agencies and international researchers in Japan, Europe and North America. Many of these substances interfere with, or mimic, normal hormone functions in experimental animals, wildlife and humans. Some of the suspected EDCs are plastics used in food packaging, phytoestrogens, food additives, pharmaceuticals, and cosmetics, all substances regulated by the Food and Drug Association in the United States. In 1996, the United States Environmental Protection Agency received a legislative mandate to develop screening and testing programs for potential EDCs in drinking water, food additives, and other sources. Over 87,000 chemicals were initially listed as possibly interfering with estrogen, androgen and thyroid functioning, but only 58,000 will be screened using the new testing procedures. These substances are classified as steroids, DESs, phytoestrogens, DDTs, PCBs, alkylphenols, phthalates, pesticides, and others.[13]

2.4 Heavy Metals and Other Elements

Most minerals, essential in the diet or not, can be found in the body and can be toxic when present in excess. Copper, zinc, cadmium, tin, lead, arsenic and mercury, and possibly other heavy metals found in the environment may be significant factors in the development of chronic diseases such as cancer and osteoporosis and more notably affect the nervous system with symptoms that may include affective disturbances and mental disorders such as depression, anxiety, and mental confusion. Permanent damage to most systems of the body have been reported, leading to anemia, kidney failure, altered skeletal growth and neurological damage.[4]

Lead poisoning associated with the food supply has decreased in the United States since food processors stopped using lead soldered cans and has become less of an environmental health problem when lead-based paints are no longer recommended. Children, prone to ingest lead-based paint peeled from walls, furniture, or toys, are more severely affected by lead toxicities.[4]

In many cultures, home remedies have been used for decades that contain lead and can have very serious consequences, particularly in children.

- "Azarcon" (a bright orange powder, also known as Ruedo, Corol, Maria Luiso, Alarcon, Ligo) and "Greta" (a yellow powder) are almost 100 percent lead and are used in some cultures to treat "empacho" (intestinal illness).
- "Pay-loo-ah" in the Hmong community is known to use this red powder to treat a rash or fever.
- "Ghasard" (brown powder), "Bala Goli" (black bean dissolved in "gripe water"), and "Kandu" (a red powder) used in Asian communities are all lead-containing home remedies to aid digestion and treat stomachaches.
- "Kohl" or "Alkohl" may be used in the Arab American community as a cosmetic eye makeup and as a remedy for skin infections and treatment for navels of newborn children.[H]

Reports of high lead levels in drinking water in bulk-water storage tanks in southwestern states of the United States have been traced to lead solder in tanks, lead-containing brass fittings and lead solder in household plumbing. Elevated blood lead levels, greater than 10–15 micrograms per deciliter (ppb) are levels of concern according to the United States Centers for Disease Control and Prevention (CDC) and the Environmental Protection Agency (EPA). Bottled water should contain less than 5 ppb lead to meet United States regulatory standards (see Chapter 2).[15]

Incidental metal toxicities have involved improper storage of foods, particularly acidic foods, in ceramic dinnerware, aluminum cookware, lead crystal, or lead-glazed pottery or porcelain.

2.5 Cleaning Materials and Food Processing Contamination

To clean and sanitize eating utensils, food preparation equipment and work surfaces various detergents and cleaners are used. Chemical sanitizers in the food processing and food service industry are also referred to as "germicides." Improper use or removal of these agents can result in human harm through incidental contamination of foods and beverages and accidental ingestion leading to corrosive actions irritating skin, eyes and nasal passages. Cleaning agents, soaps, alkaline detergents, acid detergents, degreasers, and sanitizers should be stored carefully. Chemicals used for cleaning and pest control should be clearly labeled and locked in a cabinet or separate room to prevent accidental contamination of food and food preparation and storage areas. Alkaline detergents, such as sodium hydroxide (caustic soda or lye) are inexpensive, chemically strong, but corrosive to skin and metals. Mild alkalis, sodium bicarbonate, are less irritating such as to the skin. Acid detergents may be mild or strong. Strong, corrosive inorganic acids are extremely corrosive compared to the less irritating organic acids. Degreasers and abrasive devices may also contribute to chemical contamination of food surfaces, utensils and equipment. Contaminated surfaces in direct contact with food are most likely to contribute to chemical hazards, yet the environmental areas, walls, floors, ceilings and shelves are also cleaned with acceptable chemical sanitizers and these cleaners can also become potential sources of contamination if the cleaning agents are not applied and removed properly.[16]

There are many chemical sanitizers available but relatively few are used in food production and preparation systems. The effectiveness of all chemical sanitizers will be dependent upon:

- Intimate contact with microorganisms
- Selectivity of sanitizer to destroy microorganisms
- Temperature of solution
- pH of solution
- Time of exposure

Chlorine containing sanitizers, generally hypochlorites, are non-toxic to humans and the most frequently used. The primary advantages of hypochlorites are that they are effective germicides against a wide range of microorganisms, they deodorize and sanitize, and are economical and easy to use. The Food Code recommends that food contact surfaces, rinsed and free of organic matter, be exposed to a 50-ppm chlorine sanitizer for at least seven seconds at the pH and temperatures recommended below. If the concentration of the solution, the pH, or the temperature limits are not met then the contact time must be at least 10 seconds. Some agencies may require longer contact times for chlorine sanitizing solutions.[17]

A chlorine solution must satisfy the minimum concentration requirements represented below according to the Food Code.[26]

Maximum Concentration	**Minimum Temperature**	
(ppm)	pH 10 or less	pH 8 or less
25	120° F/49° C	120° F/49°C
50	100° F/38° C	75° F/24° C
100	55° F/13° C	55° F/13° C

Iodine containing sanitizers, sometimes referred to as iodophors, are fast acting and effective but stain skin and metal surfaces, are slippery to handle and more expensive than other chemical sanitizers. Iodophors for immersion sanitizing are most effective at 12.5 ppm in acidic solutions and temperatures between 75° and 120° F (24° and 49° C). For swabbing and spray application 25 ppm is needed and exposure to surfaces must be at least 30 seconds to ensure the most effective germicidal action.[16]

Quaternary ammonium compounds (ammonium salts, "quats") are other chemical sanitizers that are relatively non-irritating to human skin and odorless but effective on a more limited number of bacteria. Quats are most effective at temperatures above 75° F (24° C) and in slightly alkaline solutions with contact times of at least 30 seconds. When water hardness is greater than 200 ppm, quats will leave a residue on food-contact surfaces and they should not be used at water hardness concentrations greater than 500 ppm.[16]

Chemical contamination of food and water may also be the result of contamination introduced through the use of food processing equipment. The oil or lubricants associated with mechanical equipment may accidentally cross-contaminate the food processed using these pieces of equipment.

2.6 Radon Gas and Radioisotopes

Airborne chemicals affect households, businesses, and international trade. Radon, estimated to cause thousands of cancer deaths annually, is an odorless, tasteless radioactive gas. Radon gas is highest in the lower floors of homes and buildings primarily as a result of the breakdown of uranium in soil, rock, water and air. Because we spend the better part of a day in our homes, household radon poses the greatest health threat. Inhalation of radon released from these sources makes the greatest contribution to radon exposure. Radon is rarely in public water supplies, yet, well water may pose a concern for some residents (see Chapters 2 and 10).[18]

Radionuclides, products of atomic fission, are the fallout of atomic weapons testing and nuclear plant accidents. Some of the important radionuclides are strontium-89, strontium-90, iodine-131, and cesium-137. Among foods, milk and plant foods are the most important transporters of radioactivity.[5]

The United Kingdom gave consideration to the contamination of the food supply by radioisotopes as early as 1957. After the Chernobyl incident in 1986, the UK quickly detected high levels of I^{131} in sheep and restricted the sale or movement of livestock. By 1987 the European Commission had issued regulations to establish procedures for determining maximum permissible levels (MPLs) of radioactivity in foods immediately following a nuclear accident or incident. Special consideration has also been given to set standards for baby foods, liquid foods, minor foods and animal feedstuffs.[19]

Following the terrorist attack on the World Trade Center in the United States in September, 2001, air contaminants at the disaster site were evaluated. Occupational exposure to toxic materials was evaluated in general air (GA) samples and personal breathing zone (PBZ) samples. The results indicated that most exposures, including asbestos, did not exceed CDC's National Institute for Occupational Safety and Health (NIOSH) recommended exposure limits (RELs) or Occupational Safety and Health Administration (OSHA) permissible exposure limits (PELs). Chemical concerns to exposure were for cadmium in torch cutters, carbon monoxide in operators of oxyacetylene torches and gasoline-powered saw operators. Toxic substances of concern included asbestos from insulation and fireproofing materials, concrete and crystalline silica, diesel exhaust, mercury from fluorescent lights, chlorodifluoromethane (Freon™ 22), carbon monoxide and polynuclear aromatic hydrocarbons from fires and engine exhaust, heavy metals from building materials, hydrogen sulfide from sewers, anaerobically decomposing bodies, and spoiled food, inorganic acids, and volatile organic compounds (VOCs). Personal breathing zone air samples were taken primarily from search-and-rescue personnel, heavy equipment operators, and workers cutting metal beams. Although no significant hazards were identified at the time of the NIOSH sampling in the ambient air at this disaster site, NIOSH has issued guidelines for addressing a variety of occupational safety and health hazards for future disaster site rapid response team members.[20]

3.0 CHEMICAL HAZARDS NATURALLY OCCURRING IN THE FOOD AND WATER SUPPLY

3.1 Microbial Toxins

Substances found as natural components of foods and beverages are called intrinsic food additives, such as the poisons in mushrooms or fish. Intrinsic substances can pose serious threats but are rare in comparison to outbreaks caused by pathogenic microorganisms.[2] Natural toxins found in seafoods and plants, aflatoxins produced by molds in foods and prions resulting from disease in cattle, for example, have been previously described in earlier chapters (see Chapters 5 and 6).

3.2 Chemicals Inherent to Foods

Chemicals inherent to foods can be consumed in excess. The mineral elements mentioned earlier, and nutritive substances can also be ingested at dangerously high levels and will be discussed in Chapter 9. Commonly consumed non-nutritive substances such as caffeine can be found naturally in foods and beverages, for example, coffee and chocolate (see Table 7.2). Consumption in moderate amounts will not have an effect at all in most people, while demonstrating only slightly observable effects in others. However, when taken in combination with other stimulants, such as a prescription drug or herb containing stimulants, such as ma huang, the additive effects may cause severe adverse reactions ranging from tachycardia to liver failure to death.[21]

Substances peripheral to foods, such as in the skin of potatoes or fruits, or substances contained in fruit seeds may also be chemical hazards. Cyanide, and other toxicants, naturally found in plant foods or herbs can be poisonous causing physical harm and even death when consumed in large amounts. For example, solanine found under the skin of potatoes, may develop in excess when exposed to light, and if consumed, be a dangerous nerve impulse inhibitor.[3]

Some substances in foods taken along with certain drugs can create harmful lethal reactions. Excellent references are available with extensive lists of drug nutrient interactions and the symptoms expressed. A good example can be given describing a harmful, even potentially lethal, reaction that may occur in persons treated for depression using monoamine oxidase inhibitors (MAOI). Monoamine oxidase is an enzyme found in human cells adjacent to nerve axons that release neurotransmitters. This enzyme inactivates the neurotransmitters after their release from axon terminals. Individuals on MAOI should be made aware of certain foods that contain high levels of tyramine. An excessive intake of tyramine, an active pressor, is generally not a problem when tyramine is quickly inactivated by monoamine oxidases. Certain cheeses and fermented beverages, high in tyramine, will not be adequately metabolized and this can elevate blood pressure to dangerous levels (see Table 7.3).[22]

3.3 Food Allergies, Intolerances, and Sensitivities

Some individuals have very individualized physiological responses to foods or food ingredients, often referred to as "idiosyncratic." They may have an immune system that is particularly sensitive or an enzyme deficiency. Persons with lactose intolerance lack the enzyme to digest lactose and suffer abdominal cramping, diarrhea, or flatulence (intestinal gas) due to the inability to digest this sugar when they eat dairy products. Removing the foods from the diet is the only known effective treatment. Food sensitivities are relatively rare and are usually in response to a food additive, most commonly sulfite, tartrazine (the colorant, Yellow No. 5) and monosodium glutamate (MSG). MSG, a popular approved additive ingredient in some foods, if used in large amounts, may cause physiological responses often in less than one hour in some individuals sensitive to MSG. Symptoms of MSG poisoning may include burning sensations in the chest, neck and abdomen and the extremities, and the face may feel abnormal.[5]

Certain chemicals in foods and food ingredients cause immune responses in 5 to 8 percent of children and 1 to 2 percent of adults. Common symptoms of food allergies include "hives," swelling of the lips, tongue and mouth, difficulty breathing or wheezing, and

Table 7.2
SELECTED CHEMICAL HAZARDS NATURALLY OCCURRING IN THE FOOD AND WATER SUPPLY

Substance	*Where Found*
	Recognized as Inherent Chemicals in Plants
Caffeine (stimulant)	In coffee and chocolate
Cyanide (poison)	In seeds of apricots
Favism	In fava beans
Glycoalkloids (poison)	Solanine with greening in cortex of tubers, potatoes; Phalloidine in *Amanita* mushrooms (see Chapters 6, 7, 9)
Goitrogens	Block iodine absorption (destroyed by cooking)
Oxalic acid (poison)	In rhubarb leaves eaten in excess
Phytates	Interfere with absorption of calcium, magnesium, zinc, iron
Trematol (poison)	In milk of cows grazing on snakeroot
	Recognized as Inherent Response in Consumer
Idiosyncratic	Metabolic, enzyme deficiency intolerances (lactase, sucrase-isomaltase and celiac disease)
Immune mediated	Food allergens_physiologic adverse reactions to food: milk, egg, soy, wheat protein, tree nuts, peanuts, fish, shellfish
Pharmacologic in origin	MSG reactions (see Chapters 6, 7, 9)

Notes: An extensive review of the active substances and metabolic consequences of these compounds and more can be found in Shils, M.E., Olson, J.A., Shike, M. and Ross, A.C. *Modern Nutrition in Health and Disease,* 9th ed. Lippincott, Williams and Wilkins, Baltimore, 1999 Metabolic.
Codex Committee on Food Additives and Contaminants (CCFAC) (Rees).
Source: Compiled from Chapter 7 References 1, 4–6, 12, 16, 19.

vomiting, diarrhea, and cramps. These acute responses of an "overactive" immune system can even lead to life-threatening allergic reactions called anaphylaxis. A person experiencing an anaphylactic response may experience some of the symptoms listed above in addition to swelling of the throat impairing breathing, lowered blood pressure, and unconsciousness.

The only preventative action that can be taken by persons with food allergies is to avoid eating the food causing the allergic reaction. It doesn't take very much of the food to cause a reaction, sometimes as little as half a peanut. Most food reactions, 90 percent, are caused by only eight foods:[16]

Milk	Egg	Soy	Wheat Protein
Tree nuts	Peanuts	Fish	Shellfish

3.4 Other Ingested Chemicals

Alcohol, another intentionally consumed substance, when ingested in excess results in devastating consequences in pregnant females who may give birth to a child diagnosed with Fetal Alcohol Syndrome. Prescription drugs and medications necessary for employees' health are allowed in a food establishment according to the Food Code.[17] The employee medication must be clearly

Table 7.3
FOOD SOURCES OF TYRAMINE

Tyramine Content	*Food Sources*
Very High	Cheeses, aged (Boursalt, Camembert, Cheddar, Stilton), yeast extracts
High	Bologna, dried, salted, or pickled herring, dried, salted, or pickled cod, pepperoni, salami
Moderately High	Cheeses (Blue, Brick [natural], Brie, Gruyere, Mozzarella, Parmesan, Romano, Roquefort), Chianti wine, meat tenderizers
Low	Ale, avocados, bananas, beer, cheeses (American [processed]), Cottage, Cream, Ricotta), figs, sherry, sour cream, white wine

Source: Groff, L. L. and Gropper, S. S. *Advanced Nutrition and Human Metabolism.* 3rd ed. Belmont, Wadsworth Thomson Learning, 1999.

labeled and stored in an area away from food, equipment, utensils, linens, and single items such as straws, eating utensils, and napkins. Medications in a refrigerator must be kept in a clearly labeled and covered container located on the lowest shelf of the refrigerator.[16] Illicit drugs and chemicals, again, voluntarily introduced into the human body, are other substances with possible dire consequences but beyond the scope of this publication.

4.0 CHEMICAL HAZARD DETECTION, MONITORING, AND COMMUNICATION

4.1 Information Needed

Volumes have been written delineating the rules and regulations set forth by the local, state, national, and international organizations, all with the intent to provide, worldwide, all persons with safe food and water, considered a given human right. Throughout this book numerous agencies have been referenced that participate in food and water safety issues such as the discussion on the Codex Alimentarius in Chapter 10. All of these agencies must depend on reliable information to detect, monitor and communicate chemical hazards. In a pesticide incident, for example, some of the factors, to be considered are:

- The amount of the contaminated food eaten
- Which pesticide was used
- How much of the chemical was used
- When the food item was last sprayed
- How the produce was prepared at home, washed, peeled, cooked, etc.
- How the body eliminates or stores the pesticide

Food handlers and consumers should strive to obtain as much information about these factors as possible. The more information known about chemical contamination, the better-prepared health officials will be to treat victims, minimize long-term effects to human health and the environment, and prevent future incidents.

4.2 Marker Doses

Also useful are "marker dosages" used by consumers and agencies in the detection, monitoring and communication of chemical hazards.[4]

NOAEL–No Observable Adverse Effect Level, the largest acute dose of a chemical an individual may be exposed to before detecting negative effects.

ED–Effective Dose, the minimum amount of a chemical required to produce an observable effect in an individual.

ED_{50}–Effective Dose required to produce an effect in half of the population.

MTD–Maximum Tolerated Dose is the largest amount that can be consumed without causing a health problem.

LD–Lethal Dose, concentration that upon acute exposure causes death.

RfD/ADI–Reference Dose and Acceptable Daily Intake are the largest amounts of a chemical to which an individual may have chronic exposure with no observable adverse effect, generally 1/100th of the NOAEL.

LADD–Lifetime Average Daily Dose is estimated to an individual averaged over a lifetime of 70 years.

4.3 Detection by Individuals

In the United States, effective control of chemical hazards depends on prompt detection and reporting to local health authorities. Food service workers will typically be the "first responders" and should be aware of chemical contaminations in order to protect themselves as well as consumers. Many employers voluntarily provide staff training to educate their employees on safety issues. In the United States laws such as the "Right-to-Know" ruling state that employees should know about the hazardous chemicals they may be exposed to at work. The Occupational Safety and Health Administration (OSHA) in the United States[24] and the Office of Laboratory Security in Canada[25] are two agencies that require employers to provide this information in material safety data sheets (MSDS) available in an accessible location.[24,25]

MSDS forms provide the ingredients and chemical characteristics of a product in addition to information about, fire, explosion, reactivity, and health hazard data. Emergency procedures if spilled, ingested or otherwise misused are also described. MSDS list personal protective equipment needed and other devices that will reduce risks to individuals. See Appendix C, page 265.

4.4 Monitoring by Individuals

Individual consumers have, in some instances, the opportunity to monitor their own risk to hazardous substances. Homeowners, for example, are instructed by the EPA on the use of two home testing procedures for determining radon levels in the home. Short-term testing requires monitoring the home for 2 to 90 days depending on the device. Long-term testing devices will require more than 90 days and will provide a better estimate of year round average radon levels. The most commonly used detectors are "charcoal canisters," "alpha track," "electretion chamber," "continuous monitors," and "charcoal liquid scintillation" detectors. These may be purchased at retail stores ranging in cost from $15 to $100. Interpretation of the results, and follow up actions can be performed by the homeowner, again relatively inexpensively according to EPA recommendations.[26]

4.5 Detection and Monitoring by Government Agencies and Industry

Some chemical hazard detection and monitoring practices are beyond the scope of individual consumers, homeowners and employees. Detection often requires medical testing, population surveillance, and accurate science to dispose of contaminated products and stockpiled chemicals. Various government agencies have invested time, money and expertise to oversee food safety. Food industries have implemented self-regulating practices to thwart the fears associated with their products, particularly any chemical hazards.

Establishing safe food handling practices to avoid chemical hazards in the food supply, again like biological and physical hazard controls, will increase not only the safety of the food supply but also the margin of profit, reduce legal liabilities, and promote good will to improve consumer confidence. Chapter 12 provides a list of representative government agencies in the MSA that participate in chemical hazard communication, detection and monitoring.

Examples of specific responsibilities of major agencies in the United States include:

- prevention of chemical hazards by food additives thorough testing prior to commercial use (FDA Food Additives Amendments)
- enforcement of pesticide tolerances at the time of harvest for 366 different pesticides on imported foods and foods shipped through interstate commerce (FDA Pesticide Program)
- monitoring trends in levels of certain nutrients and over 300 different chemicals consumed; the most frequently identified contaminants are DDT, malathion, chlorpyrifos-methyl, endosulfan, and dieldrin. (FDA Total Diet Study)[4]
- monitoring raw produce, processed grains and fluid milk (USDA Pesticide Data Program)
- calculation of exposure estimates for a contaminant in air, food and drinking water (arsenic, chlordane, DDT, dieldrin, dioxins, and polychlorinated biphenyls (PCBs) have cancer hazard ratios greater than 1.[4]

Each food and water chemical contamination situation has the potential to be unique in detection, routes of contamination, treatment, disposal and hazard communication. The following scenarios will attempt to depict a small number of chemical contamination cases that vary in methods of detection, monitoring, disposal, and reporting.

4.6 Regional Monitoring of a Pesticide Contamination

The FDA and USDA monitoring programs report that most pesticide residues are within tolerable limits according to the EPA.[8,28,29] This is the result of vigilant monitoring that has been long-term and extensive, not to mention expensive as the following situation demonstrates (FBDO #36). Today kepone, from a manufacturing plant closed over 25 years ago, is still monitored regularly in and around Hopewell, Virginia. Initially, the chemical hazard was detected in a single blood sample submitted by an attentive physician to the CDC who then alerted regional OSHA officials. The response by the National Institute of Occupational Safety and Health (NIOSH) shortly thereafter resulted in a report showing that half of the 113 kepone plant employees had medical histories reporting clinical signs of kepone poisoning; tremors, visual disturbances, vertigo, lack of muscle coordination, loss of weight, nervousness, insomnia, pain the chest and abdomen, and in some cases, infertility, and loss of libido.

At the time of the incident there was no data available regarding the effect of kepone on humans. Within the year the National Cancer Institute had completed bioassays that led to the issuance of a report that kepone must be assumed to be a potential carcinogen and that workplace levels for kepone be limited to 1 μg/cu m as a time-weighted average concentration for up to a 10-hr. workday, 40-hr. workweek, as an emergency standard.[28]

Environmental monitoring for kepone in nearby waterways has continued three times per year, sampling finfish at five stations, ground water at six stations and sediment at 25 stations since 1976. By the 1996–98 biennium, detectable levels of kepone were reported in fish, ground water and sediment but were found to be consistently below the U.S. FDA action levels as in the previous biennium reports. Detection and monitoring in this instance involved responsible individuals and regulatory agencies at all levels of government in many different agencies.[29]

4.7 International Monitoring of a Nuclear Contamination

The problems magnify when the contamination is not confined to the immediate site of the accident. The nuclear incident resulting from poor plant design in Chernobyl, Russia in 1986 affected most of the Northern Hemisphere and received immediate media attention and worldwide concern. According to a World Nuclear Association report in March of 2001, 15 years following the incident, the impact resulted in 30 deaths, 28 confirmed due to radiation exposure, and up to ten deaths from thyroid cancer. An authoritative United Nations report in 2000 confirmed that there is no scientific evidence of any significant radiation-related health effects to most people exposed.[30]

Another report has concluded that the long-term effects of the Chernobyl incident affected another 140 persons who suffered various degrees of radiation sickness and health impairment and identified a significant increase of carcinomas of the thyroid among children living in the contaminated regions of the former Soviet Union. Between 1990 and 1998, reported cases of carcinomas of the thyroid totaled 1,791 among children.[31] The impact of the Chernobyl accident on agricultural practices, food production and use appears to continue to be much more widespread than the direct health impact initially reported in humans.

International agencies were unprepared to handle an emergency of this magnitude. Steps should be taken to improve the harmonization, communication, and involvement in emergency planning, preparedness, management and consistency in reporting of short and long-term effects of nuclear contaminations.[32]

4.8 Limitations to the Regulations

The federal monitoring systems are not without limitations. The FDA system monitoring food additives is designed to protect consumers ingesting products containing these chemicals. The FDA system does not consider the safety of workers exposed to inhalation of high concentrations of food additives. In May of 2002, workers at a microwave popcorn factory in Missouri were diagnosed with fixed obstructive lung disease due to exposure to the flavoring additive. Four of the patients were on lung transplant lists (see Ch. 15, page 255).[27]

4.9 International Agency Coordination

Worldwide coordinated efforts between local, state, federal and international agencies must be vigilant in their efforts to detect, monitor, and communicate chemical hazards.[7] Agencies with these responsibilities exist in most countries of the world. However, international cooperation will be essential to assure worldwide safety from chemical hazards in our food and water supply for years to come.

When international cooperation is lacking, chemical hazards persist. Situations in Belize and Belgium demonstrated the need for international cooperation when disposing of chemicals and contaminated products.[10,11] Officials in Belize have struggled with the responsibility of disposing of a supply of DDT that remained after national regulations banned its use. The recommended method for disposal is incineration. However, there is no incinerator or hazardous waste landfill facility in Belize. The Belize Ministry of Health and the Department of the Environment (DOE) contacted the United States Environmental Protection Agency for assistance in disposing of the unused DDT. The DDT is still under temporary storage in Belmopan, Belize.

In Belgium, as recently as January, 1999, dioxins still posed a human health risk, when the chemical (Ch. 15, page 254) made its way into the food supply due to improper disposal of industrial oil containing dioxin and PCBs. In Asia, authorities were puzzled about how to dispose of potentially contaminated foods that they may have imported from Belgium. Burial in landfills is again the common choice for disposal, however, danger may well return in another form if the chemicals leach into the ground water.

The situations above remain unresolved today. In both situations authorities were aware of the potential hazards and attempted to dispose of the chemicals properly. For continued responsible disposal of chemical waste, international cooperation will be needed to prevent accidental contamination of the food and water supply, and prevent negligent spills of chemical hazards into the environment.

4.10 Communicating Chemical Hazards

In Belize, the chemical hazard went unreported for years. In Chernobyl, the long-term effects reported are conflicting. Communication depends on the prompt reporting of each suspected incident to local health authorities. Once the incident is confirmed as a chemical hazard, local health authorities relay the information to agencies such as the Centers for Disease Control and Prevention (CDC) in the United States. The CDC is recognized as the lead federal agency for protecting the health and safety of consumers at home and abroad. One of the principle publications of the CDC is the *MMWR Weekly,* reporting on morbidity and mortality issues globally. The Adverse Effects Reported (AER) in this publication help authorities identify chemical hazards that are not acute as in the case of ephedrine containing dietary supplements (see Chapter 9).[24]

A number of agencies have well established information and reporting strategies developed for consumers and professionals to use regarding the harmful effects of chemical contamination.

- In the United States, the agencies developing effective radiation surveillance methods have been the US Public Health Service and the US Atomic Energy Commission.
- The National Toxicology Program provides chemical health and safety infor-

mation, short-term toxicity and long-term carcinogenicity definitions, toxicity definitions for genetic and organ systems.

NIOSH provides a *Pocket Guide to Chemical Hazards*. The National Institute of Environmental Health and Safety (NIEHS) has found three tests that when used in combination provide a rapid assessment of potential estrogenicity of environmental contaminants. In six weeks or less this combination of assays can be used to screen chemicals with known or suspected estrogenic activity, such as 17 beta-estradiol, diethlstilbesterol (DES), tamoxifen, methoxychlor, endosulfan, o,p-DDT, and kepone.

- Neurological and behavioral effects of exposure to toxic substances can be found in "Neurotox" tables
- Local health departments require eating establishments to prominently post facility inspection reports for customers. These reports also appear weekly in local newspapers.
- United States Centers for Disease Control and Prevention publishes Adverse Effects Reported (AER) in *MMWR Weekly*
- The WHO IPCS/ILO has established Chemical Safety Cards for hundreds of chemicals and substances, including exposure occupational exposure limits (OELs)
- The WHO has also provided extensive information in their Principles for the Safety Assessment of Food Additives and Contaminants in Food. That information was complied by the International Programme on Chemical Safety in cooperation with the Joint FAO/WHO Expert Committee on Food Additives. http://www.who.int/pcs/jecfa/ehc70/html

5.0 PRACTICAL GUIDELINES TO REDUCE OR PREVENT CHEMICAL HAZARDS

5.1 For Consumers

- Scrub food surfaces with water and or a mild soap to remove most pesticide residues.
- Carefully label all IPM products such as rat poisons, all cleaning products.

5.2 For Employees

- Follow OSHA guidelines
- Maintain and use MSDSs
- Report all accidental contaminations to the proper agencies

5.3 For Government

- Seek ways of minimizing the effects of fallout, reducing the uptake of radionuclides from soil, preventing entry of radionuclides to animals, and removal of radionuclides from milk and food.[5]

5.4 For Business and Industry

- Develop safer and more effective chemical pesticides.
- Use agricultural practices that reduce pesticide usage.
- Adopt IPM practices that emphasize natural toxins, more effective applica-

tion procedures and disease resistant species.

REVIEW QUESTIONS

1. Are natural foods toxic? Explain your answer.
2. Once pesticide residues enter the food chain they diminish in concentration from plant to animal to human. True or False? Explain
3. Who can report a chemical hazard?
4. What is the most frequently used chemical cleaner in food establishments?
5. What is the recommended way to dispose of organic halogens?
6. What are endocrine disrupting chemicals?
7. Are all home remedies for illnesses safe?
8. What are the eight foods that most commonly cause food allergies?
9. How can homeowners reduce the radon gas in their homes?

REFERENCES

1. Claudio, V. S., Leocadio, C. G., De Leon, S. Y., Serraon-Joves, L. *Food Safety and Sanitation for Philippine Consumers.* Manila, Philippines, Merriam & Webster Bookstore, 2001.
2. American Dietetic Association (ADA). Position of the American Dietetic Association: Food and Water Safety. *J Am Diet Assoc 97:*184–189, 1997.
3. Boyle, M. A. *Personal Nutrition.* 4th ed., Belmont, California, Wadsworth, 2000.
4. Cody, M. M., and Kunkel, M. E. *Food Safety for Professionals.* 2nd ed. Chicago, American Dietetic Association, 2001.
5. Longree, K., and Armbruster, G. *Quantity Food Sanitation.* 5th ed. New York, John Wiley & Sons, 1996.
6. Grosvenor, M. B., and Smolin, L. A. *Nutrition from Science to Life.* Orlando, Harcourt, 2002.
7. Alegria, M. Problems with Final Disposal of DDT in Belize. United Nations Environmental Programme. Available at http://www.chem.unep.ch/pops/POPs_Inc/proceedings/cartagena/ALEGRIA.html. Accessed March 21, 2002.
8. Fishing Restrictions and Health Advisories in Effect for Virginia Rivers. Available at http://www.vdh.state.va.us/HHControl/fishing_advisories.htm. Accessed March 21, 2002.
9. Astudillo, P. US study establishes link between dioxin and cancer. *WSWS: News & Analysis: Medicine & Health.* Available at http://www.wsws.org/articles/1999/jun1999/diox-j01.shtml. Accessed March 22, 2002.
10. The Great Dioxin Scare. *Asia Week.* Available at http://www.pathfinder.com/asiaweek/99/0625/feat6.html. Accessed March 25, 2002.
11. CVM and International Dioxin Concerns. Available at http://www.fda.gov/cvm/index/dioxin/dioxin_intl.html. Accessed March 25, 2002.
12. Hubbert, W., Hagstad, H., Spangle, E., Hinton, H., and Hughes, K. *Food Safety and Quality Assurance,* 2nd ed., Ames, Iowa State University Press, 1996.
13. Tong, W., Perkins, R., Fang, H., Hong, H., Xie, Q., Branham, W., Sheehan, D. M., and Anson, J. F. Development of Quantitative Structure-Activity Relationships (QSARs) and Their Use for Priority Setting in the Testing Strategy of Endocrine Disruptors. *Regulatory Research Perspectives: Impact on Public Health.* Vol. 1:3, 2002.
14. The California Department of Health Services. *Lead in home remedies.* Available at http://www.parentsplace.com/health/safetyrecalls/articles/0,10335,239332_110076,00.html. Accessed April 20, 2002.
15. Epidemiologic Notes and Reports Lead-Contaminated Drinking Water in Bulk-Water Storage Tanks–Arizona and California, 1993. *MMWR Weekly, 43*(41); 751,757–758, 1994.
16. McSwane, D., Rue, N., and Linton R. *Essentials of Food Safety and Sanitation,* 3rd ed. Upper Saddle River, NJ: Prentice Hall, 2003.

17. US FDA CFSAN Food Code 2001. Available at http://www.vm.cfsan.fda.gov/~dms/food-code.html. Accessed April 20, 2002.
18. Ritchie, I., and Martin. S. J. *The Healthy Home Kit.* Chicago, Real Estate Education Co., 1995.
19. Rees N., and Watson, D. *International Standards for Food Safety,* NY, Kluwer Academic, 2000.
20. Occupational Exposures to Air Contaminants at the World Trade Center Disaster Site–New York, September–October, 2001. *MMWR Weekly, 51*(21); 453–456, 2002. Available at http://www.cdc.gov/niosh/pdfs/76-kepon.pdf. Accessed April 26, 2002.
21. Stone, B. FDA Warns Consumers Against Nature's Nutrition Formula One. *HHS NEWS.* February 28, 1995.
22. Groff, L. L., and Gropper, S. S. *Advanced Nutrition and Human Metabolism.* 3rd ed. Belmont, Wadsworth Thomson Learning, 1999.
23. *C C MMWR Weekly.* Available at http://cisat.isciii.es/mmwr/mmwr wk.html. Accessed April 26, 2002.
24. Where to find Material Safety Data Sheets on the Internet. Available at http://www.ilpi.com/msds/osha/index.html. Accessed July 20, 2002.
25. Material Safety Data Sheets. Health Canada, Population and Public Health Branch, Office of Laboratory Security. Available at http://www.hc-sc.gc.ca/pphb-dgspsp/msds-ftss/index.html. Accessed July 20, 2002.
26. United States Environmental Protection Agency. *A Citizen's Guide to Radon: The Guide to Protecting Yourself and Your Family From Radon.* 3rd. ed. Available at http://www.epa.gov/iaq/radon/pubs/citguide .html#how-totest. Accessed April 26, 2002.
27. *CDC MMWR Weekly.* Fixed Obstructive Lung Disease in Workers at a Microwave Popcorn Factory–Missouri, 2000–2002, 51(16); 345–347, April 26, 2002. Available at http://www.cdc.gov/mmwr/preview/mmwrhtml/mm5116a2.htm. Accessed April 26, 2002.
28. National Institute for Occupational Safety and Health. *Recommended Standard for Occupational Exposure to Kepone.* Available at http://www.cdc.gov/niosh/pdfs/76-kepon.pdf. Accessed March 25, 2002.
29. Biennial Report to the Governor and General Assembly on Toxic Substances in the Commonwealth. State Board of Health, Virginia Department of Health. July 30, 1999
30. World Nuclear Association Energy for Sustainable Development, Information and Issue Briefs, Chernobyl. Available at http://www.world-nuclear.org/info/chernobyl/inf07.htm. Accessed July 20, 2002.
31. UNSCEAR Vienna Meeting Focuses on Chernobyl Incident, United Nations Scientific Committee on the Effects of Atomic Radiation, Press Release. Available at http://www.unscear.org/pressrelease.htm. Accessed July 20, 2002.
32. Nuclear Energy Agency, Organization for Economic Cooperation and Development (OECD–OCDE. Available at http://www.nea.fr/html/rp/chernobyl-update.pdf. Accessed July 20, 2002.

Chapter 8

CONTROL OF PHYSICAL HAZARDS

1.0 INTRODUCTION

One food-related hazard is one too many. As discussed previously, food safety hazards are generally caused by biological, chemical or physical contamination.[1-4] Biological hazards, usually microbial contaminations, generally pose the greatest threat to food safety, followed by chemical hazards (see Chapters 5, 6 and 7). In reality, it is difficult to singularly categorize all food related hazards as biological, chemical or physical hazards. For example, physical contamination can introduce both biological and chemical hazards into products. Also, in many instances, foodborne illnesses go undetected and, thus, are never reported, and of those reported, the CDC estimates that nearly half are of unknown cause.[1–4]

The objective of this chapter is twofold, to 1) address physical hazards that affect consumers and food handlers, and 2) address physical facilities in food and water safety. Physical hazards result from accidental contamination and poor food handling practices at any point in the food chain–from the source to the consumer. Unfortunately, in severe situations physical hazards such as choking or internal punctures can even cause death. Physical hazards may statistically not be as important as other food hazards, however, they can be considered obnoxious, irritating, unsightly, unsanitary, as well as, inconvenient. Another real consequence of physical hazards in the food supply is the economic impact, placing unnecessary costs on regulatory agencies, small businesses, and the community.

Poorly managed physical facilities contribute to physical contamination of food as well as physical injuries to food handlers. Food handlers on the farm, involved in food transport and food service are subject to regulations to protect themselves and their products. Although inadequate time will be devoted here to agricultural and industrial facilities for food systems the reader is encouraged to remember that food safety applies from "farm to fork."

Careful attention to physical hazards that may enter the food system at any point will prevent devastating consequences to both food consumers and food handlers. On the farm, workers are exposed to a range of physical hazards, farm implements, production animals, and adverse weather conditions. The USDA, OSHA, and various other agencies are resources for educating employees about the extensive regulations in place to detect, monitor and control physical hazards in food production environments. Proper animal handling facilities can prevent farm animal related injuries. Proper silo ventilation and employee safety will prevent deaths due to suffocation. Dairy parlor inspections will assure that raw, fluid milk will be transported without contamination in a closed milking system from cow to cooler. Many of the issues addressed in reference to food service facilities also apply to production facilities.[15] Regardless of the position in the food system, the farm or the fast food restaurant, covered or shatterproof light fixtures, screened windows, tight doors, and facilities designed to accommodate the demands are needed to prevent physical hazards from entering the food chain.

1.1 Impact of Physical Hazards

Australia's current food hygiene regulatory system costs government agencies $18.6 million (net) in enforcement, small businesses $337 million in compliance, and the Australian community an additional $2.6 billion every year. In 1996–97, absenteeism due to food poisoning resulted in productivity losses of over $370 million. Physical contamination of food was the reason for over 40 percent of food recalls in Australia during 1997 and there can be an extreme financial liability to the offending company. In 1988, the New South Wales Supreme Court awarded almost $500,000 in damages to a consumer who had eaten a toothpick in a can of beans and suffered a perforated bowel and peritonitis.[5]

The new national food safety standards report incorporates requirements that can reduce the incidence of foodborne illness in Australia through lower health care costs, less absenteeism, improved business productivity, increased competitiveness on world markets and a reduction in business failure and associated costs, including civil litigation. Public health and safety outcomes directed the development of the new standards by the Australia-New Zealand Food Standards Council (ANZFSC). The evidence-based standards take into account standards developed by the Codex Alimentarius Commission and countries including the United States, Canada and the United Kingdom.[4,5]

Other countries have dealt with many of the same issues faced by Australia, New Zealand, the United States and the European Union when seeking common markets. Argentina, Brazil, Paraguay, and Uruguay in 1991 created the Southern Common Market (MERCOSUR), a single common market, in Latin American under the Treaty of Asuncion to assure food safety in a harmonious international trade environment.[7]

Food safety in the US is a top public health priority, driven by an estimated 76 million illnesses, 323,914 hospitalizations and 5,104 deaths attributable to foodborne illnesses each year in the US. The estimated cost of foodborne illness is $10–$83 billion annually. The Healthy People 2010 campaign targets food safety as a public health goal with specific aims to reduce outbreaks of foodborne illnesses, improve food employee behaviors and food preparation practice.[6]

1.2 FDA Food Code 2001

The FDA Food Code 2001 serves as a valuable reference and a basis for state and local requirements if adopted by regulating agencies in state health organizations (see Appendix I). Throughout this discussion of physical hazards endless references are made to the Food Code 2001.[6] Throughout this chapter, the sections of the code the reader may want to refer to for further details will be referenced as "FC 4-1," for example, for more information about the limited the use of wood products, sponges, and numerous chemicals in food service facilities.

1.3 Definitions

To some a *physical hazard* is simply defined as a physical contaminant in food. The Australia New Zealand Food Safety Authority (ANZFSA) considers food contaminants to be those substances present in food at levels that serve no technological function and whose presence may lead to adverse health effects. They usually serve no nutritional function; even if some elements needed for normal body functioning, such as copper, selenium, and zinc have adverse effects at high levels of intake.

The Codex Alimentarius Commission defines a contaminant as a substance not intentionally added to food and specifically states that the term does not include insect fragments, rodent hairs and other extraneous matter. As such, fish bones can be considered a physical hazard when they are present in a boneless fillet, but not when they are in a whole fish or a cutlet. Some products, for example, harvested from fields or orchards, physical contamination may be tolerated provided further processing, through sieving or the use of flotation tanks for example will remove sticks from dried beans or dirt from root vegetables (see Table 8.1).[5]

2.0 INJURIES FROM PHYSICAL HAZARDS ADDED TO THE FOOD AND WATER SUPPLY

2.1 Consumer Concerns

Foreign objects can injure consumers when swallowed accidentally or unknowingly along with their food or fluids. Children are naturally curious and inclined to put everything they get their hands on into their mouths. The bodily harm inflicted, lacera-

Table 8.1
EXAMPLES OF PHYSICAL HAZARDS IN FOOD AND BEVERAGES[8,10]

Physical Hazard Source	*Likely Items Found in Food or Beverages*
Food	Gristle, seeds, nut and seed shells, bone (see definitions) egg shells, orange peels, hair and shuck from corn, nut shells, inedible seeds, fish scales, gristle, chicken pin feathers, vegetable or fruit peels
Glass	Chipped glassware, light fixtures, bottles, jars, gauge covers
Ceramics	Crockery
Wood/Plants	Splinters from pallets, boxes, buildings; toothpicks; sticks; grass clippings
Metal	Machinery, wire, shavings from cans, staples from cartons, steel wool, tops from aluminum cans, chips from corroding kitchen equipment, nails, screws, wire
Cookware metals	Lead in cast iron, ceramic, china and crystal utensils; copper; galvanized metal; lead in pewter alloys; lead in solder flux; nonstick resin peelings; perflurocarbon compounds
Stones	Rocks, pebbles, sand
Rubber	Seals, packaging
Plastic	Packaging and storage materials, single-use items fragments, straws, chipped cups, spatula pieces, decorations, candles
Cloth	Fragments of rags, hot pads, roasting ties, sponges
Insects and rodents	Fur, hair, fecal pellets, eggs, wings, legs, nesting materials, discarded seed shells Personal effects Hair, nails, gum, jewelry, bandages, cigarette butts

tions, damaged teeth, or possibly a punctured gastrointestinal tract may be a painful consequence.

Unlike chemical hazards, physical hazards do not have to enter the body passing through cell membranes when digested and absorbed in the digestive tract. Instead physical hazards, and fecal material, are technically considered "outside the body" when they remain in the tract or pass through until eliminated from the body through defecation.

Again, unlike chemical hazards, reference doses or average intakes are not calculated for physical hazards. There is nil tolerance of most physical hazards in food, either on the basis of safety (such as glass fragments and wire) or suitability (insect parts). In Australia, the dried fruit industry has a nil tolerance for contamination with spiky weed seeds (African boxthorn) because of the potential damage if ingested.[7]

A clear distinction between chemical and physical hazards is again blurred when we consider plastic packaging materials. Some of these materials can be physical hazards if swallowed and chemical hazards if heated with food in a microwave oven. Nonstick coatings, perfluorocarbon compounds on kitchenware and non-food-contact surfaces can easily chip off, again posing both chemical and physical hazards if these materials enter the food supply. As consumers we can protect our selves from this kind of chemical and physical hazard by using nonscoring or nonscratching utensils and cleaning aids on frying pans, griddles, sauce pans, cookie sheets, and waffle bakers coated with these nonstick compounds.[6]

Injuries from physical hazards generally begin in the oral cavity. Teeth can become cracked or broken when biting down on a hard foreign object that was not anticipated, such as a cherry seed, a bone chip or a stone. Soft tissues in the mouth and pharynx can sustain cuts, scrapes, and burns from both extremes in temperature or exposure to chemicals. In the esophagus a piece of meat, a large bolus of sticky food like peanut butter, or a hard object can get stuck in the food passage and cause choking. Eating utensils may also accidentally damage lips cheeks, tongues or palates. Foods and beverages passing down the gastrointestinal tract can also continue to be hazardous if capable of puncturing, irritating, or inflaming the stomach or intestines.

2.2 Food Handler Concerns[11]

Physical injuries at home in the kitchen or in food establishments may be:

- Cuts from food preparation equipment and implement use
- Slipping caused by improper footwear or spills on the floor
- Accidents caused by jewelry or clothing catching on equipment or furniture
- Burns from hot stove surfaces, hot cookware, hot food and water
- Electrical burns
- Concussion injuries from falling supplies from storage shelves

3.0 PHYSICAL FACILITIES AND CONSUMER AND FOOD HANDLER SAFETY

Physical facility design contributes to the efficient and safe handling of food to protect consumers from biological, chemical and physical food hazards and the prevention of injury to food handlers. The physical facilities, to be efficient, effective and safe must be designed, maintained, and cleaned using appropriate methods.[6]

3.1 Layout and Construction Materials

Both indoor and outdoor food establishments, according to the 2001 Food Code are required to have materials for the floors, walls and ceilings that are smooth, durable and easily cleanable. Utility lines should not be unnecessarily exposed and should not obstruct or prevent cleaning of floors, walls or ceilings.[6]

3.2 Floors, Walls, and Ceilings

All floors subject to washing or spray cleaning methods must be nonabsorbent, including food preparation areas, walk-in refrigerators, warewashing areas, toilet rooms, and mobile food establishment serving areas. Flush washing area wall and floor junctures must be tight and floor drains graded. All mats in these areas must be easily removable for cleaning. Closely woven and easily cleanable carpets, tightly installed against the wall or with edges secured with strips or tacks, are permitted in customer areas (FC 6-1). Generally, any sawdust, wood shavings, granular salt, baked clay, diatomaceous earth, or similar materials may not be used on floors FC 6-5.[6]

Walls and ceilings also must be easily cleanable; finished and sealed to provide a smooth nonabsorbent, easily cleanable surface, with the exception of areas used for dry storage; and concrete, porous blocks or bricks may be used. All wall and ceiling fixtures, lights, fans, vents and decorative items must also be easily cleanable (FC 6-2). Doors and windows must be tight fitting and secured, protected against entry of insects, rodents and animals. Wire screens and air curtains to control pests need to be cleanable. Walls and roofs must adequately serve as barriers to weather, insects, rodents, and animals.[6]

3.3 Lighting, Air Flow, Electricity, and Plumbing

Light fixtures need to be shielded, coated, or otherwise shatter resistant in areas where there is exposed food, clean equipment, utensils and linens, or unwrapped single-service, single-use articles. Ample lighting, properly distributed as needed, is necessary in food preparation areas to prevent mistaking tie strings on roasts for spaghetti, for example, and to see rodent droppings or stones in dried beans, etc. In these areas, where the food service employee is working with food or equipment such as slicers, grinders or saws at least 540 lux (50 foot-candles) is required. Also, cleaning and hand washing require adequate lighting for employees to effectively do their jobs. These areas, inside equipment such as reach-in and under-counter refrigerators and consumer self-serve areas, all expect at least 220 lux (20 foot-candles) on all working surfaces, with less intense light required in other areas, 110 lux (10 foot-candles) (FC 6-2) (FC 6-3).[6,9]

Ventilation, heating and air-conditioning system designs should not cause contamination from airflow in food, equipment or utensil work areas. Intake and exhaust ducts need routine maintenance to assure adequate airflow, prevent dust or grease accumulation and detect unlawful discharge.[6,9] Fans may be needed in areas subject to excessive heat, steam, condensation, vapors, obnoxious odors, smoke and fumes.

Electrical appliances must be of proper construction, materials and design and meet the standards of regulations, and bear the UL seal. Proper sanitary plumbing is extremely important in food sanitation. If plumbing is not properly installed or maintained, the risk of backflow, flooding, and stoppages may contaminate food preparation and storage areas. Leaking sewer lines must be avoided and quickly repaired. Plumbing should meet the capacity needs of the facility, installed and maintained according to local and state laws. Equipment with plumbing connections, i.e. garbage disposals, dishwashers, etc. need to be given special attention. Grease traps should be easy to clean and with out cross connections between potable water and any nonpotable water supplies. Toilets must be designed to maintain good working order, and be kept clean (FC 5-2).[6]

4.0 PHYSICAL FACILITY OPERATION AND MAINTENANCE

4.1 Handling Capacity

Being able to handle capacity again transcends across all facets of the food system. Food production systems must have the milking stanchions for the number of cows in production, and dairy parlor storage tanks must be able to hold the volume of milk produced until processing plant transport tanks arrive for milk pickup. Cleaning frequencies and methods must be feasible for the volume of each type of food handled, i.e. fresh fish, beef, lamb, poultry, pork, and raw fruits and vegetables (Table 8.2). All of these examples

Table 8.2
FOOD UTENSILS AND EQUIPMENT TEMPERATURES SCHEDULE

Temperature		*Cleaning Frequency*
F°	C°	
41	5.0	24 hrs
41–45	>5.0–7.2	20 hrs
45–50	>7.2–10.0	16 hrs
>50–55	>10.0–12.8	10 hrs

Source: US Food Code 2001.

illustrate the importance of facility planning and design.

4.1.1 Equipment, Utensils, Linens

Likewise, food service equipment must be of sufficient weight and be smooth, easily cleanable and resistant to pitting, chipping, crazing, scratching, scoring, distortion, and decomposition.

Equipment must be safe, durable, corrosion resistant, and nonabsorbent. In many cases the use of cast iron is prohibited for utensils or food contact surfaces or equipment, but may be used for cooking surfaces and brazing to endure repeated washing (FC 4-1). Other possible means of chemically contaminating food through lead in ceramic, china and crystal utensils as well as, copper, galvanized metal, lead in pewter alloys, solder and flux are described in Chapter 7 (Table 8.3) (FC 4-1).

Single-use and single-service items should not allow the migration of deleterious substances or impart colors, odors, or tastes to food and shall be safe and clean (FC 4-2). Equipment and utensils need to be designed and constructed to be durable, strong enough to perform adequately, seamless, and free of crevasses that might harbor food particles.

Temperature measuring devices for food, air and water need to be accurate, easy to read, and hot water sanitization temperatures and pressures maintained and other measuring devices calibrated for water pH, concentration and hardness (see Chapter 7). Manual and automatic dishwashing machines need to be operated according to code (4-2).

Type of food involved, amount of food residue, and temperature of food is maintained during the laundering linens, drying utensils, cookware, flatware,

4.2 Storage

Critical to proper storage is proper labeling. Even upon delivery at the loading dock it is critical that each shipment be inspected and properly identified before storing. Labeling, again, from any point in food systems, from farm to fork, is critical. Proper, clear labels that will not fall off, wear off, or be illegible. A plan should be designed to adequately inform family members, consumers, and employees of all substances, not just those that are potentially dangerous.[6]

FBDO #39 (Ch. 15, page 250) illustrates the importance of being able to properly identify a product by its label. A black pepper can refilled with pesticide led to a terrible consequence at a company picnic in the summer of 1998. Fourteen of sixteen persons became ill, and ten were even hospitalized when the pesticide, aldicard, was mistakenly added to a cabbage salad instead of black pepper.[6]

Table 8.3
LEAD IN UTENSILS–LIMITATIONS FOR CONTAMINATION

Utensil Category	*Description*	*Maximum Lead mg/L*
Hot beverage mugs	Coffee mugs	0.5
Large hollowware	Bowls greater than or equal to 1.1 L (1.16 QT)	1
Small hollowware	Bowls < 1.1 L (1.16 QT)	2.0
Flat utensils	Plates, saucers	3.0

Stressed merchandise such as damaged, spoiled, and recalled products must be labeled and segregated and held in designated areas that are separated from food, equipment, utensils, linens, and customer serving items. Maintenance tools, such as brooms, mops, vacuum cleaners, and similar items need to be stored neatly and in a location that prevents contamination of food and food contact items (food equipment, utensils, linens, and single-service and single-use articles) (i.e. straws and plastic serving utensils). The premises must be free of items that are unnecessary, i.e. old or nonfunctioning equipment and litter (FC 6-5).[6]

4.3 General Sanitation

Again, consumers, food handlers and production workers will benefit from good general sanitation practices.

4.4 Cleaning the Facility

Cleaning should occur as often as necessary. Appropriate methods used at times when the least food is exposed is best. Cleaning may be needed due to spills or to prevent accidents from occurring during peak hours of operation; equipment needs to handle capacity.

Follow cleaning frequency and methods for each type of food, i.e. fresh fish, beef, lamb, poultry, pork, raw fruits and vegetables. Dustless methods should be used to clean floors: wet cleaning, vacuum cleaning, mopping with treated mops or sweeping with a broom and dust-arresting compounds. Cleaning equipment such as mops should never be in food preparation sinks or hand washing sinks, and warewashing equipment may not be in contact with body parts; cigarette butts with saliva are potential sources of food handler contamination.

4.5 Integrated Pest Management

Insects, rodents and birds contribute to diseases, including foodborne illnesses discussed in Chapter 6. Fecal droppings and animal fur contribute to physical contamination. Vermin feeding and nesting practices may result in hidden deposits of seed shells remaining from scavenged foods in food storage areas. Dead or trapped birds, insects, rodents, and other pests need to be removed from control devices such as electric insect traps and mouse traps (FC 6-5).

Rodents and insects are attracted to discarded food, odors and unsanitary toilet rooms. To reduce the likely hood of vermin and insect infestations, empty containers, crates and boxes should be disposed of. Garbage and rubbish should be stored in tight durable containers that do not corrode, leak or retain odors. Garbage cans should be cleaned using brushes and decontaminated in hot water (180° F; 82° C) or steam.

Garbage disposals need to be installed, used, and maintained according to manufacturer's directions. Toilet facilities must be kept exceptionally clean.[6,9]

4.6 Waste Management

Sewage is one of the most dangerous sources of human microbial disease. Sanitary sewage disposal should prevent the contamination of the ground and water supply. All waste should be disposed of by a public sewage system or by a sewage system constructed and operated according to health laws. Temporary food establishments must make special arrangements to meet these criteria. Waste should be protected from pets and rodents at all times (FC 5-4).[6,9] (For more details, see also Chapters 6 and 10.)

4.6.1 Refuse, Recyclables and Returnables (FC 5-5)

Sponges may not be used in contact with cleaned and *sanitized* or in-use *food-contact surfaces* (FC 4-1).

Dispensing equipment, protection of equipment and food should avoid splashing, clean, and free from customer or employee contamination, i.e. spout recessed (4-2 FC).

Consumers can also be sources of contamination, especially with displayed food, on buffets and salad bars; attention to the proper use of tongs, forks, and spoons is critical.

5.0 PERSONAL HYGIENE

Infected cuts and burns are also capable of contaminating foods, as are unwashed hands following a trip to the toilet (see Chapter 5). It is the responsibility of the supervisor to send employees home if symptoms of illness arise. Employees should call attention to illnesses that are not apparent.

Personal employee habits such as clean hair, hands, nails, garments, and sanitary habits are critical to good food sanitation (see Chapters 3 and 6).

The opportunities for contamination of hands are endless and cannot possible be listed. Examples such as picking up a dropped pencil, recovering a pot holder from the floor, unclogging a sink drain, and all unsanitary actions that may be subconscious and overlooked. Using a hand sink for the cleaning of maintenance tools, the preparation or holding of maintenance materials, or the disposal of mop water and similar liquid wastes violates Food Code 2001 recommendations (FC 6-5).[6,9]

Food Code regulations prohibit the use of food establishments as living or sleeping areas. Dressing rooms, lockers, hand washing facilities, toilet rooms, and other employee accommodations are outlined in the 2001 Food Code. They should be of adequate capacity to meet the needs of the establishment's employees, conveniently located, accessible, and clean. Areas for employee smoking, eating and drinking should also be located to prevent contamination of food, equipment, utensils, linens, and serving items (FC 6-4, 6-5).

5.1 Hygienic Practices

Family members in the home, employees in food service, and food production workers need to be aware of hygienic practices to prevent food contamination of all kinds, including physical hazard contamination. The FC 2001 provides guidance on:

- Hair Restraints–caps or nets should be used to prevent hair from contacting food surfaces and the food itself.
- Clothing–must be clean, laundering may occur on premises or employees should be allowed to change to discourage traveling in work attire.

- Education–of employees on personal hygiene.
- Animals–live animals are generally prohibited in food establishments except for decorative or edible fish in tanks, patrol or service dogs, or pets in common areas of institutional care facilities. At all times pets should not be in food preparation areas and they are not permitted in situations where a health or safety hazard may result from the presence or activities of the animal (FC 6-5).

6.0 PRACTICAL GUIDES FOR CONSUMERS[12,13]

- Wash raw fruits and vegetables.
- Peel outer layers on leafy produce, such as heads of lettuce and spinach, to remove layers directly in contact with the environment (soil, topical pesticides, etc.).
- Carefully watch the flow of food through your establishment or home to prevent physical contamination.
- Contamination from food packaging–the actual packaging materials–use only microwaveable products intended for use in microwave ovens.
- Visibly inspect foods not washable–ground beef.
- Do not use glasses to scoop ice, use only commercial food-grade plastic or metal scoops with handles.
- Do not chill glasses or any food items in ice that will later be used for drinks.
- Do not store toothpicks or non-edible garnishes on shelves above food storage or preparation areas.
- Place and maintain protective shields on lights over food storage and preparation areas.
- Clean can openers before and after each use and replace or rotate blade often.
- Remove staples, nails, and similar objects from boxes and crates when food is received so these materials do not later fall into the food.
- Proper food handling will help prevent physical contaminations.
- Always use good lighting in food preparation areas so visual inspection of food is optimal.
- No cockroach eggs adhering to the carton inspect packaging, not moist or wet, or wrinkled or dented.
- Proper labeling of cleaning materials–not in oil containers . . . or poison in black pepper box.
- Anti-slip floor coverings, mats or applications may be used in wet, smooth areas to prevent falls.
- Glass candy thermometers should be properly scaled in Celsius or Fahrenheit, if glass sensors or stems, encased in a shatterproof coating.
- Pressure measuring devices, mechanical warewashing equipment–accurate.
- Can openers must be disassembled for cleaning.
- Kickplates should be removed periodically for cleaning.

REVIEW QUESTIONS

1. Preventing physical hazards will benefit consumers in what ways?
2. Why are physical facilities an important issue in preventing physical hazards in foods?
3. When can physical hazards enter a food?
4. What considerations should be given to facility layout and design to prevent

physical contaminations by animals, rodents, insects, and birds?

5. Why is labeling and storage important in the prevention of physical contamination?
6. What are the maximum lead concentrations that are permitted in food utensils?

REFERENCES

1. American Dietetic Association (ADA). Position of the American Dietetic Association: Food and Water Safety. *J Am Diet Assoc.* *97*:184–189, 1997.
2. National Restaurant Association Educational Foundation. *ServeSafe® Coursebook.* Chicago, NRAEF, 2002.
3. Cody, M. M., and Kunkel, M.E. *Food Safety for Professionals,* 2nd ed., Chicago, American Dietetic Association. 2001.
4. McSwane, D., Rue, N., and Linton R. *Essentials of Food Safety and Sanitation,* 3rd ed. Upper Saddle River, N.J., Prentice Hall, 2003.
5. *Food Standards Australia New Zealand: Executive Summary.* Available at http://www.foodstandards.gov.au/search/index.cfm. Accessed June 20, 2002.
6. Incidence of foodborne illness-foodborne pathogens, chemicals and physical contaminants Australia New Zealand Food Safety (ANZFS) Available at http://www.foodstandards.gov.au/mediareleasespublications/publications/foodsafetystandardscostsandbenefits/incidenceoffoodborne633.cfm. Accessed June 20, 2002.
7. US FDA CFSAN Food Code 2001. Available at http://vm.cfsan.fda.gov/~dms/foodcode.html. Accessed July 16, 2002.
8. Rees, N., and Watson, D. *International Standards for Food Safety,* New York, Kluwer Academic, 2000.
9. Grosvenor, M. B., and Smolin, L. A. *Nutrition from Science to Life.* Orlando, Harcourt, 2002.
10. Longree, K., and Armbruster, G. *Quantity Food Sanitation.* 5th ed. New York, John Wiley & Son, 1996.
11. Claudio, V. S., Leocadio, C. G., De Leon, S. Y., Serraon-Joves, L. *Food Safety and Sanitation for Philippine Consumers.* Manila, Philippines, Merriam & Webster Bookstore, Inc., 2001.
12. Boyle, M. A. *Personal Nutrition.* 4th ed. Belmont, California, Wadsworth, 2000.
13. Hubbert, W., Hagstad, H., Spangle, E., Hinton, H., and Hughes, K. *Food Safety and Quality Assurance,* 2nd ed. Ames, Iowa State University Press, 1996.
14. US FDA CFSAN Food Code 2001. Available at http://vm.cfsan.fda.gov/~dms/foodcode.html. Accessed July 16, 2002.
15. *Food Standards Australia New Zealand: Executive Summary.* Available at http://www.foodstandards.gov/au/search/index.cfm. Accessed July 16, 2002.

Chapter 9

FOOD CONTROL AS APPLIED TO COMMODITIES

1.0 INTRODUCTION

An international discussion of food and water safety encompasses a vast number and variety of foods and beverages. Today, where food distribution is equitable, the traditional food industry provides the safest and most abundant variety of foods in history. With innovative and active global marketing, foods are commodities that are distributed far and wide. Food commodities in international food trade are, and always have been, big business. The types of products entering the food industry differ considerably from the traditional foods that contribute to most of the world's energy and nutrient needs. Genetically modified foods, dietary supplements, herbal remedies, organically grown foods and new processed foods continually "stretch" the traditional food groups designed for regulatory standards that assure food safety.

1.1 Food Groups of Commodities

How do we structure detection, monitoring and control programs to maintain and continue to improve the safety and quality of today's world food supply? The Food and Agriculture Organization (FAO) categorizes foods that represent the most significant nutrient sources worldwide into food commodity groups on the basis of plant and animal origin.[1] The Food Drug & Cosmetic Act (FD&CA) in the US, initially passed in 1938, has been continually revised to define ten statutory food categories. The ten categories specifically identified the foods for each group and the statutory restrictions relating to claims on labels made for each of the categories (see Table 9.1).[2]

Reducing the world's dauntingly vast and variable food supply into a few representative groups is by no means an easy task for any agency. Regardless of how the categories are designed, it is difficult to include all foods that enter global markets or all foods that contribute to the nutritional status of consumers. In many instances foods fall into several categories, others are not included. The FAO food group list does not include many minor foods of plant origin, such as mushrooms and marshmallows. People also consume flesh from vertebrate classes such as sharks, amphibians (frog legs), reptiles (alligators, snakes, turtles), wild birds, turtle and fish eggs (caviar), and gelatinized nest material from Southeast Asian swallows. In all parts of the world invertebrates are also eaten, depending on availability and culture, including edible insects (larvae, grasshopper legs, slugs, snails, squid and earthworms).[1] Although these novel items are of interest, the greatest impact on the world's food supply is still determined by the traditional food commodities consumed in the greatest quantities, regardless of the system, as listed in Table 9.1.

1.2 Commodity Control by Food Handlers

Globally, food safety involves every food handler involved in the food chain, from "farm-to-fork" or "paddock-to-plate." Agricultural preharvest and industrial postharvest practices in food production involve many employees; all vital to food safety in the food chain.[1] For example, strict sanitation codes apply to every aspect of food production. Veterinary agencies and farm management practices promote safe and effective animal breeding, feeding, transport, and slaughter. In dairy processing plants, just like in food establishments, facility inspections dictate that strict standards are maintained. Regulatory codes in milk production facilities require integrated pest management, proper handwashing, approved chemicals for cleaning udders and milking equipment, milking parlors with tight doors, windows and screens, and holding tanks that cool milk to the required temperatures at the specified rates. Temperatures continue to be tightly maintained as milk passes through the farm gate, progressing from preharvest to postharvest facilities, and then to the final destination, the consumer (see Chapter 8).

1.3 Commodity Boards

The importance of food commodity boards should not be overlooked in food safety. Commodity boards in the United

Table 9.1
FOOD COMMODITY GROUPS CLASSIFIED BY ORIGIN ACCORDING TO THE FAO

Plant	*Animal*	*Plant and Animal*
Cereals	Meat and offals*	Sugars and honey**
Roots and tubers	Eggs	Oils and fats
Pulses	Fish and seafood	
Nuts and oilseeds	Milk	
Vegetables		
Fruits		
Spices		
Stimulants		
Alcoholic beverages		

Food commodity groups for regulatory purposes according to the US FDA.[2]

1. Food–articles used for food or drink and their components
2. Food for special dietary use
3. Food intended to affect the structure or any function of the human body
4. Food intended for the prevention or treatment of human disease
5. Medical food
6. Vitamin and mineral products
7. Infant formula
8. Food with claimed characteristics for nutrient levels (nutrient descriptors)
9. Food with claimed characteristics for disease prevention and treatment disease prevention and treatment claims.
10. Dietary supplement

*offals refers to edible parts of the animal other than muscle meat, e.g., blood and liver
**honey is included as of both plant and animal origin because plant nectar is concentrated and partially hydrolyzed by honeybees.[1]
Source: United States Congress. Dietary Supplement Health and Education Act of 1994. Public Law 103-417, 108 Stat. 4325-4333. October 25, 1994.

States, like the National Dairy Council[3] and the California Avocado Commission,[4] actively engage in-self regulating programs, consumer education, marketing, political lobbying and research to support their products. The National Dairy Council in the US has extensive consumer education programs that help keep consumers informed of new products and provide product visibility. Most nonprofit boards are supported by the membership, comprised mostly of producers and affiliated businesses, all willing to invest in programs that maintain the safety and marketability of their commodity.

1.4 Commodity Control by Consumers

Today, particularly in developed countries, consumers are using their purchasing power not only to demand a safe and economically priced food supply but also to "voice" their interest in improving the health of their families. US consumer surveys report that 85 percent of Americans consider diet and nutrition personally important. Also, 75 percent of American consumers state that they carefully select food in order to achieve balanced nutrition and a healthful diet.[5]

Historically, consumers have driven the need for regulations that assure the safety and availability of a wide range of food products in the market. Passage of the US Pure Food and Drug Act in 1906 was the result of consumer movements, some of which were in response to Upton Sinclair's book, *The Jungle,* which described meatpacking plants in Chicago in that day.[6]

1.5 New Food Commodities

The number of new products that come onto the market every year is staggering. Once again, we find it difficult to fit a burgeoning number of new foods into traditional commodity food groups. The definitions of the traditional food groups are simplistic and do not make allowances for dietary supplements, genetically modified foods or functional foods. New regulatory actions are emerging to establish comparable detection; monitoring and control measures to assure that our food safety programs include these new products. An organization instrumental in the self-regulation of the dietary supplement industry is the National Nutritional Foods Association (NNFA) founded in 1936 in the US (www.nnfa.org). Their membership is comprised of over 4,000 representatives from retail, distributing, manufacturing, brokering and processing businesses in the dietary supplements, cosmetics and natural products industries. NNFA has eight regional offices and is recognized for its strong, aggressive lobbying presence in Washington, DC. NNFA was influential in the efforts leading to the passing of DSHEA in 1994. This commodity lead organization has developed programs to proactively direct dietary supplement and related industries:

- Good Manufacturing Practices (GMP) Certification Program
- TruLabel Program
- Mandatory Label Registration
- Finished Product Testing Program
- FDA notification initiatives and
- Other trade organizations:
  - Council for Responsible Nutrition (CRN) www.crnusa.org
  - Consumer Healthcare Product Assoc. (CHPA) www.chpa-info.org
  - American Herbal Products Assoc. (AHPA) www.ahpa.org
  - American Botanical Council (ABC) www.herbalgram.org
  - Citizens for Health www.citizens.org
  - U.S. Pharmacopeia (USP) www.usp .org

1.6 Dietary Supplement Health and Education Act

Many of the recently introduced foods have resulted from the growing interest in complementary and alternative medicine (CAM). The recent expansion of a new auxiliary multibillion dollar industry has followed the passage of the Dietary Supplement Health and Education Act of 1994 (DSHEA).[7] DSHEA was passed as an amendment to the Federal Food, Drug, and Cosmetic Act of 1938. DSHEA classifies herbal preparations and dietary supplements as food supplements. In essence, DSHEA deregulated the sale of any product taken by mouth that contains a so-called "dietary ingredient" and the label indicates that it is intended to supplement the diet by increasing total dietary intake.[7]

Legislation has also broadened to allow Supplement Facts Labels to make health claims that state a product will:

- Maintain a healthy cholesterol level
- Support the immune system
- Promote relaxation
- Maintain healthy bones, cartilage, and teeth

- Reduces stress and frustration
- Improves urine flow

However, legislation does not permit statements on labels that claim a product will:

- Protect against the development of cancer
- Reduce the pain and stiffness associated with arthritis
- Alleviate constipation
- Relieve headaches
- Reduce joint pain
- Lower cholesterol

2.0 SOUND DIETARY ADVICE FOR CONSUMERS

With so many choices in so many parts of the world, how do consumers make the best choices when planning diets? Dietary guidelines have been developed in 25 countries and several basic recommendations are shared throughout the world. The following overview was adopted from an International Food Information Council publication.[8]

- *Eat a variety of foods*–Worldwide the most consistent message is "variety." Japanese guidelines very specifically recommend eating at least 30 different foods each day to achieve variety.
- *Eat a diet low in fat*–Chronic diseases such as heart disease and diabetes are spreading throughout the human populations. However, the level of recommended consumption, particularly for total fat, varies greatly across the world. American guidelines recommend keeping fat below 30 percent of total daily calories consumed. Korean guidelines recommend "keeping fat consumption at 20 percent of energy intake," and in the Netherlands recommendations are for 35 percent of total energy intake.
- *Achieving and maintaining an appropriate weight & physical activity*–Many different messages are used to communicate the importance of appropriate body weight and energy balance. Japanese consumers are advised to "take energy corresponding to daily activity." In the United Kingdom, advise focuses on weight, "Eat the right amount to be a healthy weight." A few countries currently mention "physical activity."
- *Moderating sodium and sugar intake*

Many countries do not quantify levels of recommended intake of sodium or salt. The United States recommendations can be found to promote a diet that does not exceed 2.4 grams of salt a day. In Singapore, 4.5 grams of salt a day is targeted and in Japan 10 grams of salt a day. Most countries do not quantify recommended sugar intakes. Other countries, Canada, Korea, Japan and the Philippines, for example, do not mention sugars at all in their guidelines.

- *Alcohol consumption*–Most countries mention alcohol, and moderation is a key term used for these recommendations. Messages range from "If you drink, keep within sensible limits," in the United Kingdom, to "Alcohol is forbidden for children and pregnant women," in Hungary.
- *Enjoyment of eating*–Many nations' dietary guidelines recognize that eating is more than just nutrition–food is a pleasure and has strong links to family, traditions and culture.

This is illustrated internationally:[8]

- The United Kingdom's first dietary guideline stated, "Enjoy your food."
- Vietnamese guidelines recommend "a healthy family meal that is delicious, wholesome, clean and economical, and served with affection."

- French guidelines also emphasize the enjoyment of eating–a prevalent part of their culture. The second French guideline recommends eating "three good meals each day."
- Thailand promotes, "A happy family is when family members eat together, enjoy treasured family tastes and good home cooking.
- Norway simply states, "FOOD + JOY = HEALTH."

Japan's dietary guidelines promote culture and family values:[8]

- Eating together as a family is an occasion for happiness and promotes cultural tradition.
- Obtain well-balanced nutrition with a variety of foods; eat 30 foodstuffs a day; take staple food, main dish and side dish together
- Take energy corresponding to daily activity
- Consider the amount and quality of the fats and oils you eat: avoid too much, eat more vegetable oils than animal fat
- Avoid too much salt, not more than 10 grams a day

In the Netherlands more specific guidelines are given:[8]

- Achieve or maintain a normal body weight
- Balance the diet; supply adequate amounts of all essential nutrients
- Ensure an average total fat intake of 30 to 35 percent of dietary energy
- Make sure that saturated fat consumption is around 10 percent of total energy and polyunsaturated fat is 50 to 100 percent of saturated fat
- Do not let dietary cholesterol exceed 33mg/MJ*
- Maintain carbohydrate consumption at 50 to 60 percent of energy; sugars 15 to 25 percent energy
- Maintain protein consumption at 10 to 25 percent of energy
- Eat dietary fiber, target 3 gm/MJ
- Realize that current alcohol consumption is far too high in many cases
- Eat no more than 8 gm salt per day
  * MJ = European measurement of food energy

The US approved the fifth edition of the *Nutrition and Dietary Guidelines for Americans,* promoting healthful eating and physical activity (see Figure 9.1). Like cultures and lifestyles, diets differ throughout the world, so it is natural that some dietary guidelines vary. These differences are likely to occur depending on how the dietary guidance is utilized, for example, policy makers using them to define and set standards, or as a basis for public education on nutrition and health. As explained by Linda Meyers, Ph.D., Deputy Director, Office of Disease Prevention and Health Promotion, US Department of Health and Human Services, the US Dietary Guidelines serve as a framework for policy activities and they are simple enough for almost all people at all ages to understand.[8]

Since 1916 the USDA has designed and published food guides.[9] Currently, the Food Guide Pyramid is the visual designed to help individuals put the US Dietary Guidelines into effect on a daily basis.[10] Other health organizations such as the American Diabetes Association and the American Dietetic Association have published dietary recommendations, such as the Exchange Lists for Meal Planning.[11] Most of these plans emphasize how much food and which foods one should eat.[12]

2.1 Nutrition Facts Label

A more quantifiable approach to guiding the American public with healthful food choices may be through recommendations that emphasize nutrients rather than foods. In

Aim for a healthy weight.

Be physically active each day.

Let the pyramid guide your food choices.

Choose a variety of grains daily especially whole grains.

Choose a variety of fruits and vegetables daily.

Keep food safe to eat.

Choose a diet that is low in saturated fat and cholesterol and moderate in total fat.

Choose beverages and foods to moderate your intake of sugars.

Choose and prepare food with less salt.

If you drink alcoholic beverages, do so in moderation.

Figure 9.1. Nutrition and Your Health: Dietary Guidelines for Americans

the US the required "Nutrition Facts" labels appear on the back of food packages. The Nutrition Labeling and Education Act of 1990 defines how food is labeled in accordance with definitions established by the FDA, and provides for the use of claims about the relationship between nutrients and diseases or health-related conditions.[13] "Nutrition Facts" include "daily values" (DVs) which are used exclusively for food labeling purposes and are derived from the Dietary Reference Intakes (DRIs) (see Figure 9.2 "Nutrition Facts Label"). The DVs represent the highest recommendations for each nutrient for all age and gender groups to form one set of nutrient standards for labeling purposes. For example, the highest iron needs are for women of childbearing age, 18 mg per day are based on National Academy of Sciences' 1968 Recommended Dietary Allowances (RDA). Men of the same age require 10 mg of iron per day. The amount used for food labeling purposes is 18 mg (see Table 9.2).

2.2 Essential Nutrients

It is hard to believe that essential nutrients (carbohydrates, proteins, fats, vitamins, minerals, and water) , necessary to support life, can also be the cause of death. Nutrient defi-

Oats 'N' More

Nutrition Facts

Serving Size 1 cup (30g)
Servings Per Container About 14

Amount Per Serving	**Cereal**	**with 1/2 cup fat-free milk**
Calories	110	150
Calories from Fat	15	20
	% Daily Value**	
Total Fat 2g*	**3%**	**3%**
Saturated Fat 0g	**0%**	**3%**
Polyunsaturated Fat 0.5g		
Monounsaturated Fat 0.5g		
Cholesterol 0mg	**0%**	**1%**
Sodium 280mg	**12%**	**15%**
Potassium 95mg	**3%**	**9%**
Total Carbohydrate 22g	**7%**	**9%**
Dietary Fiber 3g	**11%**	**11%**
Soluble Fiber 1g		
Sugars 1g		
Other Carbohydrate 18g		
Protein 3g		
Vitamin A	10%	15%
Vitamin C	10%	10%
Calcium	4%	20%
Iron	45%	45%
Vitamin D	10%	25%
Thiamin	25%	30%
Riboflavin	25%	35%
Niacin	25%	25%
Vitamin B_6	25%	25%
Folic Acid	50%	50%
Vitamin B_{12}	25%	35%
Phosphorus	10%	25%
Magnesium	8%	10%
Zinc	25%	30%
Copper	2%	2%

*Amount in Cereal. A serving of cereal plus fat-free milk provides 2g total fat (0.5g saturated fat, 1g monounsaturated fat), less than 5mg cholesterol, 350mg sodium, 300mg potassium, 28g total carbohydrate (7g sugars) and 7g protein.

**Percent Daily Values are based on a 2,000 calorie diet. Your daily values may be higher or lower depending on your calorie needs:

	Calories:	2,000	2,500
Total Fat	Less than	65g	80g
Sat Fat	Less than	20g	25g
Cholesterol	Less than	300mg	300mg
Sodium	Less than	2,400mg	2,400mg
Potassium		3,500mg	3,500mg
Total Carbohydrate		300g	375g
Dietary Fiber		25g	30g

Ingredients: whole grain oats, (includes the oat bran), modified corn starch, wheat starch, sugar, salt, oat fiber, trisodium phosphate, calcium carbonate, vitamin E (mixed tocopherols) added to preserve freshness. **Vitamins and Minerals:** iron and zinc (mineral nutrients), vitamin C (sodium ascorbate), vitamin B_6 (pyridoxine hydrochloride), riboflavin, thiamin mononitrate, niacinamide, folic acid, vitamin A (palmitate), vitamin B_{12}, vitamin D.

Figure 9.2.Nutrition Facts Label

Table 9.2
DRVS AND RDIS

Daily Reference Values*		Reference Daily Intakes**	
Food Component	*Amount*	*Nutrient*	*Amount*
Total fat	65 grams	Vitamin A	5000 International Units
Saturated fat	20 grams	Vitamin C	60 milligrams
Cholesterol	300 milligrams	Calcium	1.0 gram
Total carbohydrate	300 grams	Iron	18 milligrams
Dietary fiber	25 grams	Vitamin D	400 International Units
Sodium	2400 milligrams	Vitamin E	30 International Units
Potassium	3,500 milligrams	Thiamin	1.5 milligrams
Protein***	50 grams	Riboflavin	1.7 milligrams
		Niacin	20 milligrams
		Vitamin B_6	2.0 milligrams
		Folate	0.4 milligrams
		Vitamin B_{12}	6 micrograms
		Biotin	0.3 milligrams
		Panothenic acid	10 milligrams
		Phosphorus	1.0 gram
		Iodine	150 micrograms
		Magnesium	400 milligrams
		Zinc	15 milligrams
		Copper	2 milligrams

*Daily Reference Values are based on a daily intake of 2,000 calories and are for adults and children over 4 only.

** Reference Daily Intakes are based on National Academy of Sciences' 1968 Recommended Dietary Allowances

***Reference Daily Intakes for protein have been established for the following groups:

Infants under 1 year: 14 grams
Children 1 to 4 years: 16 grams
Pregnant women: 60 grams
Nursing mothers: 65 grams

Source: http://www.fda.gov/fdac/special/foodlabel/rditabl.html

ciencies have long been recognized as a cause of death and unfortunately these situations still exist in some parts of the world. The most critical essential nutrient to life is water, making water the most important food commodity of all. A normal human body contains 65 to 75 percent water, with infants having a higher percentage. A typical distribution of water in the various organs and tissues of a normal adult is presented in Figure 9.3 (see Chapters 1 and 2).

Harper, in a review traces the first formal action to establish a dietary standard to the passage of the British Merchant Seaman's Act of 1835 which made provision of "lime" or lemon juice compulsory in the rations of the merchantile service.[12] Harper states that this action was taken as a result of Lind's treatise in 1753 on the prevention of scurvy and the success that was achieved in preventing scurvy after 1796 when lemon juice was included in the rations for the British Navy. It is interest-

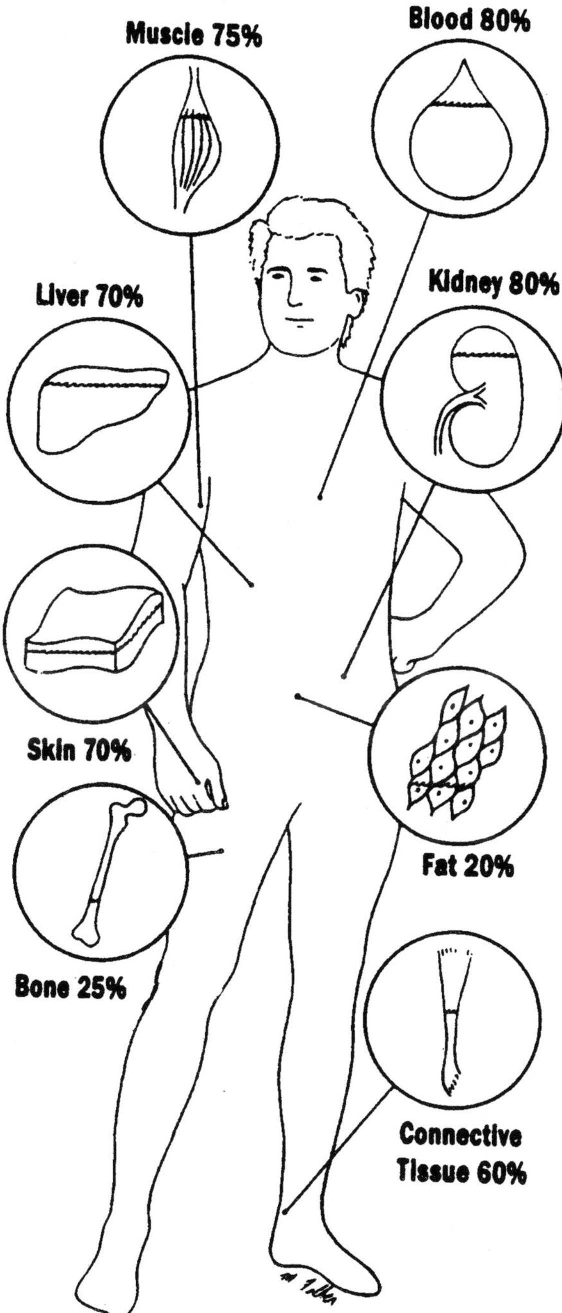

Figure 9.3. Water: The Medium of Life. *Source:* Clark County Health District, Health Education Office, Las Vegas, Nevada. Flyer for August 2000. *Note:* The percent (%) values above are average water content of organs or tissues.

ing to note that it took over 80 years to make an initial dietary treatment observation, implement the treatment in practice and support the treatment with British legislation.[12,14]

In the United States researchers are methodically updating national nutrient standards for optimal health and for the first time establishing tolerable upper levels to safeguard against toxicities. In the US the RDAs have been defined as "the levels of intake of essential nutrients that, on the basis of scientific knowledge, are judged by the Food and Nutrition Board to be adequate to meet the known nutrient needs of practically all healthy persons." The RDAs that have been the basis for nutrient guidelines since the 1940's in the United States and Canada have recently been reevaluated, renamed, and revised.[17-22] Currently available are contemporary studies that address topics ranging from the prevention of classical nutritional deficiency diseases, such as rickets, to the reduction of risk of chronic diseases such as osteoporosis, cancer, and cardiovascular disease. These compelling factors have extended the basis for the development of the new nutrient guidelines.[12, 17-18]

2.3 Dietary Reference Intakes

The new term DRIs is the inclusive "umbrella" name being given to the set of recommended intake values developed for Americans and Canadians (see Table 9.3).[12,17-22] In partnership with Health Canada, the Food and Nutrition Board in the US has responded to these developments by making fundamental changes in its approach to setting nutrient reference values. The resulting DRIs were designed to help people maintain their health while at the same time, avoid potential risks from taking too much of a particular nutrient. The recommended intake values established as DRIs are:[12,17-22]

- *Dietary Reference Intakes* (DRI)–A set of values for the dietary nutrient intakes of healthy people in the United States and Canada.
- *Estimated Average Requirement* (EAR)–The amount of a nutrient that will maintain a specific biochemical or physiological function in half the people of a given age and sex group.
- *Recommended Dietary Allowance* (RDA)–The average daily amount of a nutrient considered adequate to meet the known nutrient needs of practically all healthy people; a goal for dietary intake for individuals.
- *Adequate Intake* (AI)–The average amount of a nutrient that appears sufficient to maintain a specified criterion; a value used as a guide for nutrient intake when an RDA cannot be determined.
- *Tolerable Upper Intake Level* (UL)–The maximum of a nutrient that appears safe for most healthy people and beyond which there is an increased risk of adverse health effects.

3.0 DIETARY SUPPLEMENTS AS POTENTIAL FOOD SAFETY HAZARDS[23,25,27]

The original dietary standards were designed in the 1940s to avoid nutrient deficiencies. The current dietary concerns are also designed to safeguard against nutrient toxicities. As many as 50 percent of Americans take some kind of dietary supplement, to complement the diet, alter macronutrient use in the body, or enhance performance, promote weight loss, relieve symptoms of disease, or prevent chronic diseases. These dietary supplements may be pills, tablets, liquids, or powders. A product intended for consumption as a supplement to the diet is classified as a food, not a drug, and regulated by the FDA. They are vitamins, minerals, herbs, botanicals, or other plant-derived substances (other than tobacco), amino acids, enzymes, concentrates and extracts, collectively called "dietary supplements."

The introduction of so many new products to the food commodities market since 1994 introduces many new issues, including food hazard and food safety concerns. The following discussion attempts to place appropriate emphasis on the perceived benefits and risks of dietary supplements. An attempt is also made to recognize the role of dietary supplements in today's food commodity market and acknowledge the role of dietary supplements in medical nutrition therapy, formerly referred to as "clinical nutrition." In this discussion it will be helpful to clarify a selection of the current terms used in today's food commodities market, which will broadly encompass most of the products most likely to be considered food or health hazards, such as, dietary supplements, antioxidants, dietary fiber, functional foods, phytochemicals, and organic foods. Many other terms have been adopted (i.e., nutraceuticals), however, again, consistency in the industry is lacking.

3.1 Supplement Facts Label

These new food commodities must be identified and carry the words "dietary supplement" on the label. The product label must contain the standardized label, "Supplement Facts" similar to the "Nutrition Facts" label for food. This label will list the recommended serving size, the name, and quantity of each ingredient per serving. The source of the ingredient must be given and the nutrients for which a Daily Value has been established listed, followed by other ingredients in descending order by weight.[23]

Regulations are designed to prevent manufacturers from making false marketing claims about the effectiveness of their products luring customers to checkout counters. Claims on dietary supplements are allowed if they are nutrient content claims, health claims, or nutrition support claims. A product can claim it is an "excellent source" of a nutrient, if it contains at least 20 percent of the Daily Value of that nutrient. A health claim can be used if it has been approved by the FDA, i.e., a supplement could claim "vitamin C prevents scurvy" or state that "calcium builds strong bones." They must also print on the Supplement Facts label that: "This statement has not been evaluated by the Food and Drug Administration. This product is not intended to diagnose, treat, cure or prevent any disease."[23]

3.2 Vitamin and Mineral Supplements

Vitamin and mineral supplements play a beneficial role in medical nutrition therapy at moderate supplementation levels. Multivitamins and minerals should be well balanced, not containing doses greater than 150 percent of the DV of each nutrient. These intakes, when food and beverage sources of vitamins and minerals are included, are generally within the ranges recommended and often equal to the nutrient intakes consumable through a nutrient-rich diet. Moderate supplementation is especially useful for persons on low calorie diets. Others that may benefit from moderate supplementation are those who may have elevated nutrient needs such as pregnant and breastfeeding women, heavily menstruating females, children in rapid growth phases, infants, people with severe restrictions, vegans and the elderly.[25]

Therapies using megadoses of vitamins or minerals have not proven effective in the

Figure 9.4. Dietary Supplements Sample Label

treatment of cancer, colds, or heart disease. Megadosing poses serious concern when interfering with the body's effective balancing act for all nutrients. In some instances nutritional products may be poorly balanced offering less than 10 percent of the Daily Value for some nutrients and over 1,000 percent for others.[25]

High doses of vitamins have been used in conventional medicine when medications deplete or destroy vitamin and mineral stores. For example, some medications for tuberculosis and seizure control interfere with B vitamin status. People with malabsorption syndromes, colitis and cystic fibrosis, often take large nutrient doses of multivitamins and minerals to compensate for poor absorption. Others may have pharmacological activity, such as niacin, when used 50–100 times the recommended daily intake to act as a drug to lower cholesterol. At these high levels some persons have reactions to too much niacin, experiencing flushing (hypotension), itching and other symptoms.[25]

Not all vitamins or minerals have ULs established. A lack of adequate information to make claims or set definitive levels has limited the DRI panel's ability to make such recommendations. However, consumers should be cautioned that excesses of unknown amounts of these vitamins and minerals could cause health hazards and food safety concerns.[17-22]

3.3 Adverse Effects of Essential Vitamins and Minerals

DRI panel reports emphasize, through their estimates of tolerable upper limits, that even essential nutrients can be harmful if consumed inappropriately, as reported above with niacin. These nutrients have been the focus of public attention and media advertising as researchers continue to examine whether increased intakes of food components, in either food or supplement form, can protect against certain chronic diseases.[12,17-22]

Many individuals are self-medicating with nutrients for curative or treatment purposes (DRI). The possible therapeutic benefits of higher nutrient intakes that may offset the risk of adverse effects have not been studied for most nutrients. The DRI committees are attempting to establish upper tolerable levels of intake that are likely to pose no risk of adverse health effects in most individuals in the healthy, general population. The newest recommendations have established UL for some nutrients (see Table 9.3) For most nutrients upper levels were not established for infants, again, because of lack of data.[17-22]

3.4 Antioxidants

Several essential vitamins and minerals have been identified as antioxidants in the body. Antioxidants are substances that prevent oxidative injury to cells and tissues. The DRI report establishes an UL for the daily intakes of antioxidant vitamins C and E, and the mineral selenium, to reduce the risk of harmful side effects from overconsumption (see Table 9.3). These limits for adult males and females are: 1) 2,000 mg/day for vitamin C; 2) 1,000 mg/day for vitamin E; and 3) 400 µg/day for selenium.[21]

Another potential group of antioxidants are compounds found naturally in foods and beverages, the carotenoids. Of the approximately 600 carotenoids that have been identified, 50 are typically found in the average diet. Only 34, however, have been isolated in human blood samples and human milk.[24] Carotenoids are naturally existing pigment compounds that give the orange, deep yellow, and red colors to fruits and vegetables such as tomatoes, carrots, and sweet potatoes. They are also plentiful in dark green vegetables, but the more abundant chlorophyll overpowers their colors.[24]

The most common and most studied carotenoid is beta-carotene, others include alpha-carotene, beta-cryptoxanthin, lycopene, lutein, and zeaxanthin. For many years, research has been underway to identify the role of these antioxidants in reducing the risk of developing chronic and lifestyle diseases such as cancer, cardiovascular disease, eye diseases such as macular degeneration, and neurodegenerative diseases such as Alzheimer's and Parkinson's. However, the relationship between antioxidants and disease prevention remains unclear.[21,24]

The panel did not set recommendations for beta-carotene or the other carotenoids. The panel felt that the current state of research on these nutrients lacks the strength and consistency to support any recommendations at this time.[21] No risk reduction for any cancer, however, was found and, furthermore, other studies have suggested that beta-carotene supplements may actually harm current smokers and people exposed to asbestos.[2] The panel, however, does advise people to avoid intakes beyond the levels required to prevent vitamin A deficiency. The final, and perhaps most important point, is that the panel stressed the role of obtaining these nutrients through food rather than supplements and emphasized food as the primary source of nutrition.[21,24]

3.5 Dietary Fiber

Recommended intakes are 10–13 grams for every 1000 kcal consumed, or 20–35 g/day for healthy adults and for children, the child's age in years plus 5 g/day. Dietary fiber intake continues to be at less than recommended levels in the US with usual intakes averaging only 14 to 15 g/day because of intakes of low intakes of good sources of dietary fiber, fruits, vegetables, whole and high-fiber grain products, and legumes. The benefits of adequate dietary fiber intakes are still being studied in relation to gastrointestinal health as well as the known benefit of lowering blood cholesterol. Excessive intakes of dietary fiber may have negative health implications, including dehydration, intestinal distress, flatulence, etc.[22]

Table 9.3
DIETARY REFERENCE INTAKES

Vitamin	*UL*	*DV*
Vitamin A	3,000 mg	5000 International Units
Vitamin D	50 mg	400 International Units
E	1,000 mg	30 International Units
C	2,000 mg	60 mg
B6 (pyridoxal phosphate)	100mg	2 mg
Folic Acid	1 mg	0.4 mg
Niacin	35 mg	20 mg
Pantothenic Acid		10 mg
Biotin		300 μg
Choline	3.5 g	NA
Boron	20 mg	NA
Calcium	2.5 gm	1 gm
Chloride		3400 mg
Chromium		120 μg
Copper	10,000 mg	2 mg
Fluoride	10 mg	NA
Iodine	1,100 mg	150 mg
Iron	45 mg	18 mg
Magnesium	350 mg	400 mg
Manganese	11 mg	2 mg
Molybdenum	2,000 μg	75 μg
Nickel	1 mg	NA
Phosphorus	4 gr	1 gr
Selenium	400 μg	70 μg
Vanadium	1.8 mg	
Zinc	40 mg	15 mg

*However, Tolerable Upper Limits (UL) are being set.[Ch.9 17-21]

3.6 Nonvitamin/Nonmineral Supplements

Proteins and amino acids, enzymes, hormones, lipoic acid, ubiquinone, and SAMe are other naturally occurring substances not essential in the diet. Although these are found on retail shelves or ordered through the mail, the FDA must approve all health claims appearing on the label to guard against false advertising.

Enzymes, extracts, herbs, and botanicals might be helpful to the body in optimal physiological amounts. How much is optimal? How much is optimal over a lifetime? So many answers to these questions remain unanswered for products already on the market. Although it is beyond the scope of this work to discuss the nutritional benefits of all dietary supplements, care should be taken to acknowledge the potential harm that these products might cause in individuals unaware of nutritional toxicities. Most of these nutrients are not considered essential to life, but after thorough testing, might be supported by scientific evidence and considered beneficial to life.

3.7 Functional Foods[22,23,25,26,27]

Foods that provide health benefits beyond basic nutrition have been termed functional foods. In the broadest sense, almost any food can be considered a functional food. In today's world, substances that provide a physiological benefit beyond fulfilling the body's need for essential nutrients are functional foods. Even popular chocolate confectionaries, for example, may have redeeming value and be considered a functional food if the benefits of this commodity contribute to well being. Chocolate contains a variety of chemicals that might contribute to satiety and euphoric feelings. Theories have proposed that the caffeine and related stimulants in chocolate provide a satisfying taste. Others have looked at the marijuana "high" inducing substances in chocolate that may trigger the release of opiates in the brain, or amphetamine-like compounds, or maybe the fatty acids providing the extra energy leads to satiety and a sense of well-being.[23]

Functional foods are also those that have had nutrients added to replace nutrients lost in processing (enrichment) or nutrients added to enhance the nutritive value of foods (fortification). These processing practices have been used for decades, i.e. vitamins A and D to fluid milk and B vitamins added to breads. More recently folic acid and calcium can be found in products not originally considered good sources of these nutrients (i.e. calcium added to orange juice).

Regardless of the sources, nutrient intakes from fortification, supplementation and all foods and beverages should collectively be considered in dietary assessments. The National Academy of Sciences Food and Nutrition Board provides recommendations that state intakes exceeding those recommendations have no demonstrated benefit for the normal, healthy population.[17-22]

Additional examples of substances naturally found in foods that are considered functional foods are:

- phytochemicals, plant chemicals that have healthful benefits
- carotenoids
- polyphenols
- saponins
- phytoestrogens, compounds that have structures that block or mimic hormones
- omega 3 fatty acids, the anticancer substances in fish

3.8 Organic Foods[25]

In response to the overuse and excessive contamination of pesticide residues in our food and water supplies, consumers, again, have initiated the need to reevaluate the chemicals we introduce into our bodies and into the environment. Organic foods are grown without the use of synthetic fertilizers, pesticides, and herbicides, etc. New labeling requirements for organic foods were established in the United States in 2000. Consumer confidence in organically grown foods can be reflected in the 20 percent per year growth in annual sales, with sales of organic foods totaling $3.5 billion in 1996. The labeling requirements set forth are a result of consumer and producer driven organizations. The resulting Organic Foods Production Act and the establishment of the National Organic Program (NOP) have established labels that identify organic foods as:

- "100% organic" or "organic"–if it contains only organically produced raw or processed products and must consist of 95 percent organically produced ingredients (excluding water and salt). Products that meet the requirements may display these terms on their principal display panel and the USDA seal and seal trade mark of the certifying agent may appear on product packages and in advertisements.

- "made with organic (name of ingredient)"–if a product contains 50 to 95 percent organic ingredients and lists up to three of the organic ingredients on the principal display panel, for example: organic beef stew, "made with organic beef, potatoes and carrots."

The certifying agents seal may be used on the package, but not the USDA seal. For products with less than 50 percent organic material the word organic must state the actual percentage of organic ingredients and use the word organic to modify each organically produced ingredient.

Consumers have had a great impact on new product formulations. Many, for example, genetically modified foods were mentioned in previous chapters (see Chapter 6).

4.0 SAFE AND EFFECTIVE NUTRITION THERAPIES[28,29]

Consumers are driving a growing trend that reaches beyond conventional (western, allopathic) medicine and normal nutrient intakes. Consumers want health care approaches that:

- avoid the adverse effects of chemical medicines,
- personalize health treatments and
- provide greater public access to health information

Conventional medicine, complementary and alternative medicine (CAM) and traditional medicine (TM) are all part of the world's health care systems, and current policies and practices are not always in place to accommodate these approaches. CAM is increasingly used simultaneously with conventional medicine in Australia, Europe and North America. The National Center for Complementary and Alternative Medicine in the United States National Institutes of Health describes complementary medicine as those practices that are used together with conventional medicine. An example of a complementary therapy is using food extracts to reduce the need or the amount of a conventional drug to treat cancer, i.e. adjuvant therapy. Alternative medicine is used in place of conventional medicine. An example of an alternative therapy is using a special diet to treat cancer instead of undergoing surgery, radiation, or chemotherapy that has been recommended by a conventional doctor.

Integrative medicine combines conventional or mainstream medical therapies with complementary or alternative practices when safety and effectiveness are supported by scientific evidence. Nutritional therapies are recognized by NCCAM as "biologically based therapies," based on using substances found in nature, such as herbs, foods, and vitamins. The popularity of CAM can be seen by those countries, primarily developed countries, with consumers who have used CAM at least once: Canada–70%, Australia–48%, France–49%, USA–42%, Belgium–31%.

Traditional medicine, used throughout Africa, Asia, and Latin America, helps meet the primary health care needs of a large percentage of these populations. Again, the popularity of this health care modality can be seen in developing countries with consumers who report having used traditional medicine at least once: Ethiopia–90%, Benin–70%, India–70%, Rwanda–70%, Tanzania–60%, and Uganda–60%. In developing countries TM is accessible, affordable, and part of a wider belief system, and considered integral to everyday life and well-being. Traditional

Figure 9.5. Organic Food Label

medicine includes a diverse array of practices and beliefs, some which are considered nutritional that use plant, animal and or mineral-based medicines. Herbal remedies are a part of Chinese medicine, Ayurveda, unani, naturopathy, osteopathy, homeopathy, and chiropractic techniques. In the year 2000, 25 countries had a national TM policy defining delivery, ensuring regulation and maintaining good practices that were fair, authentic, safe and effective.

4.1 Complementary and Alternative Medical Nutrition Therapies

Complementary and alternative (CAM) practices outside of the traditional medicine mainstream are becoming increasingly popular and many involve nutrition. The scientific support for most restrictive diets, supplementation diets or food prescriptions for the treatment and prevention of diseases is not always available.[25,27,28,29] Herbal medicine is a traditional form of healing in many cultures. Some herbal medicines have shown enough promise to warrant clinical trials and large-scale studies. Others, such as ephedrine containing products have posed serious public health concerns, contributing to side effects, interfering with prescription medications and implicated in deaths (Table 9.4).

Complicating the potential side effects and interferences herbal medicines may introduce is the difficulty assuring product identity. It is difficult to document the accurate identity of the plant and when and where the raw materials are collected. Good evidence of efficacy has been estimated for some herbal medicines. Of the randomized clinical trials showing benefits 48 percent reported benefit unlikely due to design or analytic flaw, 34 percent claimed a benefit compared to the placebo, and 18 percent claimed to have the same benefits as the placebo (TM–growing needs and potential).

Regardless, persons using herbal therapies have increased by more than 350 percent from 1990 to 1997, more than any other alternative medicine. In Table 9.4 is a list of herbal products and the associated adverse effects associated with each product.[23] Clearly the wide availability of these products, and their popularity, is creating a new food safety concern. The numbers of adverse effects reported by consumers are growing. The FDA is now evaluating the adverse effects reported by users of ephedrine products. As a result of these reports the FDA is proposing that a dietary supplement containing ephedrine will be considered adulterated:

Table 9.4
POPULAR HERBAL AND SUPPLEMENTAL INGREDIENTS

Ingredient	*Possible Health Hazards*
Herbs	
Chaparral (a traditional American Indian medicine)	Liver disease, possibly irreversible
Comfrey	Obstruction of blood flow to liver, possibly leading to death
Slimming/dieter's teas	Nausea, diarrhea, vomiting, stomach cramps, chronic constipation, fainting, possibly death (see "Dieter's Brews Make Tea Time a Dangerous Affair" in the July–August 1997 *FDA Consumer*)
Ephedra (also known as Ma huang, Chinese Ephedra, and epitonin)	Ranges from high blood pressure, irregular heartbeat, nerve damage, injury, insomnia, tremors, and headaches to seizures, heart attack, stroke, and death
Germander	Liver disease, possibly leading to death
Lobelia (also known as Indian tobacco)	Range from breathing problems at low doses to sweating, rapid heartbeat, low blood pressure, and possibly coma and death at higher doses
Magnolia-Stephania preparation	Kidney disease, possibly leading to permanent kidney failure
Willow bark	Reyes syndrome, a potentially fatal disease associated with aspirin intake in children with chickenpox or flu symptoms; allergic reaction in adults. (Willow bark is marketed as an aspirin-free product, although it actually contains an ingredient that converts to the same active ingredient in aspirin.)
Wormwood	Neurological symptoms, characterized by numbness of legs and arms, loss of intellect, delirium, and paralysis
Vitamins and Essential Minerals	
Vitamin A (in doses of 25,000 or more International Units a day)	Birth defects, bone abnormalities, and severe liver disease
Vitamin B6 (in doses above 100 milligrams a day)	Balance difficulties, nerve injury causing changes in touch sensation
Niacin (in slow-released doses of 500 mg or more a day or immediate-release doses of 750 mg or more a day)	Range from stomach pain, vomiting, bloating, nausea, cramping, and diarrhea to liver disease, muscle disease, eye damage, and heart injury
Selenium (in doses of about 800 micrograms to 1,000 mcg a day)	Tissue damage
Other Supplements	
Germanium (a nonessential mineral)	Kidney damage, possibly death
L-tryptophan (an amino acid)	Eosinophilia myalgia syndrome, a potentially fatal blood disorder that can cause high fever, muscle and joint pain, weakness, skin rash, and swelling of the arms and legs

Source: FDA Statement before Senate Committee on Labor and Human Resources, Oct. 21, 1993. *FDA Consumer,* September–October 1998

1. if it contains 8 milligrams (mg) or more of ephedrine alkaloids per serving
2. if its labeling suggests or recommends conditions of use that would result in intake of 8 mg or more in a 6-hour period or a total daily intake of 24 mg or more of ephedrine alkaloids

The proposed legislation will:

- require that the label of dietary supplements that contain ephedrine kaloids state "`Do not use this product for more than 7 days"
- prohibit the use of ephedrine alkaloids with ingredients, or with ingredients that contain substances that have a known stimulant effect (e.g., sources of caffeine or yohimbine), which may interact with ephedrine alkaloids
- prohibit labeling claims that require long-term intake to achieve the purported effect (e.g., weight loss and body building)
- require a statement in conjunction with claims that encourage short-term excessive intake to enhance the purported effect (e.g., energy) that "Taking more than the recommended serving may result in heart attack, stroke, seizure or death"; and require specific warning statements to appear on product labels.

4.2 Function Specific Products and Practices

Weight loss products, such as fiber pills, prescription drugs, over-the-counter drugs and assorted other dietary supplements can contain benzocaine (that numbs the tongue), caffeine (a stimulant) and, as just discussed, ephedra, a stimulant that can be dangerous in people with hypertension, heart disease, and diabetes. Fiber pills can lead to dehydration, and very-low-calorie diets high in protein and low in calories alter body fluids, electrolyte balance, metabolic activities, hormone levels, and organ functions, at times resulting in deaths without medical supervision. Individuals engaging in these practices frequently develop eating disorders, another topic closely aligned to food safety. Likewise, obesity can be considered another food safety issue, due to overindulgence. However, both of these topics are more appropriately addressed in detail in discussions of clinical nutrition, yet, in the future more and more attention will be focused on the "health hazards" of too much food.

Additional "food commodities" have created health hazards that have led to deaths. In the 1970s reported deaths from persons participating in weight loss programs that relied solely on meal replacement formulas were tragic. More recently ergogenic aids, or performance enhancing aids, have been implicated as the cause of death in athletes. A variety of ergogenic aids are marketed in retail stores and are easily available, even to young, adolescent athletes, including caffeine and ephedrine-contain products. A brief selection of products popular among sports enthusiasts used to enhance performance is:

- Andostenedione–claims to increase muscle strength, no known long- term studies are available on safety or effectiveness; risks may be similar to illegal steroid drugs; stunted growth, acne, unwanted hair growth, premature baldness, increased blood cholesterol, and decreased sperm production
- Bee pollen–no evidence that it improves training; some persons are allergic
- Branched chain amino acids–conflicting study results, no toxicity (expand list)

Another grave reality in the competitive arena is the desire by weight lifters, boxers, wrestlers, gymnasts, and dancers to "make weight." Unfortunately, several talented athletes have become statistics in the *MMWR Weekly Report* when their desire to drop body weight rapidly ended in death due to dehydration.

5.0 SORTING FACT FROM FALLACY

How can food handlers and consumers identify nutrition quackery and false advertising? One of the best indicators, as mentioned earlier, that food handlers and consumers can use to identify good quality products is the "USP" designation on Supplement Facts labels. USP stands for US Pharmacopeia, a non-government organization that promotes public health by establishing state-of-the-art standards to ensure the quality of medicines and other health care technologies. These standards are developed by a unique process of public involvement and are accepted worldwide. USP is a not-for-profit organization that achieves its goals through the contributions of volunteers representing pharmacy, medicine, and other health care professions, as well as science, academia, the US government, the pharmaceutical industry, and consumer organizations. USP's Internet address is www.usp.org.

Also, consumers will want to be aware of products that are of questionable quality. Possible indicators of products to avoid are those that have:

- Claims that a product has a "secret, magical, or miracle cure"
- Terms that are pseudomedical, "detoxify, purify, energize"
- Claims that cure a wide range of unrelated diseases
- Claims with only benefits and no side effects
- No references from legitimate sources that can be found
- Claims that the medical profession is withholding information

6.0 PRACTICAL GUIDELINES

- Carefully select the source of complementary dietary products you purchase, based on efficacy and purity.
- Evaluate the claims for dietary supplements, and based on your research of the scientific literature evaluate your purchases.
- All dietary supplements should have a Supplement Facts label.
- Physicians should be made aware of your decisions regarding complimentary and alternative medical nutrition practices.
- Try a new fruit or vegetable each week.
- Eat fruits and vegetables for snacks.
- Put fruit on your cereal in the morning or vegetables in your eggs.
- Try dried fruit instead of candy.
- Drink fruit and vegetable juices instead of soft drinks.
- Try baked fruit for dessert.
- Double your typical serving of vegetables.
- Increase your use of herbs and spices such as garlic, basil, turmeric, parsley, oregano, and hot peppers.
- Eat a vegetarian dinner at least once a week.
- Add vegetables to your favorite entrees such as spaghetti sauces and casseroles.
- Try tofu in cooking.
- Do not give herbs to children or pregnant and lactating women.
- If you are ill or taking medication, consult your doctor before taking herbs.

- Do not assume herbal products are safe.
- Do not take herbs with known toxicities.
- Read label ingredients and the list of precautions.
- Start with low doses and stop taking any product that causes side effects.
- Do not take combinations of herbs.
- Do not use herbs for long periods.

REVIEW QUESTIONS

1. What are traditional medicine, allopathic medicine, and complementary and alternative medicines?
2. What is an antioxidant?
3. What are phytochemicals?
4. How are organic foods labeled?
5. Are dietary supplements safe?
6. Why should someone taking herbal remedies report these to his or her doctor?
7. What groups of people might benefit from vitamin and mineral supplements?
8. Can herbs and weight loss products be dangerous?

REFERENCES

1. Hubbert, W., Hagstad, H., Spangle, E., Hinton, H., and Hughes, K. *Food Safety and Quality Assurance,* 2nd ed., Ames, Iowa State University Press, 1996.
2. Federal Food Drug, and Cosmetic Act of 1938, ch 675,52 Stat 1258.
3. National Dairy Council.
4. California Avocado Commission.
5. Tracking Trends. *DAD Dietetics in Practice,* vol 2. no. 1, Summer, 2002.
6. Sinclair, Upton. *The Jungle.* New York, Random House, 2002. (Originally published 1905).
7. United States Congress. Dietary Supplement Health and Education Act of 1994. Public Law 103-417, 108 Stat. 4325-4333. Oct. 25, 1994.
8. FOOD INSIGHT Mar/Apr 1998 http://www.ific.org/proactive/newsroom/relesase.vtml. Accessed April 29, 2002.
9. US Departments of Agriculture and Health and Human Services. *Nutrition and Your Health: Dietary Guidelines for Americans,* 5th ed. Home and Garden Bulletin No. 232. Washington, DC: US Government Printing Office, 2000.
10. US Department of Agriculture. *The Food Guide Pyramid,* Home and Garden Bulletin, No. 252. Washington, DC, US Government Printing Office, 1992.
11. American Diabetes Association and American Dietetic Association. *Exchange Lists for Meal Planning,* Alexandria, 1–33. 1988.
12. Meacham, S., Johnson, L., and Kruskall, L. The Recommended Dietary Allowances–Then and Now. *J of Agromedicine,* in press.
13. Food labeling regulations implementing the Nutrition Labeling and Education Act of 1990, final rule, opportunity for comments. *Fed. Register* 1993; 58b: 2066.
14. Harper A. Origins of recommended dietary allowances–an historic overview. *Am J Clin Nutr* 1985; *41:* 140–148.
15. Food and Nutrition Board. *Recommended Dietary Allowances.* National Academy of Sciences, National Research Council, Reprint and Circular Series No. 115, Washington, DC, 1943.
16. National Research Council. *Recommended Dietary Allowances,* 10th ed. Report of the Subcommittee on the Tenth Edition of the RDA, Food and Nutrition Board, and the Commission on Life Sciences. Washington, DC, National Academy Press, 1989.
17. Food and Nutrition Board. Available at http://www4.nas.edu/iom/iomhome.nsf.
18. Health Canada. *Nutrition Recommendations: The Report of the Scientific Review Committee.* Ottawa, Health Canada, 1990.
19. Committee on Dietary Reference Intakes. *Dietary Reference Intakes for Calcium, Phosphorus, Magnesium, Vitamin D, and Fluoride.* Washington, DC, National Academy Press, 1997.

20. Committee on Dietary Reference Intakes. *Dietary Reference Intakes for Thiamin, Riboflavin, Niacin, Vitamin B_6, Folate, Vitamin B_{12}, Pantothenic Acid, Biotin, and Choline,* Washington, DC, National Academy Press, 1998.
21 Committee on Dietary Reference Intakes. *Dietary Reference Intakes for Vitamin C, Vitamin E, and Carotenoids.* Washington, DC, National Academy Press, 2000.
22. Committee on Dietary Reference Intakes. *Proposed Definition of Dietary Fiber.* Washington, DC, National Academy Press, 2001.
23. Grosvenor, M. B., and Smolin. L.A. *Nutrition: From Science to Life.* Orlando, Harcourt College, 2001.
24. Committee on Dietary Reference Intakes. *Dietary Reference Intakes for Vitamin A, Vitamin K, Arsenic, Boron, Chromium, Copper, Iodine, Iron, Manganese, Molybdenum, Nickel, Silicon, Vanadium, and Zinc.* Washington, DC, National Academy Press, 2002.
25. Insel, P., Turner,E.R., and Ross, D. *Nutrition.* Sudbury, MA, Jones and Bartlett, 2001.
26. Health Implications of Dietary Fiber, Position of ADA, *J Am Diet Assoc. 102:* 993–1000, 2002.
27. Food Fortification and Dietary Supplements. Position of the ADA, *J Am Diet Assoc. 101*:115–125, 2001.
28. WHO Policy Perspectives and Medicines. *Traditional Medicine–Growing Needs and Potential.* No. 2, May 2002
29. National Center for Complementary and Alternative Medicine. Available at http://nccam.ni.gov/. Accessed August 5, 2002.
30. United States Pharmacopeia. Available at www.usp.org. Accessed August 3, 2002.

Chapter 10

ADDITIONAL FACTORS FOR ENVIRONMENTAL SANITATION

1.0 INTRODUCTION

The world we live in is getting smaller, figuratively, when one thinks of the faster means of transportation and communications; the globalization of trade including food; the transfer of knowledge by high technology; cultural diversity; and many other developments in the past three decades. Inevitably, the number of environmental factors affecting a person's health and life style has increased and one has to make adjustments or changes with current trends. However, these changes should be aimed at improving the quality of life.

Prevention of disease is still the main public health concern worldwide, especially in the less developed countries. Maintaining a safe and sanitary environment is the key to the reduction of morbidity and mortality rates, which is the main objective of Chapter 10.

Selected environmental factors will be taken up in the next sections, since many of them have been explained in previous chapters. The reader will be guided accordingly, in which chapter(s) a specific topic has already been discussed.

1.1 Definitions

Environmental sanitation is " the promotion of hygiene and the prevention of disease, and other consequences of ill health, relating to environmental factors."[1]

Environmental health is "concerned with the medical effects of pathogenic organisms, chemicals, and physical factors of our environment and is related to every branch of medicine. The most immediate health threat has always been pathogenic organisms."[2]

1.2 Components of Environmental Sanitation

Figure 10.1 is a chart showing various environmental components and how they are interrelated or linked together to bring about environmental sanitation. Each environmental issue, associated with maintaining water safety, healthy air quality, proper waste management, housing, and other considerations, has ecological, economic, social, and political implications. Regulatory efforts need the collaboration of policy makers, food processors, agriculturists, food service operators, health professionals, and organizations concerned with this complex issue of environmental sanitation.[3]

In this chapter, selected components of the environment that impact directly on the transmission of disease are discussed, such as: waste disposal, indoor air quality, household and personal sanitation.

1.2.1 Waste Disposal

The term "waste," as discussed in this chapter, refers to human excreta, wastewater, and solid waste like cans, plastics, paper, glass, and the like. "Hazardous waste" is a material that exhibits ignitability, reactivity, corrosion, or toxicity. The Environmental Protection Agency (EPA) has monitored a comprehensive program to ensure that hazardous waste is managed safely in what is referred to as a "cradle-to-grave" management system.[3]

Some of the cleaning and sanitizing agents belong to this category and have been discussed in Chapter 7 on the control of chemical hazards.

1.2.1.1 Human Excreta. It is estimated that about 66 percent of the world's population has no access to safe human excreta disposal and 25 percent to safe water supply. The main problem seems to be related to the insufficient awareness of people living in unsanitary conditions and the lack of support by their national and local authorities. The latter is due in part to the costs of operation and maintenance of water supply and waste disposal systems.[4]

In areas without proper excreta disposal facilities, local public health authorities should assist the community in building or setting up latrines or acceptable sanitary means of disposing human excreta. Sewage consists of human fecal matter and other waste such as laundry and bath water, and residues from community household garbage.

Bacteria from the intestinal tract of humans and from soil make sewage a real source of pathogenic organisms. Therefore, raw sewage is rendered safer by collecting in septic tanks, digesting into sludge mostly by useful aerobic or anaerobic microorganisms and making the sludge into powder for use as fertilizers.[5]

Toilet facilities are required for all employees in food establishments. The restroom must be completely enclosed and provided with a tight-fitting and self-closing door. The floors, walls, sink, and fixtures must be clean and sanitized regularly.[6]

Toilets and urinals shall be designed such that they are easily cleanable. Toilet rooms for women shall have at least one covered receptacle for sanitary napkins. Lavatories for handwashing should be installed in the restroom or immediately adjacent to it. Kitchen sinks should never be used for handwashing after using the toilet. Be sure the rest rooms have adequate paper and soap supplies and a step-on covered receptacle for trash.

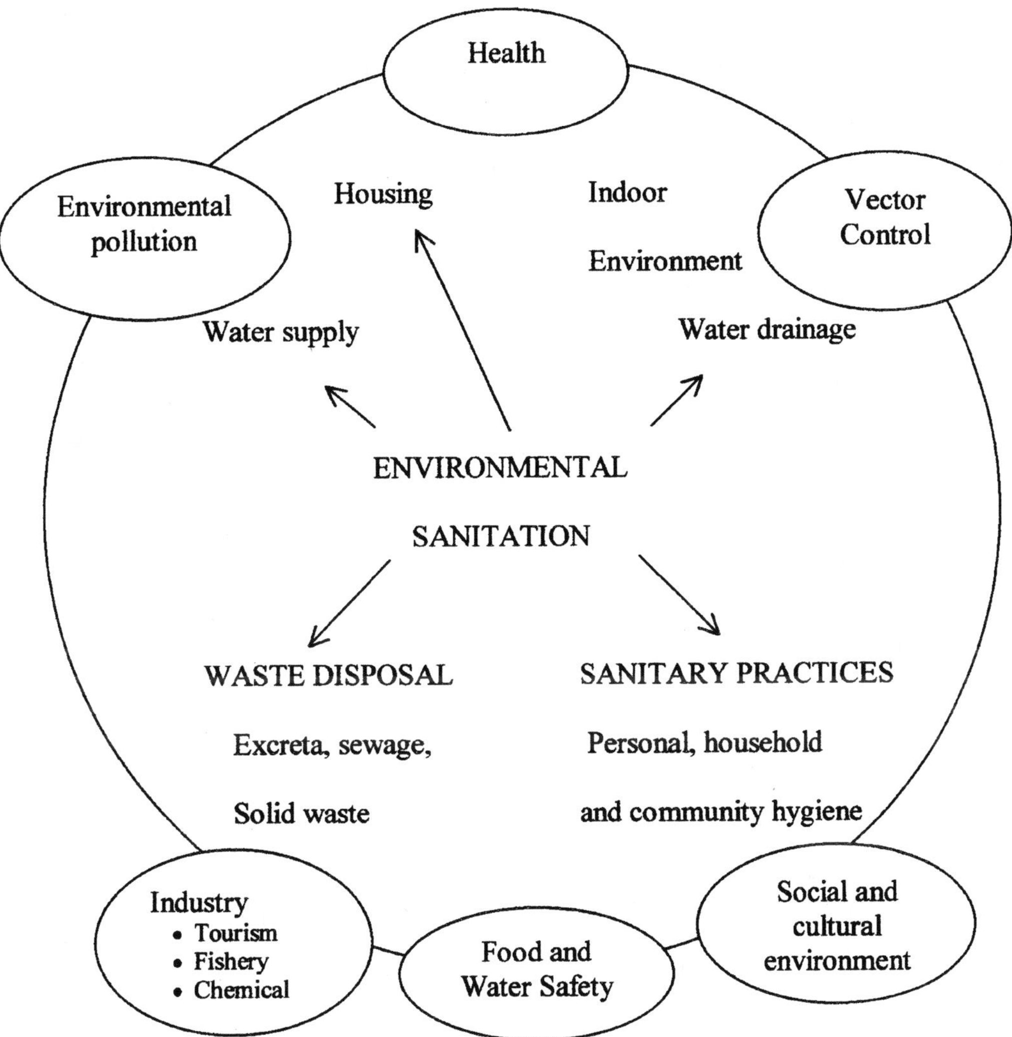

Figure 10.1. Interrelationships of factors for environmental sanitation. (Adapted from: World Health Organization. *Protection of the Human Environment.* Available at http://www.who.int/water-sanitation-healthsanitation/envindex.htm. Accessed June 12, 2002.)

To ensure compliance, some restaurants or grocery stores post a form to record who cleaned and sanitized the restroom showing the time and date, and signed by the employee who did the job. This is a very good system of monitoring sanitation in toilet areas to avoid the spread of disease.

Ecological sanitation (also called "ecosan") is a closed-loop system, which treats excreta for use in agriculture after it is sanitized to be free from pathogenic organisms. This practice has been used for hundreds of years in some Asian countries.[7] Principles may be applied across a range of socio-economic conditions. The fertilizing value of human excreta comes from its nitrogen, phosphorus, and potassium content. About 65 percent to 95 percent of these nutrients come from urine. If ecosan could be adopted on a larger scale worldwide, the groundwater, streams, seas and lakes would be protected from fecal contamination.

A research corporation in Japan has developed a two-staged human excreta treatment process, called "Nishihara's Total System." The process consists of nitrification-denitrification of human excreta followed by chemical and physical treatments and finally, a deodorizing process.[8]

1.2.1.2 WASTEWATER MANAGEMENT. All household wastewater should go into the septic tank, which should be located at a specific distance away, according to regulations. For households, the distance should be at least five feet away from the house. It should be properly designed and constructed such that wastewater will not leak and contaminate groundwater and wells that supply drinking water. The septic tank should be at least 50 feet away from a water supply well. It must be large enough and should follow strictly local building code. For example: the capacity of a septic tank for a single-family home with two bedrooms should be 750 gallons. Check the tank once a year if it needs cleaning by hiring a licensed waste hauler. A malfunctioning septic tank would give off foul odors. Flooding indicates poor drainage. See Table 10.1 for more problems and possible solutions about septic systems.

The plumbing system should be properly constructed to avoid any cross connection that could result in drinking water contamination. Be sure that the pipes for the water distribution system do not contain lead. All fixtures should have backflow devices. Plumbing traps will keep sewer gases from entering the living area.[5,6]

The best protection is to be sure the plumbing system is installed according to current strict building codes (see Chapter 5 of the US Food Code 2001).[6] Another source of guidelines for plumbing is given by the Food and Drug Administration (FDA) in its *Food Service Sanitation Manual.* The regulations include the prevention of backflow, use of grease traps, garbage grinders with proper drainage, and proper connections of pipes so that there will be no cross-connection between drinking water supply and non-potable water.[10]

1.2.1.3 SOLID WASTE DISPOSAL. This includes dry, bulky trash, such as glass, cans, plastics, paper and cardboard boxes. To cite some facts about waste in the United States: in 1990, the average American produced four pounds of garbage daily; and Americans threw away 2.5 million plastic bottles every hour, and threw away enough iron and steel daily that could supply aluminum for the auto makers' needs daily. With proper waste management, recycling paper takes 60 percent less energy and 15 percent less water. One ton of recycled paper saves 7,000 gallons of water and 4,200 kilowatts of energy.[9] Educational campaigns are needed for consumers to reduce solid waste because of the ill effects on health. Examples are given below:

- Plastics, such as polyurethane foam, which can irritate the skin, eyes, and lungs; vinyl chloride that is carcinogenic; and fluorocarbon plastic, which can irritate the skin, eyes, and lungs.
- Garbage from kitchens attracts insects and rodents that are carriers of disease-causing organisms.
- Particleboard, which has urea-formaldehyde, which could be carcinogenic.
- Glue, permanent ink markers, and correction fluids, which are toxic.

Proper disposal of garbage (i.e., food waste that cannot be recycled) is very important to protect food and equipment from contamination by household pests that got attracted to the garbage. Remove garbage as soon as pos-

Table 10.1
CHECK LIST FOR PROBLEMS WITH HOUSEHOLD PLUMBING SEPTIC SYSTEMS

Questions To Ask	*What It Means If Your Answer Is "Yes"*
1. Is there a "glugging" sound when you use fixtures?	A dry trap could be the cause. Flush water after the sound stops. If sound does not stop, call a plumber.
2. Are there any fixtures with S-shaped traps or no traps?	S-shaped traps can allow the backflow of wastewater and sewer gas odors. Replace these traps with U-shaped traps and install U-shaped traps on any fixture that does not have a trap.
3. Are there any fixtures without air gaps?	Fixtures without air gaps should be corrected because they do not stop contaminated water from flowing into clean water.
4. Have you had a problem with a cross-connection?	Eliminate these connections to prevent potential water contamination.
5. Is flooding a problem on your lot?	Flooding indicates that the soil does not drain quickly. Septic systems are likely to have problems in these areas.
6. Does there appear to be good surface drainage on the lot?	Good surface drainage will assist in the proper function of the septic system.
7. Does the ground slope away from the house?	Ground that slopes away from the house assists in the drainage of rainwater. Slopes of 2 to 6 percent are suitable for septic systems. (Lots with greater slopes may be suitable with special absorption field designs.) A lot with a very steep slope or a lot with ground that slopes into the house is not suitable for septic systems.
8. Is the septic system more than ten years old?	The average life span of a well-installed system can be up to 15 years. Have the septic system checked by a qualified professional after ten years, even if it appears to be working well.

Source: Ritchie, I., and Martin. S.J. *The Healthy Home Kit.* Chicago, Real Estate Education Co., 1995.

sible. Provide containers that are durable, waterproof, and easy to clean and sanitize, and should be pest-proof with a tight-fitting lid. Clean and sanitize your containers regularly. Place them on smooth surfaces that repel liquids (e.g., sealed concrete), and away from food preparation and storage areas.

For the other solid waste that is not accepted to be recycled, pulpers and grinding machines may be used. Observe guidelines on how to reduce the amount of the material received or disposed of. Examples of such practices are:[5,9,11]

- Reuse as much as possible: paper bags, plastic bags, cardboard boxes, and bottles
- Use biodegradable products.
- Buy more durable products and buy in bulk.
- Buy less commercially prepared cleaners and sanitizers in cans or bottles. Use

less hazardous compounds available in bulk (see Table 10.3).

- Check with your locality and follow incineration rules.
- Support legislation for deposits of solid containers.

More and more food service operators are using composting to reduce their fees for landfill use. All food waste and unbleached napkins can be composted. Discarded utensils and food scraps are ground up, composted, and degraded to dirt within 40 days.[12]

The disposal of solid waste continues to be a serious urban issue. Governments in Japan and in the US use three main ways to dispose of solid waste: composting, incineration, and landfill.

Composting relies on the action of bacteria and fungi to decompose waste materials into soil additives. Incineration is burning the waste from which energy is produced. Landfill is the terminal means for solid waste management; however, it could pollute surface water and underground aquifers. Incinerator smoke gives off toxic substances like dioxins, sulfur dioxide, and oxides of nitrogen. More research is needed to find alternate ways of solid waste management or to improve on current methods to be more environmentally safe.[13]

Composting is gaining more attention as an environmentally sound way of managing yard wastes at household levels. It is safe (burning pollutes the air and could lead to uncontrolled fires) and the reduced residue could be used for potting soil, increasing air and water absorption in soil, and suppressing weed growth. Farmers use compost for enhancing crops and landscapers apply them for covering landfills and as a soil amendment for decorative purposes. Check with your local authorities about composting.[14]

To store solid waste, large food establishments provide a separate room for storing garbage containers and refuse, e.g., solid waste that is not disposed of through the sewage disposal system. The flooring should be smooth and nonporous, such as cement or asphalt; the containers are labeled to separate paper, glass, plastics, and cans; and the outside refuse and garbage stations must be emptied at least twice a week. These outdoor storage areas must be kept clean, without littering around. The large refuse receptacles must have drains and drain plugs.[15]

There are communities that require the separation of garbage and recycled items in homes. Find out collection days and bring out your garbage on schedule to prevent pest and domestic animals from ripping the bags apart looking for food. Also, garbage collectors inform the community which items they will not collect, such as hazardous waste and corrosive liquids. An example of separating solid waste is done in a county in England:[16] An average bin of solid waste from households contains paper/cardboard = 30%; plastics = 10%; glass = 5%; and metals = 3%.

1.2.2 Indoor Air Quality (IAQ)

Air pollution is defined as "the presence of substances in the air that are at concentration levels that interfere directly or indirectly with human comfort, health, and safety."[3]

The US Environmental Protection Agency (EPA) conducted studies of human exposure to air pollutants, which indicated that indoor levels of pollutants might be two to five times greater than outdoor levels. This is significant to know, because most people spend about 90 percent of their time indoors. Twenty percent of the US population, or nearly 55 million people, spend their days in elementary and secondary schools. Bear in mind that children are especially susceptible to the ill effects of pollutants.[17] Also, in the past decade, concern about indoor air quality has increased in food establishments, such as the smoking ban. Radon is another contemporary issue of consumers. Therefore, the next discussions are focused on learning how to reduce or avoid air contaminants that are deleterious to health.

1.2.2.1 Air Pollutants. The following are the main sources of indoor pollutants:

- Combustion sources like coal, wood, oil, gas, and tobacco products
- Building materials like deteriorating asbestos-containing insulation and plastics
- Furniture made from selected types of pressed wood and damp carpets
- Central heating systems and humidification devices
- Products for household cleaning
- Personal care products or hobbies
- Dust or soil particles carried by wind movement
- Other chemical substances, airborne allergens and pathogens including molds
- Radon, ozone, pesticides, and other outdoor air pollutants that enter indoors.[18]

1.2.2.2 Consequences of Poor Air Quality. The movement of air into and out of houses and buildings is called air exchange. This occurs when doors and windows are open, when air passes through cracks and other openings, and when fans are used. When air conditioning exchange is inadequate, moisture accumulates and will support mold growth. The polluted air breathed in by a person is unhealthy for the respiratory system and may carry pathogens that could cause allergies or sickness.[19]

"Sick building syndrome" is defined as an illness that occurs in persons working in a building, (i.e. working indoors) with air quality poor enough to produce health complaints among 20 percent of its occupants. Residents in a house or apartment may experience problems with their eyes, nose, throat, skin, and respiratory system.

Table 10.2 summarizes outdoor contaminants and their effects on people. It also lists the regulations and US federal standards for acceptable air quality.

1.2.2.3 Regulation of Air Quality. Consumers should check with their local health authorities or the governing agency regulations for environmental sanitation, and air pollution in particular. Recent estimates in the USA indicated a range of 2 to 14 percent of deaths nationwide, which are related to outdoor air pollution. The EPA reported in 1992 that 150 million people lived in areas that exceeded at least one air quality standard.[19]

In the United States the Clean Air Act amended by Congress in 1990 established safe levels of contaminants. The quality of air is monitored by a nationwide network that samples outdoor air and tests it for specific pollutants listed in Table 10.2.

1.2.3 Household Sanitation

A clean house has manifold benefits. It reduces the risk of illnesses, especially those from polluted air and soil, contaminated food and water, and from pests that carry infectious diseases. The quality of air a person breathes in is healthful. The responsibility of maintaining a clean, sanitary indoor environment depends on the vigilance of the consumer or household members who must habitually observe safe personal hygiene in addition to household sanitation practices. Guidelines for food handlers and consumers have been discussed in previous chapters.

1.2.3.1 Sanitizers. The use of chemical compounds is needed for effective sanitizing of surfaces around the house. Currently, many commercially prepared chemicals are

Table 10.2
OUTDOOR AIR CONTAMINANTS REGULATED BY THE GOVERNMENT

Contaminant and Major Sources	*Effects on Human Health and the Environment*	*US Federal Standards to Protect Human Health*
Particulate matter PM-10* Sources are: power plants, industries, fires, motor vehicles, wood stoves and fireplaces.	Aggravates heart and lung disease. Causes eye and lung irritation and decreases visibility. Corrodes metals and causes grime on buildings.	150 micrograms per cubic meter (24-hour average)[1,2] 50 mcg. Per cubic meter (annual average)
Sulfur dioxide Sources are: coal-burning plants, metal smelters, oil refineries and industrial boilers that burn sulfur-containing fuel.	Irritates the eyes and lungs. Aggravates existing lung diseases. Corrodes metals and stone. Damages textiles, toxic to plants. Forms acid rain.	0.13 parts per million[3] (24-hour average) 0.03 parts per million (annual average)
Carbon monoxide Sources are: the incomplete burning of fuel in motor vehicles, wood stoves, gas stoves and fireplaces.	Enters the bloodstream and reduces the amount of oxygen that gets to the body's tissues and organs.	9.0 parts per million (8-hour average) 35.0 parts per million (1-hour average)
Nitrogen dioxide By-product of fuel combustion by motor vehicles, industries and power plants.	Irritates the lower lungs and lowers resistance to respiratory infections.	0.053 parts per million (annual average)
Ozone Produced by reactions that involve volatile chemicals released into the air from motor vehicles, dry cleaners, paint shops and other users of solvents.	Causes coughing, congestion and chest pain, and reduces lung function. Annual studies suggest that long-term exposure can permanently damage the lungs and cause premature aging of the lungs.	0.120 parts per million (maximum daily 1-hour average)

Lead From smelters, lead battery manufacturing or recycling. Lead gasoline additives were a major source in the past. Currently, unleaded gasoline is used.	Lead affects all of the body's systems, especially the central nervous system. Can cause a decrease in IQ, mental retardation and behavioral problems. Infants and children are especially sensitive.	1.5 micrograms per cubic meter (averaged quarterly)

*pm-10 particles are very small particles of dust, dirt, soot, and smoke that are easily inhaled into the lungs.

[1] One microgram per cubic meter (u/m[3]) means that one microgram of the contaminant exists in one cubic meter of air; this is a very small unit of measurement (one microgram is the same as one-millionth of a gram).

[2] A 24-hour average means the concentration is calculated for a period of 24 hours; similarly, 1-hour, 8-hour, quarterly or annual averages are calculated for those periods of time. When a standard includes different time periods for a given contaminant, the numerical value of the standard will be higher for the shortest period to time. This means that standards allow greater exposure to a contaminant for shorter periods of time than for longer time periods.

[3] One part per million (ppm) is a concentration unit that means that one part of the contaminant exists in one million parts of air.

Source: US EPA, 1993 Report on Air Contaminants Regulated by the Government, as read from Ritchie, I., and Martin. S. J. *The Healthy Home Kit.* Chicago, Real Estate Education Co., 1995.

in the grocery and hardware stores. One may also get some supplies from the drugstore. However, they tend to be expensive and are potential health hazards. Some may cause allergic reactions to sensitive individuals. Table 10.3 has alternatives to use, which may be more affordable for people with limited money income. ALWAYS USE HAND GLOVES in applying cleaners and sanitizers.

1.2.3.2 MOLDS. Molds and mildews are not only unsightly but can be deleterious to health. Molds can cause allergies and asthma in susceptible persons. For molds that are foodborne, see Chapter 5.

Molds grow favorably in warm, humid places. They can grow on practically anything: food, fabrics, carpet, tiles, cement, leather, wood, wallpaper, and even metals. A moldy smelling room does not speak well for the restaurant, hotel, or household. These off-odors are due to the gases given off by proliferating molds from their metabolic processes. Their threadlike filaments can cause permanent stain and can damage walls and furnishings.

Ventilation is necessary to control mold growth and to promote a healthy air exchange for respiration. Control room temperature and humidity with the use of thermometers and hydrometers.

A relative humidity of 40 percent is acceptable for the skin and mucous membranes, but too low for molds and mildews. If affordable, use humidifiers, air filters, and air conditioners.

In food establishments, ventilation is very important to remove odors, grease, dirt and molds. Condensation of moisture and grease build-up should be prevented, especially over stoves. The hoods over cooking area should be regularly cleaned and maintained. All fans and ducts should be cleaned and sanitized to avoid drippings onto the food, or food equipment, and table surfaces.[20]

1.2.3.3 RODENTS. Rodent control is probably the most unpleasant task for a consumer. Health hazards caused by rodents have been discussed in Chapter 6. The focus in this section is how to prevent them from entering the house and how to eliminate them once they are inside the house.

Guidelines to Prevent Rodents from Entering the House:

- Seal all holes in walls and floors with steel wool or concrete. Remember that a mouse can fit through a hole 1/4-inch wide–about the size of a US dime, and a rat can enter a hole about the size of a US quarter. Check around the opening where plumbing and electrical wires enter the house.
- Create a barrier to entry by placing metal roof flashing around the base of wooden, earthen or adobe dwellings. The flashing should be buried six inches deep into the soil and extend up to a height of 12 inches.
- Place 3 inches of gravel under the base of the house or under mobile homes to discourage rodent burrowing.

A. Do not provide food and shelter for rodents inside the house.

- Keep food (including pet food) and water covered and stored in rodent-proof metal or thick plastic containers with tight-fitting lids. Do not leave pet food in feeding dishes.
- Store garbage inside homes in rodent-proof metal or thick plastic containers with tight fitting lids. Empty the garbage even if not yet full, daily. Do not leave inside house overnight.
- Wash dishes and cooking utensils immediately after use and remove all spilled food.
- Dispose of trash and discarded tires and other dark containers that can be used for rodent nesting or shelter.

Table 10.3
ALTERNATIVES TO HAZARDOUS HOUSEHOLD CHEMICALS

Common Household Product	*Less Hazardous Alternatives*
Laundry aids	Instead of fabric softener, try adding 1/4 cup of baking soda to the final rinse, or try using borax instead of liquid bleach.
General purpose cleaners	Dissolve 1/2 to 1 cup of borax in 1 gallon of hot water.
Heavy duty cleaner	Mix 4 tablespoons of trisodium phosphate (TSP) with 1 gallon of hot water. Be sure to wear rubber gloves. TSP is available at hardware stores and is effective on dirt, grease, and some other stains. Be sure to test painted surfaces before applying TSP to them.
Carpet cleaner	Spot clean with a solution of 1/2 cup of borax and one quart of water. If commercial cleaning is needed, use water-based steam cleaning whenever possible.
Rug cleaner	Buy rugs that are 100% cotton or a fabric that can be hand washed or machine washed. Some Oriental rugs can be cleaned outdoors with the use of mild soapy water and soft scrubber or brush.
Wood and floor polishes	1. For furniture, mix 1/2 cup of lemon juice with 1 cup of vegetable or olive oil. Apply with a clean, absorbent cloth and wipe with a second cloth to remove excess. 2. For wood floors, mix 3 parts of olive oil with 1 part of vinegar (or lemon juice) or mix 1 teaspoon of lemon juice with 1 pint of mineral or vegetable oil.
Window cleaner	Combine 1 tablespoon of white vinegar and 1 quart of warm water (some recipes call for 2 to 5 tablespoons of vinegar in 1 quart of warm water). Put the solution into a pump sprayer and wipe treated surface with a clean, absorbent cloth.
Air freshener	1. To remove odors, place an opened box of baking soda (several will be needed for a larger space) in a refrigerator or closet. 2. Sprinkle baking soda or borax in the bottom of garbage pails. 3. Use pine boughs or sachets of herbs and flowers to scent the air.
Drain cleaner	1. To prevent clogs, install a drain sieve or hair trip. 2. To open clogs, use a plunger or metal snake or pour 1/4 cup of baking soda followed by 1/2 cup vinegar down the drain. Let the mixture sit until fizzing stops, then flush with boiling water.
Tub and tile cleaner	1. Mix together equal parts of warm water and vinegar. Apply to soap film and spots, rinse and wipe dry. 2. Combine either baking soda or borax with water to form a paste and add a squeeze of lemon juice. Apply to the surface, rinse and wipe dry.

Continued on next page

Table 10.3–*Continued*

Common Household Product	*Less Hazardous Alternatives*
Mildew remover	Combine 1/2 cup of vinegar, 1/2 cup of borax and 1 cup of warm water.
Silver polish	1. Clean with a paste of baking soda and warm water. Rinse object well with warm water and dry thoroughly. 2. Add 1 tablespoon of baking soda and 1 tablespoon of salt to boiling water. Drop silver pieces into the water and boil them for 3 minutes, then remove and polish them with a soft cloth.
Copper and brass polish	Use equal parts of salt and lemon juice or white vinegar.
Oven cleaners	Use baking soda sprinkled on a wet sponge or dish cloth (piece of rug you can throw away) to clean top of stoves and inside ovens.

Source: Bower, L. *Creating a Healthy Household.* Bloomington, The Healthy House Institute, 2000. Ritchie, I., and Martin, S. *The Healthy Home Kit.* Chicago, Real Estate Education Co., 1995.

- Use spring-loaded rodent traps in the house continuously, but cautiously, if children are in the house.
- As an adjunct to traps, use rodenticide with bait under a plywood or plastic shelter (covered bait station) on an ongoing basis inside the house.

B. Reduce rodent shelter and food sources within 100 feet from your house.

- Cut grass, brush and dense shrubbery within 100 feet of the house.
- Use raised cement foundations in new construction of sheds, barns, outbuildings or woodpiles.
- Plant gardens and compost heaps (which should not contain food scraps) and trash cans at least 100 feet away from the house. Use rodent-proof garbage cans (in infested areas these should be raised to 12 inches above the ground).
- Haul away trash, abandoned vehicles, discarded tires and other items that could provide rodents with nesting areas.
- On farms, store grains and animal feed in rodent-proof containers. Store hay on pallets, and use traps or rodenticides to keep off rodents.

C. How to Eliminate Rodents Inside the House

Rodent infestation can be inferred from the presence of feces in closets or cabinets or on floors or from evidence that rodents have been gnawing at food. In cases of heavy rodent infestation (e.g., piles of feces or numerous dead animals), or if it is associated with a confirmed case of hanta virus disease, get professional help to eradicate the rodents.

- Before rodent elimination work is begun, ventilate closed buildings or areas inside buildings by opening doors and windows for at least 30 minutes. Use an exhaust fan or cross-ventilation if possible. Leave the area until the airing-out period is finished.
- This airing may help remove any aerosolized virus inside the closed-in structure.
- Next, treat the interior of the structure with an insecticide labeled for flea control, and follow specific label instructions.

Rodenticides may also be used while the interior is being treated, as outlined below.

1. Remove captured rodents from the traps. Wear rubber or plastic gloves while handling rodents.
2. Place the carcasses in a plastic bag containing a sufficient amount of a general-purpose household disinfectant to thoroughly wet the carcasses.
3. Seal the bag and then dispose of it by burying in a 2- to 3-foot-deep hole or by burning. If burying or burning is not feasible, contact your local or state health department about other appropriate disposal methods.
4. Wash and disinfect used traps. Re-bait and reset all sprung traps.
5. Before removing the gloves, wash gloved hands in a general household disinfectant then in soap and water. A hypochlorite solution prepared by mixing three tablespoons of household bleach in one gallon of water may be used in place of a commercial disinfectant. When using the chlorine solution, avoid spilling the mixture on clothing or other items that may be damaged.
6. Leave several baited spring-loaded traps inside the house at all times as a precaution against rodent reinfestation. Examine the traps regularly. Disinfect traps no longer in use by washing in a general household disinfectant or the hypochlorite solution. Dry well before storing.
7. Disinfect and wash gloves as described above, and wash hands thoroughly with soap and water before beginning other activities.

Table 10.4 is a useful checklist for households to detect any rodent and mold problems. Bear in mind that one rat or mouse is too many. Get help immediately for rodent eradication.

For mold control, check with your local sanitarian or health authority. These are household chores that cannot be postponed for "health's sake."

1.2.4 Food and Water Safety

Next to air quality, a safe food and water supply is one of the components of environmental sanitation that is absolutely necessary for sustaining life and promoting good health. All of the chapters in this text have elucidated about food and water safety, as stated in its main title. However, this topic cannot be overemphasized. This additional information is a reminder for food handlers and consumers as stated in our subtitle.

Food safety in the house is a concern in every station or step of a food flow (see Appendix B). As soon as food enters the house, observe time-temperature control for microbial growth during storage, thawing, preparation, cooking, reheating and serving. The details have been given in Chapter 5. Safe food handling starts with proper hand washing. Wash your hands frequently and observe personal hygiene, like daily bathing, wearing clean clothes and shoes, clean short fingernails, and hair restraints. All surfaces that touch food and water should be clean and sanitized. Pay particular attention in preventing cross-contamination. Think of household germs when using sponges, rags, and towels.[21]

When preparing food for picnics, school or office lunches, and when dining out for leisure or as a traveler in other countries, observe guidelines for these occasions, which are given in this text. There are three golden rules to remember:

1. *Serve foods safe to eat for everyone.* You and your family, your guests, or your paying customers.
2. *Keep cold foods cold and hot foods hot.* The best is to cook adequately and serve promptly. For cold salads, wash

Table 10.4
CHECKLIST FOR SELECTED BIOLOGICAL HAZARDS IN YOUR HOUSE

Questions to Ask	*What It Means If Your Answer Is "Yes"*
Is there evidence of mice or rats within the home? Look for droppings inside cabinets and closets, carefully examine the basement floor area and on top of floor joists (if they are accessible) and look for entryways into the home that are at least 1/4 inch wide.	Mice and rodents carry many diseases, including hanta virus and the plague. Rodents should be eliminated from the home. Follow the rodent proofing guidelines in this chapter or call the local or state health department for assistance.
Is there evidence of mice or other rodents within 100 feet of the home?	Potential nesting sites include shrubs, woodpiles and other yard debris. Potential nesting sites and yard debris should be removed. Woodpiles should be raised to at least 12 inches above the ground and food sources should be removed. Follow the rodent proofing guidelines in this chapter or call the local or state health department for assistance.
Are there visible signs of mold, rot, or discolored areas on wood and other surfaces? Look in all areas of the house including the attic and basement. Examine areas covered by insulation.	Mold and decay are present. There may be damage to the structure. Follow the guidelines previously given on the control of molds.
Is there carpeting in the kitchen, bathroom, basement, or any room where water is used?	Carpeting in these rooms is a likely place for mold and other microbes to grow.
Do you have unexplained allergic symptoms that seem to be related to being in your home?	The problem could be caused by allergens produced by pets, dust mites or mold. (Pollen and grasses are other possible causes that are not considered in the chapter). Look for potential sources and consult with a doctor about symptoms.

Source: Bower, L. *Creating a Healthy Household,* Bloomington, The Healthy House Institute, 2000. Ritchie, I., and Martin, S. *The Healthy Home Kit.* Chicago, Real Estate Education Co., 1995.

fruits and vegetables properly with potable water. Refrigerate and serve fresh.

3. *When in doubt, throw it out.* Never taste to find out if it is spoiled or not. Bacteria and viruses cannot be seen by the naked eyes, have no smell and no taste.

With regard to water safety, detailed discussion has been presented in Chapter 2. To summarize, acceptable water quality is not only freedom from waterborne pathogens, but must also meet consumers' standards for taste, odor, appearance (clarity and color), etc. The water supply is not only safe, but also accessible for daily needs. *Report any suspected foodborne or waterborne illness immediately.* Chapter 1 listed the steps to take for reporting any case or outbreak. You are helping yourself, your community and the world population, especially policy makers and investigators, to learn more about the disease for future preventive actions and education programs.

2.0 ECONOMIC CONSIDERATIONS OF ENVIRONMENTAL SANITATION

Economics deals mainly with the allocation of scarce resources with the aim of maximizing favorable outcomes desired, e.g., for health, profit, social upliftment, improving standards of living, etc. Sanitation interventions provide challenging application of economic principles that need regulation, collaboration of multidisciplinary team members, and are influenced by culture and social behaviors of a community or nation. An example to show the complexity of this discipline is observed in "Willingness to Pay" (WTP) studies on water supply and sanitation services. Benefit analysis included:[22]

1. Commercial benefits as reflected in infrastructure improvements which in turn lead to increased investment and business opportunities, and
2. Health benefits in direct terms, like avoiding medical expenses and savings in poison control centers; and in indirect terms, such as productivity gains due to reduced morbidity, reduced sick leave, and more efficient performance at work or in school.

Environmental degradation reduces the food supply for the world at large. Soil erosion, deforestation, air pollution, and ozone depletion, all cause damage to crops. Extensive grazing causes rangelands to deteriorate and reduce food supply for livestock. Water pollution threatens marine life, thereby reducing our supply of seafood.

The advantages of lowering population growth rate and improving economic status are demonstrated by the sharing of resources and education programs from the more fortunate nations to the less developed countries. Already, population growth has slowed down in Sri Lanka, Malaysia, Costa Rica, and Taiwan. This leads to the review of how the "Sanitation Connection" campaigns in selected countries are favorably improving environmental sanitation.

3.0 PROGRAMS AND STRATEGIES FOR ENVIRONMENTAL SANITATION

To be successful in undertaking programs and strategies to improve environmental sanitation, the following principles have to be observed:[4]

- Sanitation programmers should be demand-based and the community should be fully involved in the process.
- Sanitation should be a component of other health-promoting or disease control programmers.
- Sanitation needs to be addressed as a whole, including improvement of facilities, environmental conditions and behavioral changes.
- High risk group should be identified for better targeting of funds and efforts.
- Systems have to be sustainable; cost sharing and cost-recovery need to be addressed carefully.

The WHO plays a key role in assessing the health impact of the various elements of environmental sanitation. It also identifies the high risk groups and what interventions are efficient and cost-effective in preventing the burden of disease. It assesses existing programs in environmental sanitation and identifies research and development needs.

The WHO has been concerned with drinking water quality and its effects on human health for almost fifty years now. It has published the *International Standards for*

Drinking Water, which is used as a guide by various countries. One of the primary goals of WHO is that "all people, whatever stage of development and their social and economic conditions, have the right to have access to an adequate supply of safe drinking water."[23]

The Food and Agriculture Organization (FAO) is involved with wastewater treatment and applications for reuse in agriculture. This is important, as the world water supply is getting scarce. The purpose of treated wastewater for irrigation is to provide nutrients, most of which are contained in domestic sewage, and to conserve potable water.[24]

The National Environmental Health Association (NEHA) was incorporated in California in 1937. The original impetus behind the creation of this national professional society of environmental health practitioners was to establish a standard of excellence, which is known as The Registered Environmental Health Specialist/Registered Sanitarian (REHS/RS) credential. Current membership is now 5,000 and their mission is "to advance the environmental health and protection professional for the purpose of providing a healthful environment for all." NEHA is involved in many educational programs, research and development, and publishes the *Journal of Environmental Health.* It actively promotes the US-EPA guidelines on wastewater management by conducting a series of regional outreach workshops.[25]

The Global Environmental Sanitation Initiative (GESI) resulted from a forum held in Manila in November 1997, which will coordinate a global campaign of advocacy and information sharing. Its goal is to stimulate greater attention to the sanitation issue suffered by half of the world population. It will also help in mobilizing more resources to serve the rural and urban poor with needed sanitation services.[26]

The following activities are examples of what various countries have accomplished or are currently pursuing to improve environmental sanitation, especially their water sanitation program (WSP):

Bolivia. Over a period of five years, Bolivian municipalities have founded intermunicipal consortiums and will receive more direct funding annually for water and sanitation initiatives. The WSP Andean Office is focusing its attention to Peru and Bolivia, two of the poorest countries of South America. It works closely with the Swedish International Development Cooperation Agency and the Swiss Agency for Development and Cooperation (SDC). This is a good example of industrialized countries helping poorer nations.[27]

India. In the rural sector, the WSP-South Asia works in alliance with the Rajiv Gandhi National Drinking Water Mission. For the next ten years in India, the WSP-SA will adopt significant financial and institutional reforms in government and water and sanitation agencies for water sanitation programs.[28]

Jamaica. The United Nations Environment Program (UNEP) and the Caribbean Environment Program are looking into the coastal and marine pollution of Jamaica. It was observed that the land-based pollutants constitute the greatest threat to the coastal and marine ecosystems and to the public health in the wider Caribbean Region.[29]

Australia. Poor water quality and sediment loads are the most serious known pollution issues in Australia, affecting its coastal and marine environments. Australia's "Ocean Policy" has been published by Environment Australia for details on these issues.[30]

East Asian Countries. In Vietnam, the WSP has been executing a project on capacity building for water and sanitation, financed by the SDC. In the Philippines, the Water and Sanitation Performance Project (WPEP) will explore the issues resulting from the lack of interest in sanitation. In Cambodia, the SIDA-supported Policy and Capacity-building Project sponsored a series of workshops about national and local views on key water and sanitation policies.[31]

Japan has been extending financial assistance to Pakistan for nation building and economic development since 1990. In June 2001, Japan provided over 91 thousand US dollars for a project known as the "Improvement of the Environmental Sanitation System in the Old Settlement of Altit."[32]

Sub-Sahara Africa. The use of human manure in agriculture is being explored because there may be cultural factors and health concerns that constrain its use. The UNEP invited researchers (anthropologists, sociologists, agriculturists, geographers and medical scientists) working in areas of Sub-Sahara Africa to gather information using a questionnaire. Data from this survey will be useful in planning out strategies in using treated human manure as fertilizers. In China, 30 percent of the nutrients for crops come from human excreta. Other Asian countries also reuse human manure for agriculture.[33]

Due to space limitation, only a dozen countries, out of about 120 in the world, have been included above. However, the activities in these countries just presented are examples of promising improvements on environmental sanitation. Chapter 14 gives more recommendations on future researches and educational programs for a safe and sanitary environment.

REVIEW QUESTIONS

A. Define the following key terms (see the Glossary).
   1. Indoor Air Quality (IAQ)
   2. Ventilation
   3. Relative humidity
   4. Radon
   5. Microgram
   6. Sick building syndrome
   7. Composting
   8. Waste management

B. Explain the components of the environmental sanitation linkage (see Figure 10.1)

C. What are the main sources of indoor air pollutants?

D. How is environmental sanitation regulated in your community? (By whom?)

E. List the national and international organizations that protect our environment to be safe and healthful.

F. Add more guidelines for consumers in maintaining environmental sanitation other than what are given in the text.

REFERENCES

1. World Health Organization (WHO). *What Is Environmental Sanitation?* Report by Protection of the Human Environment. Available at http://www.who.int/water_sanitation_health/Environmental_sanit/envindex. Accessed June 10, 2002.
2. Narins, B. *The World of Health.* Detroit, Gale Group, 2000.
3. American Dietetic Association (ADA). Position of the American Dietetic Association: Dietetics professionals can implement practices to conserve natural resources and protect the environment. *J Am Diet Assoc. 101*:1221, 2001.
4. World Health Organization (WHO). Past Programs and Activities to Improve Environment Sanitation. Available at http://www.who.int/watersanitation-health/waterquality/drinkwater. Accessed June 10, 2002.
5. Marriott, N. G. *Principles of Food Sanitation.* 4th ed. New York, Kluwer Academic, 1999.
6. Food and Drug Administration (FDA). *US Food Code 2001.* Available at http://www.cdc.gov/fsf/usfoodcode/2001. Accessed June 10, 2002.
7. Sanitation Connection Publications. *Ecological Sanitation Report, 2002.* Available at http://www.sanicon.net/titles/topicintro/php3/topicId=7. Accessed June 10, 2002.

8. JSIM. *Nishihara's Human Excreta Treatment Process.* Report by Nishihara Environmental Sanitation Research Corporation, LTD. 2000. Available at http://nett.21.unep.orjp/JSIM-DATA/water/water-3/html/Document-247/html. Accessed June 10, 2002.
9. Ritchie, I., and Martin. S. J. *The Healthy Home Kit.* Chicago, Real Estate Education Co., 1995.
10. Longree, K., and Armbruster, G. *Quantity Food Sanitation.* 5th ed. New York, John Wiley & Son, Inc. 1996.
11. National Restaurant Association Education Foundation. *ServeSafe® Coursebook.* Chicago, NRAEF, 2002.
12. Matsumoto J. Dirt Cheap Operators unearth way to close food chain loop through composting. *Restaurants and Institutions. 109:*106, 1999.
13. JLGC Newsletter. *Solid Waste Management,* Issue #24, Fall 1997. Available at http://www./jlgc.org/jlgnes/024/waste-management.htm. Accessed June 10, 2002.
14. EPA Region V & Agricultural and Biological Engineering, Purdue. *Feed a Bug, Starve a Landfill.* 2000 Available at http://www.epa-gov/grtlakes/seahome/housewaste/src/open.htm. Accessed June 10, 2002
15. McSwane, D., Rue, N., and Linton R. *Essentials of Food Safety and Sanitation,* 3rd ed. Upper Saddle River, N.J., Prentice-Hall, 2003.
16. Anon. *Waste Management for Householders. National Data Survey 1995.* Available at http://www.meath.je/environment/wasteman agement-house. Accessed June 12, 2002.
17. Environmental Protection Agency (EPA). *Indoor Air Quality (IAQ) USEPA Report.* June 12, 2002 Available at http://www.epa.gov/iaq. Accessed June 15, 2002.
18. Environmental Protection Agency (EPA). *Indoor Air Quality (IAQ) Report 2000.* Available at http://www.epa.gov/iaq/index.html. Accessed June 15, 2002.
19. Environmental Protection Agency (EPA). *1993 Report on Air Contaminants Regulated by the Government.* As read from Ritchie, I., and Martin. S. J. *The Healthy Home Kit,* Chicago, Real Estate Education Co., 1995.
20. National Restaurant Association Education Foundation. *ServSafe®Essentials,* 2nd ed. Chicago, NRAEF, 2002.
21. Matthews, D. D. *Food Safety Sourcebook.* Detroit, Omnigraphics, 1999.
22. Fewtrell, L. *Water Quality–Guidelines and Health.* Centre for Research into Environment and Health, Geneva, WHO, 1997.
23. World Health Organization (WHO). *Drinking Water Quality Report by the Protection of the Human Environment.* Available at http://www.who.int/water-waterquality/drinkwater. Accessed June 10, 2002.
24. Pescod, M. *Wastewater Treatment and Use in Agriculture.* Rome, Sanitation Connection Publications, 1992.
25. National Environmental Health Association. *Onsite Wastewater Management.* Reported on 3/22/02. Available at http://www.neha.org/research/onsite wastewater.htm. Accessed June 12, 2002.
26. Water Supply and Sanitation Collaborative Council (WSSCC). *Global Environmental Sanitation Initiative (GESI).* Report on April 5, 2001 c/o WHO, Geneva. Available at http://www.who.int/water-sanitation-health/GESI/htm. Accessed June 12, 2002.
27. Water Supply and Sanitation Program (WSP). *Andean Region: Rural Water and Sanitation.* Available at http://www.wsp.org/eng/andean. Accessed June 18, 2002.
28. Water Supply and Sanitation Program (WSP). *Country Data on India.* Report from the World Bank, 2000. Available at: http://www.wsp.org/eng/india. Accessed June 18, 2002.
29. Caribbean Environment Programme. *An Overview of Land Based Sources of Marine Pollution.* United Nations Caribbean Regional, Jamaica, 2002. Available at: http://www.cep.unep.org/issues/lbsp.html. Accessed June 18, 2002.
30. Environment Australia. *Australia's Ocean Policy: An Issues Paper, Chapter 5: Land Sourced Pollution.* Australia, 1998. Available at http://www.environment.gov.au/marine/ocepoly/ocean policy/public/chaper5 1 5.html. . Accessed June 18, 2002.
31. Water and Sanitation Program (WSP). *Overview; Rural Water and Sanitation.* Available

at: http://www.wsp.org/eng/asia/htm. Accessed June 18, 2002
32. Numata, S. *Improvement of Environmental Sanitation System in the Old Settlement of Altit.* June 12, 2001. Pakistan, Aga Khan Cultural Services. Speech by The Ambassador of Japan.
33. UNEP. *Human Manure in Agriculture in Sub-Sahara Africa,* December 12, 1997, Available at: http://www.ee/list/infoterra/1997/12/0019.html accessed June 18, 2002.
34. Bower, L. *Creating a Healthy Household.* Bloomington, Indiana, The Healthy House Institute, 2000.
35. Martin, S. *The Healthy Home Kit.* Chicago, Real Estate Education Co., 1995.

Chapter 11

EFFECTS OF NEWER TECHNOLOGY ON FOOD AND WATER SAFETY

1.0 INTRODUCTION

Advances in food technology have been at an accelerated pace in the past decades. Many new food products are available to consumers as a result of research and development in manufacturing, processing, preserving, and packaging. With improved means of transport and increased import-export trading, a wide variety of food commodities reach different parts of the world. However, not all consumers readily accept novel products and innovative methods in food technology. Consumer confidence has to be established by education. This chapter presents some of the major newer technologies in foods, with a discussion of the benefits gained from them on one hand and the possible disadvantages or risks on the other hand.

2.0 BIOTECHNOLOGY[1,2]

Biotechnology refers to the applications of living organisms to produce foods and chemicals with improved characteristics or qualities. Traditional biotechnology has been practiced for centuries and is almost as old as the science of agriculture. In the past three decades, biotechnology has undergone tremendous advances mainly through genetic engineering. Thus, some scientists refer to this era as modern biotechnology or the new biotechnology.

Three major areas that scientists have focused on in modern food technology are: genetically modified organisms (GMOs), genetic engineering (GE), agricultural biotechnology, and medical applications, such as, the production of drugs, antibiotics, vaccines and hormones, and gene therapy.

2.1 Genetic Engineering (GE)[3]

Genetic engineering (GE) is the use of recombinant deoxyribonucleic acid (DNA) technology. It involves the process of manipulating or inserting foreign DNA or genetic material into plants, bacteria, and animals for beneficial results as discussed in the coming sections. The era of GE started in the early 1970s and the first generation of GE foods involved crops.[1]

Since then, the use of transgenic crops has increased rapidly. Table 11.1 summarizes the number of acreage used to plant genetically engineered crops.

Genetic engineering is still in its early stages and current research is ongoing to study the pros and cons about this revolutionary technique for biotechnology.[2,4]

2.1.1 Benefits derived from genetic engineering (GE)[1-6]

Biotechnology proponents are optimistic about the direct benefits of GE, especially in developing nations. These include:

- Increase of food supplies. An example is the use of altered corn seeds that produce up to 8 percent more yield than the average seeds.
- Improved farm income. A study by the National Center for Food and Agricultural Policy, released in June, 2002 by the USA NCGAP revealed that six biotech crops produced an additional four billion pounds of food on the same acreage, plus improved farm income of $1.5 billion.[5]
- Improved nutritional quality of certain foods, i.e., increased vitamin and amino acid contents and lowered the amount of fat and cholesterol. An example for the latter is with soybeans that are genetically modified to yield lower fatty acids and higher monounsaturated fatty acids.
- Improved taste, color, texture and other palatability factors of foods. Excellent examples are the bioengineered tomatoes and peppers. They are sweeter and the colors are brighter. They do not rot on the vine.
- Reduced use of chemical sprays, like herbicides. An example is the NCFAP study (cited above), which shows that the pesticides used were reduced by 46 million pounds.
- Prolonged shelf life or storage. More pest-resistant varieties of grains and cereals are expected to have a longer storage life. Oils from GE seeds yield more stable cooking oils.

The long-range effects of the above benefits to consumers are to reduce poverty, hunger and malnutrition. Table 11.2 summarizes some of the approved bioengineered crops in the United States. The desirable traits or functional characteristics derived from each GE crop are direct benefits to the consumers.

Table 11.1
PLANTED ACREAGE OF GENETICALLY ENGINEERED CROPS

Crops	*Countries*	*1999*
Corn	United States	26 million
	Canada	500,000
Soybean	United States	40×10^6
	Canada	30,000
	Argentina	12×10^6
Canola	United States	5×10^6
	Canada	1×10^6
Cotton	Australia	200,000
	Mexico	100,000

Source: Abdullah, A. Food Safety and the Consumer: Household Perspective. Presented at the Food Safety Research and Development Proceedings, Bangkok, May 2001. Laguna, RP, SEAMEO SEARCA.

2.1.2 Risks and Safety Concerns about Genetic Engineering[1-3]

Consumer concerns that need to be resolved and explained to the public are: 1) environmental and ecological impacts and the safety of the genetically modified foods (GMFs), and 2) ethical and socioeconomic issues.

Examples of studies for the first issue involve pollen dispersed from the use of *Bacillus thuringiensis (Bt)* spores. The concern is that *Bt* may cause damage to non-target organisms, or insects may eventually develop resistance to *Bt. Bt* crops contain the bacterium *Bacillus thuringiensis* proteins that are resistant to corn borers, bollworms, and other pests.

Another study theorized that the use of just one GE fish could lead to extinction of the species within thirty-seven generations. Many are concerned about the danger to beneficial insects, like the ladybugs, some butterflies, and bees.

Some questions asked about GE foods in relation to socioeconomic issues are:

- Will GE applications render the soil infertile and force many who now save and share their seeds to purchase more expensive GE seeds?
- Will rural communities eventually be devastated when many farmers and agricultural workers would lose their livelihood from traditional farming?
- Will there be production of toxic substances and harmful substances that cause allergies?
- Are there cancer risks or cumulative deleterious effects to human health?

Some countries will not allow the sales of genetically modified foods to the public until the risks and concerns about their use are clarified. Opposition to bioengineered foods is especially strong in some European countries. The process of genetic engineering should be carefully tested to avoid any safety risks and environmental catastrophes.[3]

Table 11.3 lists the countries that have approved the use of GE crops for feed and food, as of 1999. The leading countries that plant GE crops are (total acres given in

Table 11.2
PARTIAL LIST OF APPROVED GENETICALLY MODIFIED (GM) CROPS IN THE UNITED STATES AND TRAITS

Crop	*Traits*
Canola	Herbicide tolerance; high laurate oil
Cherry Tomato	Taste, color, texture
Corn	Herbicide tolerance; insect protection
Cotton	Herbicide tolerance; insect protection
Flax	Herbicide tolerance
Papaya	Virus protection
Potato	Insect protection
Soybean	High oleic oil to reduce need for hydrogenation; herbicide tolerance; low linolenic oil to reduce need for hydrogenation; low saturated fat oil
Squash	Virus protection
Sugar beet	Herbicide tolerance
Sunflower	High oleic oil to reduce need for hydrogenation
Tomato	Altered ripening to enhance fresh market value; thicker skin; altered pectins for processing value

Source: Union of Concerned Scientists. Available at www.ucsusa.org/agriculture/gen.market.html. Accessed July 1, 2002.
Biotechnology Industry Organization. Available at www.bio.org. Accessed July 1, 2002.

Table 11.3
COUNTRIES THAT HAVE APPROVED THE USE OF GENETICALLY ENGINEERED (GE) CROPS BY 1999

Argentina	Mexico
Australia	Romania
Canada	Russia
China	South Africa
European Union	Switzerland
Japan	United States

Source: ISAAA Briefs, No. 12-1999 BIO. Available at www.bio.org/food&ag/1999Acreage.html. Accessed July 1, 2002.

parentheses): The United States (72 million acres), Argentina (17 million acres), Canada (10 million), and China (one million).

2.2 Agricultural Biotechnology[2,3,8]

This branch of biotechnology applies the principles of genetic engineering (discussed previously) in the practice of agriculture, such as plant breeding and animal husbandry (see Table 11.4). Three main areas that show beneficial outcomes are in the:

1. Production of plants that can grow in areas of low rainfall and extreme temperatures
2. Development of new strains of plants and animals that are more resistant to

Table 11.4
GENETICALLY MODIFIED (GM) FOODS APPROVED FOR THE US MARKET

Foods	*Traits*
Corn, and potato	Insect protected and virus protected
Soybeans, corn, and canola	Tolerant to herbicide
Squash and papaya	Virus protected
Tomatoes	Virus-resistant
	Improved taste, color and texture
Soybeans	High-sucrose, high-lysine, and high oleic acid; high-methionine
Canola oil	High lauric acid
Rapeseed	Herbicide-tolerant

Source: Insel, P. et al. *Nutrition*. Boston, Jones & Bartlett, 2001.
Shea, K. M. Technical report: Irradiation of food. *Pediatrics 106*.6, 505. December 2000.

pests and diseases or can resist destruction of herbicides
3. Applications of conservation tillage practices that help preserve topsoil and reduce soil erosion.

The concerns of farmers that are negative in applying agricultural biotechnology are:

1. Problem of out-crossing, i.e. accidental cross-pollination with related wild weeds that would crowd out the needed plants.
2. Socioeconomic factors that are explained earlier in this chapter.
3. Cost factors or expenses involved in the newer technologies.
4. Safety factors for consumers. An example is when farm animals are given genetically produced bovine somatotropin (BST) hormone to increase milk production. Other animal drugs, like vaccines, antibiotics, antiparasites and bactericides, might have ill effects on humans who consume foods produced from these animals.

The public must be protected by regulations to ensure that drugs are used properly in cattle, poultry, and other animals used for food. They should be informed about the details of the processes or methods, the benefit, as well as the risks involved.

2.3 Medical Applications of Biotechnology[3,9]

Genetic engineering in medicine is well accepted. Clear evidence is the widespread use of many recombinant products in health care, such as human insulin, erythropoietin, hepatitis B vaccines, several interferons, and anti-hemophilic factor. It is estimated that more than 25 percent of the leading drugs are produced using genetically modified organisms.

Gene therapy is a promising application of genetic engineering to treat genetic diseases and illnesses, like AIDS, rheumatoid arthritis, cancers, asthma, and viral infections.

Pharmaceuticals can be produced using GE methods, which will be faster (not time consuming compared to extracting the chemicals). Hopefully, the genetically engineered drugs will also be less expensive.

Bacteria can be used in genetic engineering techniques to degrade toxic agents and render allergenic substances into harmless compounds. This method is called *bioremediation,* which is the use of living systems to convert toxic, as well as nontoxic, wastes and pollutants to nontoxic substances.

Opponents of the use of genetic engineering are concerned about the disruption of natural ecosystems when introducing new, unusual organisms that have no natural place in the food chain. Also, they are worried that newly created microorganisms may mutate and cause deadly diseases to plants, animals, and humans.

Ultimately, it is the consumers' acceptance of these revolutionary new technologies and the regulations of governing agencies that decide the use of modern biotechnology in plants, animals, microorganisms, medicine, etc. The global population is increasing and there is an urgent need to improve the quality and quantity of food supply. One promising solution is by the application of modern biotechnology. Other methods to use are the newer food preservation techniques as explained in the coming sections.

3.0 METHODS OF FOOD PRESERVATION[10]

The five general methods of food preservation–dehydration, canning, refrigeration, freezing, and the application of chemicals–are basically the same. They have been used for many years and two of these traditional methods have been used for centuries. They continue to be the most common means of preserving foods worldwide, especially in developing countries (see Chapter 5 for details). The principles in the conventional methods of food preservation are extended to newer processing techniques that are less time consuming and are more effective in rendering the food product free from pathogenic microorganisms. At the same time, the retention of nutrients and attainment of desirable sensory qualities of food, like color, flavor, texture, form or shape, are additional goals of the newer methods of preservation.

3.1 Irradiation[10–14]

Food irradiation, sometimes referred to as "cold pasteurization," is the process of exposing food to an electron beam or gamma rays. The benefits of this method are:

- Elimination or significant reduction of spoilage and pathogenic microorganisms.
- Alternative method for chemicals as preservatives.
- Nutrients, taste, and appearance of the food are not significantly affected.
- Longer shelf life of food. Mold spores and insect eggs are destroyed.
- Other specific benefits: Irradiation inhibits sprouting in tubers and bulbs, retards ripening of produce after harvest, inactivating parasites in fish and meats, and prevents insect infestation of grains, spices, and fresh produce.

The hesitancy of some consumers to use irradiated foods is mainly the possibility of getting radioactive substances, which is unfounded. The sources of radiation and the low dose used for foods are regulated to be safe for humans. Public education about food irradiation, and its safe use and benefits, are important to establish consumer confidence and its acceptance. It should be emphasized that handling irradiated foods follows the same care as observed for other foods to avoid contamination with disease producing organisms. Table 11.5 lists the foods approved for irradiation in the United States.

One great advantage of irradiation is that it can be applied after the food is packaged,

Table 11.5
FOODS APPROVED FOR IRRADIATION IN THE UNITED STATES

Food	*Purpose of Irradiation*
Spices, dry vegetable seasoning	Decontamination/disinfest insects
Wheat, wheat powder	Disinfest insects
White potatoes	Extend shelf life; inhibit sprouting
Dry or dehydrated enzyme preparations	Control insects and microorganisms
Pork carcasses or fresh non-cut processed cuts	Control *Trichinella spiralis*
Fresh fruit and fresh vegetables	Delay maturation; control mold growth
Root crops like onion, garlic, and ginger	Inhibit sprouting
Dry or dehydrated enzyme preparations	Decontamination
Dry or dehydrated aromatic vegetables	Decontamination
Poultry	Control pathogens
Red meat	Control pathogens and prolong shelf life
Fresh shell eggs	Control Salmonella species

Source: Greenberg, R. *Irradiated Foods.* 4th ed. New York, American Council on Science and Health. Shea, K. M. Technical report: Irradiation of food. *Pediatrics 106*.6, 505. December 2000.

thereby preventing recontamination in subsequent handling, as long as the packaging is intact. The package should be properly labeled with RADURA, the international irradiation symbol and the words, "TREATED BY IRRADIATION: DO NOT TREAT AGAIN" clearly written. (See Figure 11.1 for the RADURA logo.)

The drawbacks to the use of irradiation include the increased cost of the process and the potential reduction of food taste. There is a possibility that some electrons are freed, which attach themselves to other components, forming harmful compounds, like benzene and formaldehyde. Some free radicals that are unidentified are also present, but to date, no ill effects about these particles have been observed.

The use of irradiated foods has been allowed in at least 40 countries, of which 24 of them use irradiation for commercial purposes, but it is the United States where irradiation is in its mature stage after more than fifty years of research and testing, and evaluation.[7,11,13]

The American Dietetic Association in its position paper dated February 2000, states "food irradiation has been identified as a safe technology to reduce the risk of foodborne illness as part of high-quality food production, processing, handling, and preservation."[14]

Dean Cliver, professor of population health and reproduction at the University of California, Davis, said: "I have been in the food safety business for almost thirty-six years and I can't think of anything else that has come along over that span that I thought had as much potential. We get an awful lot of safety for very little money with irradiation." Dean Cliver pointed out that because irradiation can penetrate muscle tissues, parasites that are buried deep within the tissues are killed by irradiation.[13]

A new process, called high-intensity pulsed light, was recently approved by the US-FDA. It is an alternative to irradiation. The high intensity pulsed light kills the microorganisms on the surfaces of food, without affecting nutritional quality. It has been

Figure 11.1. The Radura Symbol

applied successfully to produce, meats, seafood, and baked goods.[13]

3.2 High Pressure Processing[15,16]

High pressure processing (HPP) uses pressures in the range of 400 to 1000 Mpa to inactivate bacteria. Mpa stands for mega Paschal, the unit of measurement for high pressures. Ham, sausage, avocado puree and salsas have been subjected to HPP process with success.

HPP is conducted by two mechanisms: first is the rapid compression heating of 3 to 4°C per 100MPa and the second is the kinetics of bacterial inactivation, which is accelerated by the high pressure. Further studies are needed for the use of HPP with low acid foods that can support *Clostridium botulinum* growth.

3.3 Newer Methods of Pasteurization[17-18]

After forty years of research, electronic pasteurization has been approved by the US Food and Drug Administration as a safe method for killing foodborne bacteria. It is used not only for meat and poultry, but also for fresh fruits, like those from Hawaii, which have been previously banned for export due to fruit flies. Electronic pasteurization destroys the fruit flies and allows the fruit to be tree-ripened.

Since no heat is applied, the color, texture, taste, and nutritional quality are retained. After the process, consumers should handle the food just like other perishable items.

Another acceptable quick and effective method of pasteurization is by applying ultra-high temperature (UHT) on milk and milk products. They are commonly marketed as extended shelf life (ESL) products and are unique because bacteria, such as *Listeria monocytogenes,* will be killed with the intense heat of UHT. However, post-production contamination by high levels of the organisms can still thrive with UHT products, therefore, handle the products with the same safety measures as given other products. For example, refrigerate once the package is opened.[18]

Some meat processing plants are experimenting with the use of steam pasteurization. This process subjects the entire carcass of beef to a blast of steam for a short time, then rapidly cooled. Surface pathogens are killed without cooking the meat. A similar method can be applied to dressed poultry.[13]

3.4 Use of Bacteria and Enzymes

The cheese-making industry has been using genetically modified bacteria to produce the enzyme chymosin that replaces rennet that is extracted from the stomach of calves.[12]

The FDA approved a spray consisting of 29 types of living nonpathogenic bacteria that are normally present in the guts of adult chickens. When sprayed on chicks, they ingest the beneficial bacteria when they preen their feathers. The nonpathogenic bacteria then compete with pathogenic bacteria, like *Salmonella, Listeria,* and *E. coli.*[20]

Beneficial lactic acid bacteria (commonly present in yogurt and other fermented foods) can be added to refrigerated produce (fresh fruits and vegetables) to inhibit the growth of salmonellae, staphylococci, *E. coli,* and possibly other pathogens.[13]

An area that is to be further explored related to this subtopic is *probiotics.* A probiotic is a live microbial food supplement, which benefits the host by balancing/improving its intestinal flora. Most probiotics belong to *Lactobacillus* species and some are *Bifidobacterium* species. Probiotics have received scientific scrutiny recently because of their potential prophylactic and therapeutic uses.[19,21]

For more details about probiotics, these two key references by the FAO[22] and L. Hoolihan[23] give excellent reviews and guidelines. Suffice it for us to be aware that this area of using beneficial bacteria to "fight harmful bacteria" is promising in studying food safety issues.

3.5 Newer Food Packaging Methods

Interesting and practical packaging materials are the so-called *edible coatings.* Almost 100 patents and scientific papers have been granted/published about edible coatings for the past decade. The ingredients are edible polymers of carbohydrates and fatty acids or waxes. Incorporation of antimicrobial agents will retard microbial growth. An example is chitosan coatings on fruits, which induces the production of chitonase, a natural anti-fungal agent.[21]

Preformed carton packaging is sterilized by using hydrogen peroxide alone or in combination with ultraviolet (UV) germicidal lamps. The sterilization process disrupts DNA of both spores and vegetative cells of pathogens. Ultraviolet laser irradiation on food carton surfaces also prevents spore formation. This process needs further evaluation as an effective sterilization method for different food products.[24]

Aseptic packaging is a method of placing a sterilized food product in a sterilized package. Modified atmosphere packaging (MAP) is another current technique that is widely accepted. The gases (e.g., carbon dioxide) added in the package replace oxygen, thereby retarding chemical, physical and microbial changes in the food. There is no need to store in the extreme cold temperatures of a freezer or in the extreme heat of canning, thus preserving flavor and nutrients.[11]

4.0 USE OF CHEMICAL PRESERVATIVES

Approved chemical preservatives have been discussed in Chapter 7, "Control of Chemical Hazards." The search for safer and effective additives to prolong the shelf life of food products is continuous. The aim of preserving nutrients, color, flavor and freshness, and at the same time prevent or retard microbial growth that spoils food or causes disease, is indeed a challenge to food technologists and biological scientists.

A recent cheese preservative, called nisin, has been highly effective in killing bacteria without any toxicity results to humans. However, it affects only gram positive bacteria, thus research is ongoing to overcome this limitation.[25] Other antibiotics, as food preservatives, have very limited use because of a principal concern about the development of resistant strains. An antifungal (natamycin or primaricin) is occasionally used in dairy products.

5.0 REGULATIONS RELATED TO NEWER FOOD TECHNOLOGY[1,2,11,12]

Genetically modified foods (GMFs) pose the same types of inherent risks to human health as conventional foods, such as the presence of allergens, anti-nutrients, toxins, etc. Before marketing GMFs, company scientists evaluate any heightened risks compared to conventional counterparts, which will then need proper labeling. The US FDA is in charge of checking on proper labels. An example is a GM rice variety said to contain beta-carotene, which is an improvement of nutrient value compared to conventional rice.

The FDA, USDA, and EPA are all involved in the regulation of plant biotechnology. Food labeled "organic" could not be grown from genetically engineered seeds. Current information on labeling in the USA can be found at the FDA website: http://vm.cfsan.fda.gov/list.

In the European Union, all GM foods must be labeled. International organizations also establish systems to assure the safety of foods derived from biotechnology. Examples are FAO, WHO, ILSI (International Life Sciences Institute), and OECD (Organization for Economic Cooperation and Development).

Other nations have their national and regional governmental agencies to evaluate the safety of processed foods and their labeling. Some countries, unfortunately, have limited resources to advance in food technology and what may be new or modern methods in the developing countries may take years before they find application in the developing countries.[26]

6.0 PRACTICAL GUIDELINES TO CONSUMERS

1. BE INFORMED

As post-harvest food technology becomes more complex, there will be a continued need to know the method, benefits and risks, etc. about newer techniques in food technology. If the GMF is already in the market, get reliable information about it before deciding whether to buy and try for the first time.

2. OBSERVE AT ALL TIMES HYGIENIC PRACTICES AND SAFETY MEASURES IN HANDLING FOOD AND WATER.

At any point of the food chain or food flow (see Appendix B), every person has to be vigilant in preventing food spoilage and/or avoiding diseases. Modern biotechnology and newer preservation methods are instrumental but not substitutes for day-to-day sanitary practices and safe food handling.

3. KEEP IN MIND THAT: **WHEN IN DOUBT, THROW IT OUT.**

REVIEW QUESTIONS

A. Define the following key terms (see text and the Glossary).
   1. Biotechnology

2. Genetic engineering
3. Irradiation
4. High Pressure Processing (HPP)
5. Probiotics
6. Modified Atmosphere Packaging (MAP)

B. What are the different methods of pasteurization?

C. Your mother is afraid to eat foods that have been irradiated. What will you do or say?

D. The farmers in a local rural area are against the planting of genetically modified crops. As an agricultural extension professional, discuss your plan of action.

E. Besides chemical additives, what are non-chemical ways of preserving foods?

F. Cite some modern uses of beneficial bacteria and enzymes.

G. What are G.M.F.s?

REFERENCES

1. American Dietetic Association (ADA). *Biotechnology Resource Kit.* ADA Editorial Board. Chicago, ADA, 2000.
2. Mackey, M., and Santerre C. R. Biotechnology and our food supply. *Nutrition Today, 35*(102), July 2000.
3. Toor, J. D. *Genetic Engineering: Opposing Viewpoints.* San Diego, Greenhaven Press, 2001.
4. McConnell, K. Biotechnology promises to boost poor countries' incomes, *Biotechnology: Global Issues,* June 12, 2002.
5. Council for Biotechnology Information. New study shows biotech crops boost farm income, reduce spraying. Available at www.whybiotech.com. Accessed June 5, 2002
6. McConnell, K., Biotechnology promises to boost poor countries' incomes: biotech meeting during food summit. Available at www.usinfo.state.gov/topical/global/biotech/02061201/htm. Accessed June 5, 2002.
7. US Food and Drug Administration. Are bioengineered foods safe? *FDA Consumer* January–February 2000.
8. The American Dietetic Association. Agricultural biotechnology–an important food production tool. *J Am Diet Assoc Foundation.* Nutrition fact sheet. 2000.
9. Sizer, F., and Whitney E. *Nutrition: Concepts and Controversies.* 8th ed. Belmont, California, Wadsworth, 2000.
10. Hubbert, W. T., Hagstad, H. V., Spangler, E., Hinton, M. H., and Hughes, K. L. *Food Safety and Quality Assurance.* 2nd ed. Ames, Iowa State University Press. 1996.
11. Grosvenor, M. B., and Smolin, L. A. *Nutrition from Science to Life.* Fort Worth, Harcourt College, 2002.
12. Insel, P., Turner, R., and Ross, D. *Nutrition.* Boston, Jones & Bartlett, 2001.
13. Latta, S. L. *Food Poisoning and Foodborne Diseases.* Berkeley Heights, N.J., Enslow, 1999.
14. ADA. Position of the American Dietetic Association: food irradiation. *J Am Diet Assoc 100*(2) 246, February 2000.
15. Anon. Effects of HPP on foodborne pathogens. *Nutrition Research Newsletter 20:5,* February 2001.
16. FDA. High-pressure processing (HPP) Food Safety Initiative, Available at: www.vm.cfsan.fda.gov/[sim]dms/fs-toc.html. Accessed June 20, 2002.
17. The American Dietetic Association. Improving food safety with electronic pasteurization. *J Am Diet Assoc Foundation.* Nutrition fact sheet. 2000.
18. Milk Safety Consortium. Developing UHT/ESL guidelines. *Dairy Foods, 101*(9): September 2000.
19. McCullum, C. Food biotechnology in the new millennium. *J. Am Diet Assoc 100*(11) 1311, November 2000.
20. Stephenson, J. Fighting flora with flora: FDA approves on anti-Salmonella spray for chickens. *JAMA 279:*1152, 1998.
21. Schmidl, M. A., and Labusa, T. P. *Essentials of Functional Foods.* New York, Kluwer Academic, 2000.

22. FAO/WHO. *Guidelines for the Evaluation of Probiotics in Food.* Report of a joint FAO/WHO working group on drafting guidelines for the evaluation of probiotics in foods. Presented in London Ontario, Canada, May 2, 2002.
23. Hoolihan, L. K. Prophylactic and therapeutic uses of probiotics: a review. *J Am Diet Assoc 101*(2):240, 2001.
24. Anon. Laser irradiation prevents spores on food carton surfaces. *Nutrition Research Newsletter, 19*:13, July 2001.
25. ADA. Can a cheese preservative protect against "superbugs"? *J Am Diet Assoc. 100*(2):204, 2000.
26. Cohn, J. P. The international flow of food. *FDA Consumer 35*(1):25, 2001.
27. Greenberg, R. *Irradiated Foods.* 4th ed. New York, American Council on Science and Health. 2000.
28. Shea, K. M. Technical report: Irradiation of food. *Pediatrics 106*:6, 505. December 2000.
29. Abdullah, A. *Food Safety and the Consumer: Household Perspective.* Presented at the Food Safety Research and Development Proceedings, Bangkok, May 2001. Laguna, RP, SEAMEO SEARCA.
30. Union of Concerned Scientists. Available at www.ucsusa.org/agriculture/gen.market.html. Accessed July 1, 2002.
31. Biotechnology Industry Organization, Available at www.bio.org. Accessed July 1, 2002.
32. ISAAA Briefs, No. 12-1999 BIO Available at www.bio.org/food&ag/1999Acreage.html. Accessed July 1, 2002.

Chapter 12

FOOD AND WATER SAFETY STANDARDS

1.0 VALUE OF STANDARDS FOR CONSUMERS AND THE FOOD INDUSTRY

1.1 Standards for the Food

Food standards are the specifications that are set either by the company or the standard-setting body of the country for a product. The standards guide the buyer and the seller in the trade. Standards provide an easy means of communication among all those in the food chain and can make satisfactory transactions provided there is a common understanding of the standards and that there is agreement of all parties concerned.

In food service, standards are set for commodities being used for different recipes. In food processing, standards are also needed for the incoming raw materials. Then as we go down the food chain, standards are also set for the processing parameters, which form the parts of the in process quality control system. There are likewise standards for the finished product. In today's industry, most of the stakeholders appreciate the fact that quality is not a matter of end or finished product inspection but quality starts from raw material, goes through the process, and then the finished product. Standards or specifications are necessary in each of these steps.

1.2 Standards for Facilities, Equipment, and Utensils

Standard setting bodies also prepare standards on the facilities, equipment and utensils. The National Sanitary Foundation International (NSF) has published standards for food equipment, commercial type dishwashing, commercial cooking rethermalization and powered hot food holding and transport equipment water heater, hot water supply boilers, and heat recovery equipment, dispensing freezers, etc. It would do well for companies to avail of these standards particularly in their planning, upgrading and renovation periods. It will help them to have the best buy for their money, and help ensure the safety and quality of their product and consequently the health and satisfaction of their customers.

1.3 Other Standards That Are Needed for Food and Water Safety

Environmental standards also need to be set, adopted, and complied with. These standards are discussed in the chapter on environmental considerations (Chapter 10).

2.0 TYPES OF STANDARDS

2.1 Voluntary Standards

Companies or groups of companies may set standards that members are expected to comply with. The classification could be by commodities i.e., companies dealing with meat, poultry, fruits and vegetables, spices, coffee, etc. The grouping could also be based on geographical proximity, i.e., companies in a certain geographical location.

It could be by ethnic group. What is important in the setting of voluntary standards is that the members all agree on the details of the standards and all parties involved on their own volition abide by these standards. There are many successful models exemplifying that standards can be beneficial for the consumers as well as the producers and all the other auxiliary agencies servicing the particular industry or sector of the industry.

2.2 Mandatory Standards Set by Regulatory Agencies

The regulatory agencies in the country set, circulate, and monitor the compliance to mandatory standards. Mandatory standards may be community-wide or statewide, or nationwide.

3.0 INTERNATIONAL STANDARD SETTING

Many international organizations have made standard setting and implementation their main responsibility. In fact, a partnership of the World Health Organization and the Food and Agriculture Organization of the United Nations has given birth to the Codex Alimentarius Commission. Also, the World Trade Organization has come up with its own set of standards to ensure adapted and suitable guidelines for the global trade of food and water supplies.

3.1 The Codex Alimentarius Commission

The establishment of the Codex Alimentarius Commission occurred in 1961. It is the body tasked to develop a food code. The two-fold agenda of Codex are protection of consumer health and fair practices in trade.[1]

The Codex Alimentarius Commission is presently composed of 163 member countries throughout the world. These member countries appoint official representatives to different committees to meet and set standards that are then distributed to the Members for compliance. These committees meet all through the year in order to deliberate on standards. In the last few years, the direction has been for the standards to be more binding such that once adopted by the Commission can be considered binding in litigations and arguments as discussed in the World Trade Organization (WTO). The Codex Alimentarius Commission through Food Agriculture Organization (FAO) and World Trade Organization (WTO) has revitalized scientific and technological researches and discussion related to food thus increasing food safety awareness and related issues. The Codex Alimentarius is composed of 237 Food Standards for commodities, 41 Codes of hygienic or technological practice, 185 Pesticides evaluated, 3, 274 Limits for pesticide residues, 25 Guidelines for contaminants, 1,005 Food additives evaluated, and 54 Veterinary drugs evaluated. The Codex Alimentarius has always been science-based. The standards are product of works of experts and specialists in a wide range of disciplines to ensure that it passes the strictest scientific scrutiny.[1]

The procedural manual on the elaboration procedures of Codex standards is in three parts. Part I discusses the uniform procedures for the elaboration of the code standards and related texts, and has eight steps:

1. The Commission decides to elaborate a worldwide Codex Standard, taking into account the "Criteria for the Establishment of Work Priorities". It also decides which subsidiary body or other body should undertake the work.
2. The Secretariat arranges for the preparation of a proposed draft standard.
3. The proposed draft standard is sent to Members of the Commission and interested international organizations for comments.
4. The Secretariat sends the comments to the subsidiary body or other bodies concerned.
5. The proposed draft standard is submitted to the Commission or to the Executive Committee. Comments and outcome of debates and proposed

amendments are considered before the proposed draft standard is adopted or amended to come up with a draft standard.

6. The Secretariat sends the draft standard to all Members and interested international organizations for comments.
7. The Secretariat sends the comments to the subsidiary body or other bodies concerned, which can amend the draft standard.
8. The Secretariat then submits the draft standard to the Commission including any written proposals received from Members and interested international organizations for amendments prior to its adoption as a Codex standard.

Part II focuses on a uniform accelerated procedure for the elaboration of Codex standards and related texts. It consists of five steps. The first step involves the Executive Committee, or any subsidiary body, that will identify the standards that will be the subject of an accelerated elaboration process. Steps 2 to 5 are similar to steps 2 to 5 of Part I.

Part III is about the subsequent procedures concerning publication and acceptance of Codex Standards. All Member States and Associate Members of FAO and/or WHO, and concerned international organizations, are given copies of the Codex standard. The status on the use of the standard, proposed measures, or whether it is accepted or not by both Commission Members and non-Members are reported to the Secretariat. Such information is also published as part of the Codex Alimentarius.[1]

3.2 International Plant Protection Convention (IPPC)

The International Plant Protection (IPPC) is a multilateral treaty deposited with the Director-General of the Food and Agriculture Organization of the United Nations (FAO) and administered through the IPPC Secretariat located in FAO's Plant Protection Service. There are currently 117 governments contracting parties to IPPC.[3]

The main reason for the establishment of IPPC is to secure common and effective action to prevent the spread and introduction of pests of plants and plant products and to promote measures for their control. The Convention provides a framework and forum for international cooperation, harmonization and technical exchange in collaboration with regional and national plant protection organizations (RPPOs and NPPOs). It is a recognized organization by the World Trade Organization in the Agreement on the Application of Sanitary and Phytosanitary Measures (the WTO-SPS Agreement) as the source for international standards for the phytosanitary measures (ISPMs) affecting trade. The IPPC was founded in 1952 and was amended in 1979 and 1997.[3]

The 1997 revision of IPPC was done to update the Convention on contemporary phytosanitary concepts and the role of the IPPC in relation to the Uruguay Round Agreements of the World Trade Organization, particularly the Agreement on the Application of Sanitary and Phytosanitary Measures (the SPS Agreement). The IPPC was identified by the SPS Agreement as the organization providing international standards for measures implemented by governments to protect their plant resources from harmful pests.[3]

The IPPC focuses on international cooperation. Its work is not limited only to protection of cultivated plants or direct damage from pests. It also focuses on the protection of cultivated and natural flora as well as plant products, and includes both direct and indirect damage by pests.[3]

The IPPC is administered through the Plant Protection Service in FAO and imple-

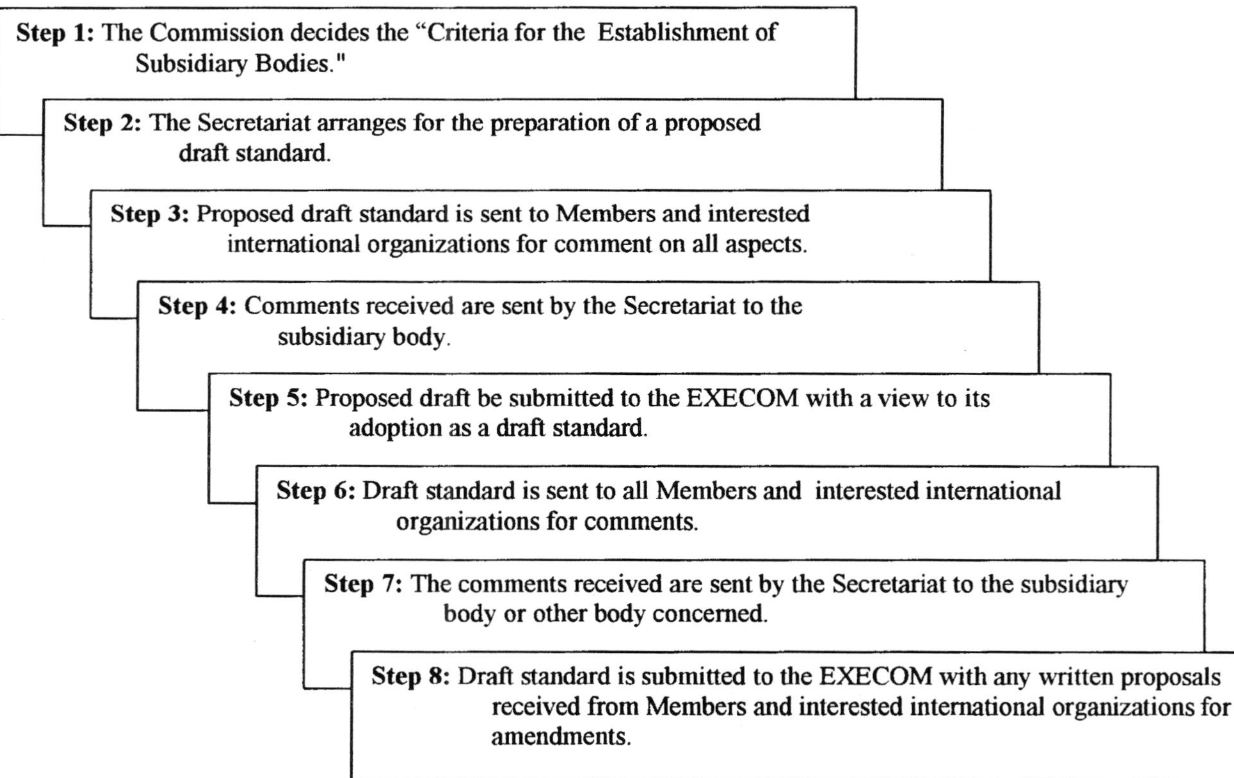

Step 1: The Commission decides the "Criteria for the Establishment of Subsidiary Bodies."
Step 2: The Secretariat arranges for the preparation of a proposed draft standard.
Step 3: Proposed draft standard is sent to Members and interested international organizations for comment on all aspects.
Step 4: Comments received are sent by the Secretariat to the subsidiary body.
Step 5: Proposed draft be submitted to the EXECOM with a view to its adoption as a draft standard.
Step 6: Draft standard is sent to all Members and interested international organizations for comments.
Step 7: The comments received are sent by the Secretariat to the subsidiary body or other body concerned.
Step 8: Draft standard is submitted to the EXECOM with any written proposals received from Members and interested international organizations for amendments.

Figure 12.1. Uniform Procedure for the Elaboration of Codex Standards and Related Tests

mented primarily through the cooperation of regional and national plant protection organizations. FAO established a Secretariat in 1992 in recognition of the expectation for standard setting associated with the WTO-SPS Agreement. The activities of the Secretariat are to establish international standards for phytosanitary measures, to provide information required by the IPPC and to facilitate information exchange between contracting parties, and to provide technical assistance through FAO and cooperation with governments. The staff of the IPPC Secretariat is composed of the Secretary, a Coordinator, a Plant Quarantine Officer, a Plant Pathologist, and an Information Officer. The process for developing International Standards for phytosanitary measures in IPPC are divided into three stages: the draft stage, consultation stage, and the approval stage.[4]

In the draft stage, suggestions to develop International Standard for Phytosanitary Measures (ISPM) coming from different places, individual, industry, the NPPO, and the RPPO are solicited then are established by priorities by the Commission on Phytosanitary Measures in consultation with the Secretariat. NPPOs or RPPOs to the Secretariat of the IPPC submits draft standards. The drafts are reviewed and edited and referred to the CEPM. The IPPC may also form international Working Group or enlist experts to help draft a standard. The CEPM considers the proposals and recommends action. It may also suggest development of new standards and guidelines to the Secretariat. After the consultation, the Secretariat arranges a technical working group or a consultant to modify draft standards if needed. The CEPM continues to review progress on the draft standard and recommends to the IPPC Secretariat the timing of submissions to Governments for technical comments.[5]

During the consultation stage, individual member countries and RPPOs review and comment on the draft. The CEPM determine the nature and extent of changes to be made in drafts based on comments from consultation. If CEPM accepts the redrafted standard, it is submitted to the Commission. If the consideration of standard made by the Commission is not relevant, the final text may be published.[5]

The last stage is the approval stage. It is here where the endorsement of the Commission results in final adoption of an International Standard for Phytosanitary Measures (ISPM). FAO publishes and distributes the Standard.[5]

3.3 Office International Des Epizooties (OIE)

The Office International Des Epizooties is an intergovernmental organization. It was created by the International Agreement of 25 January 1924, signed by 28 countries. As of May 2001, there are 158 Member Countries of OIE. Its headquarters is located in Paris, France.[6]

The missions of OIE are to guarantee the transparency of animal disease status worldwide; to collect, analyze and disseminate veterinary scientific information to provide expertise and promote international solidarity for the control of animal diseases; and to guarantee the sanitary safety of world trade by developing sanitary rules for international trade in animals and animal products.[6]

The Office is under the authority and control of an International Committee, which consists of Delegates, appointed by the Governments of Member Countries. The International Committee is the highest authority of the OIE. It is composed of all the Dele-

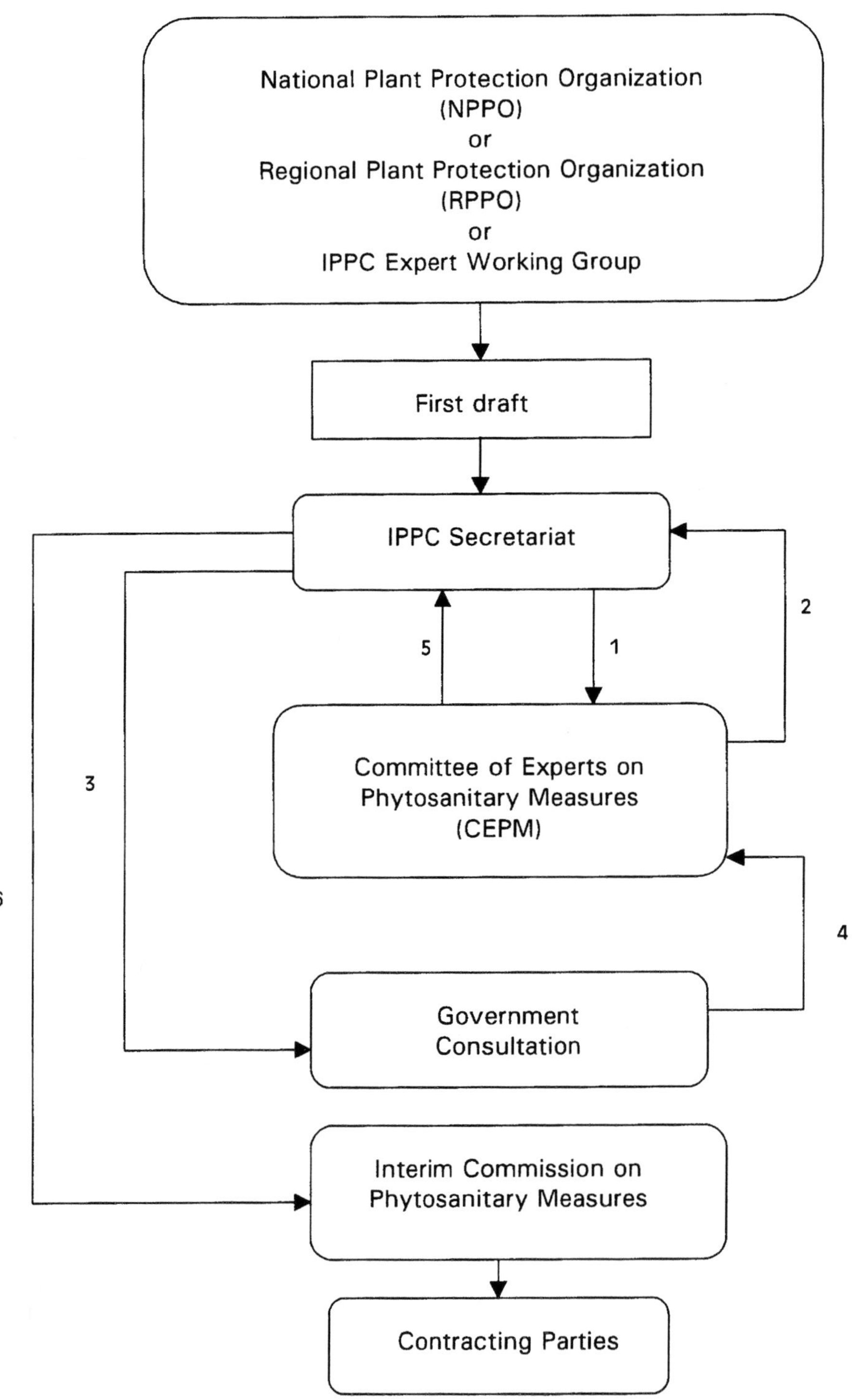

Figure 12.2. Process for Developing International Standards for Phytosanitary Measures (ISPMS)

gates and meets at least once a year. The Administrative Commission prepares the work of the International Committee.[6]

The OIE is managed by a Central Bureau located in Paris under the responsibility of a Director General elected by the International Committee. The Central Bureau implements the resolutions passed by the International Committee and developed with the support of elected Commissions, which are the Administrative Commission, Regional Commissions, and Specialist Technical Commissions.[7]

The SPS Agreement refers to the standards, guidelines, and recommendations of OIE for animal health and zoonoses. The OIE has two health codes and two manuals that contain standards, guidelines, and recommendations to prevent the introduction of infectious agents pathogenic to animals and humans into the importing country during trade in animals, animal genetic material and animal products. The health codes are *International Animal Health Code* (for mammals, birds and bees) and *Aquatic Animal Health Code.* The manuals are *Manual of Standards for Diagnostic Tests and Vaccines* and *Diagnostic Manual for Aquatic Animal Diseases.* Both codes and manuals provide a uniform approach to the diagnosis of OIE-listed diseases and other diseases of importance to international trade. This enables compliance of requirements for health certification in relation to trade in animals and animal products. The manuals provide wide internationally agreed essential scientific and technical information that is correlative with the Codes' trade provisions.[8]

The development of new standards and the revision of current standards in the OIE Codes and manuals are assigned to one of the Specialist Commissions. The Specialist Commissions are composed of members experienced in veterinary science and regulatory issues. They are elected by the OIE International Committee and taken from all OIE regions.[8]

The International Committee initially circulates a draft standard to all Member Countries for comments and preliminary discussion. Afterward, the Specialist Commission revises the draft, taking into consideration the comments received. The revised draft is submitted for adoption at the next meeting of the International Committee. Once formally adopted, the standard is made available for implementation by Member Countries. The standards published in Codes and Manuals are developed and revised through formal consultation and are the outcome of consensus among experts from OIE Member Countries.[8]

3.4 World Trade Organization (WTO)

The World Trade Organization is the only international organization that deals with global rules of trade between nations. Its main function is to facilitate trade among member countries harmoniously and orderly.[9]

The WTO is located in Geneva, Switzerland and was established January 1, 1995. It was created by the Uruguay Round negotiations (1986–94). The WTO has more than 140 members. There are over 30 countries negotiating membership.[10]

The task of the WTO are to administer trade agreements, act as a forum for trade negotiations, settle trade disputes, review national trade policies, assist developing countries in trade policy issues through technical assistance and training programs, and to cooperate with other international organizations.[11]

The decision-making is the responsibility of all members through consensus. The WTO's agreements have been ratified in all members' legislature.[11]

The highest level of decision-making body of WTO is the Ministerial Conference, which meets at least once every two years.[11]

The next lower level is the General Council. It is normally composed of ambassadors and heads of delegation in Geneva, but sometimes representatives come from members' capitals. They meet several times a year in the Geneva headquarters. The General Council works also as Trade Policy Review Body and the Dispute Settlement Body.[11]

The next levels to the General Council are the Goods Council, Services Council, and Intellectual Property (TRIPS) Council. They report to the General Council.[11]

There are numerous specialized committees, working groups, and working parties that deal with individual agreements and other areas such as environment, development, membership applications and regional trade agreements.[11]

The WTO Secretariat is based in Geneva and has an estimated staff of 550 and is headed by a director-general. The main tasks of the Secretariat are to supply technical support for the many councils and committees and the ministerial conferences, to provide technical assistance for developing countries, to analyze world trade, and to explain WTO affairs to the public and media. The Secretariat also grants some forms of legal assistance in the argument settlement process and advises governments hoping to become members of the WTO.[11]

3.5 International Organization for Standards (ISO)

The International Organization for Standards (ISO) is a worldwide federation of national standards bodies from some 140 countries with each country represented. It is a non-governmental organization founded in 1947.[12]

The ISO's mission is to promote the development of standardization and related activities in the world with a view to facilitating the international exchange of goods and services, and to developing cooperation in the spheres of intellectual, scientific, technological and economic activity.[12]

ISO is made up of members which, are divided into three categories:

3.5.1 Member Body of ISO

The national body "most representative of standardization in its country." Therefore, only one body in each country may be admitted to membership of ISO. The responsibilities of a member body is to inform potentially interested parties in their country of relevant international standardization opportunities and initiatives, to ensure that a concerted view of the country's interests is presented during international negotiations leading to standards agreements, and to provide their country's share of financial support for the central operations of ISO, through payment of membership dues.

3.5.2 Correspondent Member

An organization in a country that does not yet have a fully developed national standards activity. Correspondent members do not take an active part in the technical and policy development work but are entitled to be kept fully informed about the work of interest to them.

3.5.3 Subscriber Member

Countries with very small economies. Subscriber members pay reduced membership fees that nonetheless allow them to maintain contact with international standardization.[13]

ISO standards are developed according to the following principles:

1. Consensus–the opinions of all stakeholders are taken into account: manufacturers, vendors and users, consumer groups, testing laboratories, governments, engineering professions and research organizations.
2. Industry-wide–global solutions to satisfy industries and customers worldwide.
3. Voluntary–International standardization is voluntary because it is market-driven.

The development process of ISO standards is divided into three main phases. The first phase involves definition of the technical scope of the future standard. An industry communicates the need for a standard to a national member. The national member proposes the new work item to ISO. This phase is generally carried out in working groups, which comprise technical experts from countries interested in the subject matter.[14]

The second phase follows after an agreement has been reached on the technical aspects to be covered in the standard. It is in this phase where countries negotiate the detailed specifications within the standard. This is the consensus-building phase. The final phase is composed of formal approval of the resulting draft International Standard. After which the agreed text is published as an ISO International Standard. The acceptance criteria stipulate approval by two-thirds of the ISO members that have participated actively in the standards development process, and approval by 75 percent of all members that vote.[14]

ISO standards are regularly reviewed and undergo revision if needed. A standard undergoes revision when it is rendered outdated. Factors considered are technological evolution, new methods and materials, new quality and safety requirements. As a general rule, ISO standards are reviewed at intervals of not more than five years.[14]

Currently, ISO has already set some 12,000 International Standards, more than 300,000 pages in English and French.[14]

4.0 STANDARDS WITHIN A COMPANY

Each company has standards for its products. Ideally companies have standards for the raw materials to which their suppliers have to adhere. There are then in-process standards that the quality control officers monitor closely throughout the process. At the end, the finished product standards are also to be met before the goods are released for distribution and consumption. The standard operating procedures manual of a company then become very valuable information that help the companies meet consumer specifications over the years in a consistent manner.

5.0 STANDARDS WITHIN A COUNTRY

5.1 Australia and New Zealand

The food regulation operating in Australia and New Zealand is Australia New Zealand Food Authority Act 1991 (ANZFA). The Act grants a focal point for cooperation between the governments, industry and the community to establish and maintain uniform food regulation in Australia and New Zealand. As a result of an Inter-Government Agreement between the Commonwealth of Australia and the States and Territories, Australia and New Zealand are working towards the establishment of harmonized food standards.[15]

The management and decision-making body of ANZFA is composed of the Ministerial Council, ANZFA Board, ANZFA's Consultation Processes, the ANZFA Advisory Committee (ANZFAAC), Senior Food Officers (SFOs), Food Regulation Standing Committee (FRSC), Development and Implementation Sub Committee (DISC), Technical Advisory Group (TAG). The task of the Ministerial Council is to set food policy and eventually approve, reject, amend or seek a review of food standards developed by ANZFA. They have position in the Australia New Zealand Food Standards Council (ANZFSC) and are from all nine Australian jurisdictions and New Zealand. The ANZFA Board makes recommendations to ANZFSC Ministers on changes to food standards in Australia and New Zealand. Board members are appointed because of their expertise in different fields. The ANZFAAC advises the ANZFA Board on matters related to food standards referred by ANZFA and other jurisdictions. Senior Food Officers are members of a technical working group that provides advice on food issues and assists in promoting the Australia New Zealand Food Standards Code. The FRSC provides advice to the Ministerial Council on the development policy relating to the regulation of food. The DISC is responsible for developing implementation policy and supervises the development and implementation of jurisdictions to enforce food regulation and standards. TAG provides technical advice to assist in the development of food standards and assistance in coordinating, surveillance and interpretation and enforcement of the Food Standards Code.[15]

The Food Standards of ANZFA includes Food Standards User Guides to help manufacturers, and retailers, Nutrition Panel Calculator (NPC) to provide manufacturers the ability to readily calculate the average nutrient content of their food products, as required under Standard 1.2.8–Nutrition Information Requirements. ANZFA also has developed a means to make the Food Standards easily accessible to the public. This is through the Food Standards Advice line (advice@anzfa.gov.au).[16]

5.2 Canada

Protecting the safety of the food system involves much more than simply inspecting food products and the premises where they are produced. The food system extends from inputs, such as seed and fertilizer, through crops and livestock, to the food products that fill our shopping carts. The Canadian Food Inspection Agency (CFIA) is mandated to regulate several stages of this food continuum with an increasing number of new and diverse inputs and products from around the world. However, it must be noted that the Agency does not have sole responsibility in these areas. The primary responsibility for meeting federal standards and requirements rests with producers, processors and suppliers. While it is the CFIA's responsibility to inspect and enforce compliance with federal acts and regulations, the Agency works with these groups to take preventative measures to reduce food safety risks.[17]

The agency's activities are focused along the three business lines: Food Safety, Animal Health, and Plant Protection.[17]

The CFIA's foremost responsibility is to enhance the safety of Canada's food and protect the health of Canadian consumers. This responsibility is shared with Health Canada and other levels of government and industry. Food Safety Programs included are for Meat Hygiene, Fish and Seafood, Egg, Dairy, Honey, Fresh Fruit and Vegetables, and Processed Products.[17]

CFIA is responsible for monitoring compliance with federal legislation by those businesses engaged in the production and distribution of federally regulated food and food products. The CFIA accomplishes this objective through: working with industry to build better science-based management practices, inspects and tests to assess compliance with acts and regulations, and takes enforcement actions to achieve compliance, including seizing, removing and recalling products or, when necessary, resorting to legal action including levying administrative penalties and prosecution.[17]

In compliance with federal acts, regulations and standards, CFIA's day-to-day activities involve verifying that domestic and imported food products are compliant with federal acts, regulations and standards.[17]

5.3 United States

The United States has one of the world's safest food supplies. This is due to the combined efforts to monitor food production at every level-locally, statewide and nationally.[18]

Food inspectors, microbiologists, epidemiologists, and other food scientists working for city and county health departments, state public health agencies, and different federal departments and agencies do continuous monitoring. The local, state, and national laws, guidelines, and other directives assigned their defined duties. Some monitor only one kind of food and others work strictly with a specified geographical location while others are responsible for only one type of food establishment. These make up the US food safety team.[18]

The Food Safety Initiative of US began during the Clinton's administration in 1997 to strengthen the efforts of all members of the nation's food safety team against foodborne illness, which affects between 6.5 million and 33 million Americans every year. In May 1998, the Department of Health and Human Services (including FDA), the US Department of Agriculture, and the Environmental Protection Agency signed a memorandum of understanding to create a Food Outbreak Response Coordinating Group (FORC-G). The tasks of the new group are to increase coordination and communication among federal, state and local food safety agencies, guide efficient use of resources and expertise during an outbreak, and prepare for new and emerging threats to the US food supply.[18]

Table 12.1 shows the agencies part of the US food safety lineup. The following agencies also work with other government agencies, such as Consumer Product Safety Commission, the FBI, the Department of Transportation, and the US Postal Service.

5.4 France

The French Food Safety Agency is tasked to evaluate health and nutrition risks related to food products intended for human and animal consumption in France. It was created by the Law of 1 July 1998, the strengthening of health safety in France. Agence Francaise De Securite Sanitaire Des Aliments (AFFSA) or French Food Safety Agency was established in April 1999 under the supervision of the Ministers of Health, Agriculture and Consumer Affairs.[19]

AFFSA is a public organization that monitors and evaluates risks within the framework of food safety in France. The Agency gives opinions, drafts recommendations, conducts research, provides expertise with the framework of technical and scientific support and is responsible for education and information activities.

The Agency is made up of Board of Directors, president and 24 members from representatives of the government, consumer organizations, the Agency staff and scientists.[19]

Table 12.1
THE UNITED STATES FOOD SAFETY TEAM

Agency	*Scope of Work*	*Food Safety Role*
I. **US Department of Health and Human Services:**		
1. Food and Drug Administration	• All domestic and imported food sold in interstate commerce, including shell eggs, but not meat and poultry • Bottled water • Wine beverages with less than 7% alcohol	Enforces food safety laws governing domestic and imported food, except meat and poultry, by: • Inspecting food production establishments & food warehouses & collecting & analyzing samples for physical, chemical & microbial contamination • Reviewing safety of food & color additives before marketing • Reviewing animal drugs for safety to animals that receive them & humans who eat food produced from the animals • Monitoring safety of animal feeds used in food-producing animals • Developing model codes & ordinances, guidelines, interpretations & working with states to implement them in regulating milk & shellfish & retail food establishments • Establishing good food manufacturing practices & other production standards • Working with foreign governments to ensure safety of certain imported food products • Requesting manufacturers to recall unsafe food products & monitoring those recalls • Taking appropriate enforcement actions • Conducting research on food safety • Educating industry & consumers on safe food handling practices
2. Centers for Disease Control and Prevention	• All foods	• Investigates with local, state & other federal official sources of foodborne disease outbreaks • Maintains a nationwide system of foodborne disease surveillance • Develops & advocates public health policies to prevent foodborne diseases

		• Conducts research to help prevent foodborne diseases • Conducts research to help prevent foodborne illness • Trains local & state food safety personnel
II. U.S. Department of Agriculture: 1. Food Safety & Inspection Service	• Domestic & imported meat & poultry & related products, such as meat- or poultry-containing stews, pizzas & frozen foods • Processed egg products	Enforces food safety laws governing domestic & imported meat & poultry products by: • Inspecting food animals for diseases before & after slaughter • Inspecting meat & poultry slaughter & processing plants • With USDA's Agricultural Marketing Service, monitoring & inspecting processed egg products • Collecting & analyzing samples of food products for microbial & chemical contaminants & infectious & toxic agents • Collecting & analyzing samples of food products for microbial & chemical contaminants & infectious & toxic agents • Establishing production standards for use of food additives & other ingredients in preparing & packaging meat & poultry products, plant sanitation, thermal processing, & other processes • Making sure all foreign meat & poultry processing plants exporting to the United States meet U.S. standards • Seeking voluntary recalls by meat & poultry processors of unsafe products • Sponsoring research on meat & poultry safety • Educating industry & consumers on safe food-handling practices

Continued on next page

Table 12.1–*Continued*

Agency	*Scope of Work*	*Food Safety Role*
2. Cooperative State Research, Education, & Extension Service	• All domestic foods, some imported	• With U.S. colleges & universities, develops research & education programs on food safety for farmers & consumers
3. National Agricultural Library–USDA/FDA Foodborne Illness Education Information Center	• All foods	• Maintains a database of computer software, audiovisuals, posters, games, teacher's guides & other educational materials on preventing foodborne illness • Helps educators, food service trainers & consumers locate educational materials on preventing foodborne illness
III. US Environmental Protection Agency	• Drinking water	• Food made from plants, seafood, meat and poultry • Establishes safe drinking water standards • Regulates toxic substances & wastes to prevent their entry into the environment & food chain • Assists states in monitoring quality of drinking water & finding ways to prevent contamination of drinking water • Determines safety of new pesticides, sets tolerance levels for pesticide residues in foods, publishes directions on the safe use of pesticides
IV. US Department of Commerce:		
1. National Oceanic & Atmospheric Administration	• Fish & seafood products	• Through its free-for-service Seafood Inspection Program, inspects & certifies fishing vessels, seafood processing plants, & retail facilities for federal sanitation standards
V. U.S. Department of the Treasury:		
1. Bureau of Alcohol, Tobacco & Firearms	• Alcoholic beverages except wine beverages containing less than 7% alcohol	• Enforces food safety laws governing production & distribution of alcoholic beverages • Investigates cases of adulterated alcoholic products, sometimes with help from FDA
2. US Customs Service	• Imported foods	• Works with federal regulatory agencies to ensure that all

		goods entering & exiting the United States do so according to US laws & regulations
VI. U.S. Department of Justice	• All foods	• Prosecutes companies & individuals suspected of violating food safety laws • Through U.S. Marshals Service, seizes unsafe food products not yet in the marketplace, as ordered by courts
VII. Federal Trade Commission	• All foods	• Enforces a variety of laws that protect consumers from unfair, deceptive or fraudulent practices, including deceptive & unsubstantiated advertising
VIII. State & Local Governments	• All foods within their jurisdictions	• Work with FDA & other federal agencies to implement food safety standards for fish, seafood, milk, & other foods produced within state borders • Inspect restaurants, grocery stores, & other retail food establishments, as well as dairy farms & milk processing plants, grain mills, & food manufacturing plants within local jurisdictions • Embargo (stop the sale of) unsafe food products made or distributed within state borders

Adapted from: US Food and Drug Administration FDA Backgrounder. *Food Safety: A Team Approach.* September 24, 1998.

REVIEW QUESTIONS

1. Define important terms (see text and the Glossary):
   a. Standards
   b. Specifications
   c. Mandatory Standards
   d. Consumers
2. What are standards? Why are they important?
3. Which agencies set food standards in your country?
4. Why are Codex Alimentarius standards important?
5. What is the role of the World Trade Organization in setting standards?
6. What is the role of the International Standards Organization? Why are ISO standards important?
7. What steps still need to be done to improve the compliance to standards by local companies?
8. What are the steps for developing Codex standards?
9. Describe the process for developing international standards for phytosanitary measures? How are standards within a company set?

REFERENCES

1. Food and Agriculture Organization and World Health Organization. *Understanding the Codex Alimentarius.* Editorial Group, FAO Information Division, Rome, 1999.
2. Food and Agriculture Organization and World Health Organization. *Codex Alimentarius Commission: Procedural Manual.* 11th ed. Joint FAO/WHO Food Standards Programme, FAO, Rome, 2000.
3. Food and Agriculture Organization. *International Plant Protection Convention.* FAO, Rome.Available at http://www.fao.org. Accessed July 3, 2002.
4. Food and Agriculture Organization. *Process for Developing International Standards for Phytosanitary Measures (ISPMs).* FAO, Rome, February 1995. Available at http://www.fao.org. Accessed July 3, 2002.
5. Food and Agriculture Organization. *The International Plant Protection Convention (IPPC) Secretariat.* FAO, Rome, 24, June 2002. Available at http://www.fao.org. Accessed July 3, 2002.
6. Office International Des Epizooties. *What is OIE?,* Paris, France, 22 April, 2002. Available at http://www.oie.int. Accessed July 4, 2002.
7. Office International Des Epizooties. *The Central Bureau.* Paris, France, 22 April, 2002. Available at http://www.oie.int. Accessed July 4, 2002.
8. Office International Des Epizooties. *OIE International Health Standards,* Paris, France, 22 April 2002. Available at http://www.oie.int. Accessed July 4, 2002.
9. World Trade Organization. *Trading into the Future: The World Trade Organization.* 2nd ed. WTO Information and Media Relations Division, Geneva, Switzerland, February 1998.
10. World Trade Organization. *The WTO in Brief: The Organization. Part 2,* Geneva, Switzerland, March 1999. Available at http://www.wto.org. Accessed June 25, 2002.
11. World Trade Organization. *The WTO.* Available at http://www.wto.org. Accessed June 25, 2002.
12. International Organization for Standardization: *What is ISO?* Last updated: July 17, 2002. Available at http://www.iso.com. Accessed July 3, 2002.
13. International Organization for Standardization. *What Makes Up ISO?* Last updated: July 17, 2002. Available at http://www.iso.com. Accessed July 3, 2002.
14. International Organization for Standardization. *How are ISO Standards Developed?* Last updated: July 17, 2002. Available at http://ww.iso .com. Accessed July 3, 2002.
15. *About ANZFA.* Available at http://www.anzfa.gov.au. Accessed June 26, 2002.
16. *Food Standards.* Available at http://www.anzfa.gov.au. Accessed June 26, 2002.
17. Canadian Food Inspection Agency. *Canadian Food Inspection Agency 2000–2001 Annual*

Report. Ontario, Canada, 26 October 2001. Available at http://www.cfis.gov. Accessed June 26, 2002.

18. US Food and Drug Administration: *Food Safety. A Team Approach.* 4 September 1998. Available at http://www.fda.gov. Accessed July 11, 2002.
19. French Food Safety Agency. *Food Safety: Meeting of Agencies Responsible for Risk Evaluation in the European Union.* Paris, 7–8 December 2000.

Chapter 13

FOOD AND WATER SAFETY IN EMERGENCIES

1.0 THE IMPORTANCE OF PLANNING FOR EMERGENCIES

As the Boys (and Girls) Scouts saying goes, we must always "Be prepared." The benefits from being prepared for emergencies are many. In the first place, it helps in the mental and emotional health of all concerned. It is wise to prepare children particularly and to involve them, depending on their age, to help the family during these crisis periods.

There were 750 worldwide catastrophes in 1999 and 855 in 2000. Fires, floods, earthquakes, and volcanic eruptions are reported over the media and remind us all of the need for preparation for natural and man-made disasters. Emergency preparedness is "a mindset" and "a way of life."[10]

2.0 BIOTERRORISM

Many references are available on bioterrorism in bookstores and on the web. Some forms of bioterrorism of immediate concern from the point of view of availability are stability, deliverability, and lethality, are anthrax, botulism, brucellosis, and cholera (Tables 13.1–13.4).[1,2,3]

2.1 Anthrax

See Table 13.1 on page 216.

2.2 Botulism[2,3]

See Table 13.2 on page 217.

2.3 Cholera

See Table 13.3 on page 218.

2.4 Other Biological Agents

See Table 13.4 on page 218.

3.0 CHEMICAL THREATS

The list of possible chemical agents that might be used by terrorists range from warfare agents to toxic chemicals commonly used in the industry (Table 13.5). Criteria for determining priority chemical agents include:

1. Chemical agents already known to be used as weaponry
2. Availability of chemical agents to potential terrorists
3. Chemical agents likely to cause major morbidity or mortality
4. Potential of agents for causing public pain and social disruption. and
5. Agents that require special action for public health preparedness

Categories of chemical agents include:

Table 13.1
ANTHRAX

Disease cause:	*Bacillus anthracis*
Symptoms:	Fever, malaise, fatigue, cough, chest pain, severe respiratory distress
Incubation period:	1 to 6 days
Transmissibility:	None (except via secretions from cutaneous lesions)
Possible means of transmission:	1. Through a cut, scratch, or abrasions of the skin (cutaneous anthrax) 2. Inhalation of spores (pulmonary anthrax) 3. Eating contaminated insufficiently cooked meat and meat products (gastrointestinal anthrax)
Effective treatment:	Antibiotics: ciprofloxacin, doxycycline, others
Vaccine:	Yes

The following are the protective response strategies:
- Wash hands properly before eating or drinking, after using a bathroom facility, and after contaminating your hand with a cough or a sneeze or any work-related activity.
- Comply with the suggested guidelines distributed by your local agencies regarding how to handle mail and packages.

Sources: Btox Analytical Laboratories, Poster on Biological Warfare Agents, Aerotech Laboratories, 2001.
Tierno, P. M. *Protect Yourself Against Terrorism,* New York, Pocket Books, 2002.
Prescott, L. M., Harley J. P., and Klein, D. A. *Microbiology.* Iowa, Wm C Brown, 1993.

4.0 FAMILY PREPAREDNESS PLAN

There are many types of natural and man-made disasters. It is difficult, of course, to make provisions for all eventualities, however, a family can formulate a basic plan that could be adopted and modified to suit a particular situation. Then it would help to ask concerned neighbors and friends about their own experiences and recommendations in preparing for emergencies. "Forewarned is forearmed."

Every family should be ready for emergencies. Food, water, and electricity may not be available for days or even weeks due to disasters like earthquakes, hurricanes and typhoons. In the last decade, these natural disasters have caught many families and communities unprepared. Many more lives could have been saved were families and communities better prepared. There would have been less emotional cost to the victims as well.[10]

A wealth of information is available in libraries and on the Internet for emergency preparedness. Some time needs to be allotted for the family to be updated on the natural disasters that may occur in the place where they are residing and working.

4.1 Steps in the Family Preparedness Plan[1,2,5,16]

There are usually four steps in a family preparedness plan.

1. Do your homework

- Find out about the following from your local emergency management office or

Table 13.2
BOTULISM

Disease cause:	*Clostridium botulinum* toxin
Symptoms:	Blurred vision, difficulty in swallowing and speaking, muscle weakness, nausea, vomiting, paralysis
Incubation period:	18–72 hours
Transmissibility:	Not transferable from person to person
Treatment:	Botulism antitoxin can stop the disease from worsening but it cannot reverse any paralysis that already has occurred.
Possible means of transmission:	1. Airborne–Released as an aerosol 2. Foodborne–A large number of casualties could result from contamination of a large salad, ready-to-eat short shelf life products such as commercial beverages 3. Waterborne–Toxin cannot survive standard water treatment of chlorination and aerations
Potential targets for bioterrorism:	Salad bars, condiments, uncooked commercial food, beer, wine and bottled water
Vaccine:	Yes

The protective response strategies are as follows:

- Go to a hospital immediately if symptoms of botulism are felt after possible exposure to the toxin. Ask a family member or friend to accompany you.
- Wash thoroughly with soap and water to effectively remove most toxins from skin, clothing and equipment. A mild bleach solution (one part bleach in nine parts water) would effectively inhibit most protein toxins.
- Store enough activated charcoal tablets because these are effective absorbers of almost all toxins, thereby reducing further harm.

Sources: Tierno, P. M. *Protect Yourself Against Terrorism,* New York, Pocket Books, 2002.
Prescott, L. M., Harley J. P., and Klein, D. A. *Microbiology.* Iowa, Wm C Brown, 1993.

Red Cross Chapter before a disaster occurs, be prepared to take notes

- Ask what types of disasters are most likely to happen. Request information on how to prepare for each.
- Learn about your community's warming signals: what they sound like, what you should do when you hear them, and where the family should stay in different kinds of emergencies.
- How should you prepare and respond to each potential disaster?
- Are there any emergency preparedness plans in your workplace?
- What are the important telephone numbers you all need to know during emergencies: the doctors, hospitals, work, school, relatives in town who can serve as outside contacts.

2. Create a disaster plan.

- Find time to meet with your family to discuss the need to be prepared for a disaster.
- Explain clearly and calmly to the children the danger of such emergencies as fire and such natural disasters as

Table 13.3
CHOLERA

Disease cause:	*Vibrio cholerae*
Transmissibility:	Rare
Incubation period:	1–5 days
Symptoms:	"Rice water" stools, diarrhea without abdominal cramps
Treatment:	Rehydration and electrolyte replacement; Antibiotics–doxycycline, ciprofoxacin, erythromycin
Possible means of transmission:	Water supply
Vaccine:	Yes

The protective response strategies are:

Because cholera is a foodborne and waterborne illness, the major threat will most likely be the result of food and water sabotage. Therefore, agencies that safeguard public health and the public itself should be alert in times of possible terrorist attacks.

Compared with other agents, the causative agent of cholera is easier to identify and destroy.

- Simple laboratory tests give fast results, making treatment easier.
- Most germicides effectively kill the organism.
- Proper handwashing easily prevents rare contact transmission.

Sources: Btox Analytical Laboratories, Poster on Biological Warfare Agents, Aerotech Laboratories, 2001.

Tierno, P. M. *Protect Yourself Against Terrorism,* New York, Pocket Books, 2002.

Table 13.4
OTHER BIOLOGICAL AGENTS

Biological agents have been categorized into first, second, and third priority agents. The pathogens that are food and waterborne, in addition to Clostridia and Vibrio, are:

- Salmonella species
- *Shigella dysenteriae*
- *Escherichia coli* (O57:H7)
- *Cryptosporidium parvum*

typhoons, tornadoes, hurricanes, and floods.

- Develop a plan to share responsibilities and a plan that would include ways of ensuring food and water safety.
- Pick two places to meet outside your home in case of a sudden emergency, like a fire and meet outside your neighborhood someplace in case you can't return home.
- Ask an out-of-state friend to be your family contact. After a disaster, it is often easier to call long distance. Other family members must know your contact's phone number.

3. Complete your family's checklist

- Post emergency telephone numbers by phones (fire, police, ambulance, etc.).
- Teach children how and when to call 911 or your local emergency medical services number for emergency help.
- Show each family member how and when to turn off the water, gas, and electricity at the main switches.

Table 13.5
CATEGORIES OF CHEMICAL AGENTS

Nerve agents	Tabun (ethyl N, N-dimethylphosphorandicynadicate)
	Sarin (isopropylethylphophanofluoridate)
	GF (cyclohylmethylphophonofluroridate)
	VX (o-ethyl-{S}-{2-diisopropylethylaminoethyl}-methylphophonothiolate
Blood agents	Hydrogen cyanide
	Cyanogen chloride
Blister agents	Lewisite (an aliphatic arsenic compound, 2- cholorovinyldichloroarsine)
	Nitrogen and sulfur mustards
	Phosgene oxime

- Check if you have adequate insurance coverage.
- Teach each family member to use the fire extinguisher (ABC Type) and show them where it's kept.
- Install smoke detectors on each level of your home, especially near bedrooms.
- Keep flashlights, portable radio and batteries working
- Conduct home hazard hunts and try to solve lessening each particular hazard.
- Stock emergency supplies and assemble a disaster supplies kit.
- Take a Red Cross first aid and CPR class.
- Determine the best escape routes from each of the rooms in your home, preferably two ways out from each room and from your house.
- Find the safe spots in your home for each type of disaster.
- Designate possible places outside the home where the family should stay in different kinds of emergencies, should that be necessary.
- Prepare, distribute, and ask each member of the family to have cue cards as shown in Figure 13.1.

4. Practice and maintain your plan.

At regular scheduled periods during the year, it is good to do the following:

- Test your children's knowledge of the plan every six months.
- Conduct fire and emergency evacuation drills at home, in schools, and in offices.
- Replace stored water every six months and stored food every six months.
- Recheck the numbers in your Family Emergency Directory. It may be a good time to give a brief call to your friend or neighbor whom you have requested to be your special contact for emergencies. Their numbers may have changed or they may no longer be available or able to help you. That will mean you may have to look for other contacts, now that you have the time.

5.0 WATER SUPPLIES IN EMERGENCIES[16]

In most emergencies, it is difficult to predict how long there will be no access to food, water, and electricity. It may, therefore, be best to store emergency food and a water supply for your entire family.

The Federal Emergency Management Agency's Community and Family Preparedness Program brochures have excellent infor-

Emergency Meeting Place

1. Outside your home:

Meeting Place: ____________________
Phone: ____________________
Address: ____________________

2. Outside your neighborhood:

Address: ____________________
Family Contact: ____________________
Name: ____________________
Phone: ____________________

Figure 13.1. Emergency Meeting Place Card

mation on things to be readied for emergencies.

5.1 Location of Sources of Water[16]

1. Emergency outdoor water sources:

   If you need to find water outside your home, you can use these sources. Be sure to treat or boil the water before drinking it.

   - Rainwater
   - Streams, rivers and other moving bodies of water, ponds and lakes
   - Natural springs

   Avoid water with flooding material, an odor or dark color. Use saltwater only if you distill it first. You should not drink floodwater.

2. Hidden water sources in your home:

   - If a disaster catches you without a stored supply of water, you can use the water in your hot-water tank, pipes, and ice cubes. As a last resort, you can use water in the reservoir tank of your toilet (not the bowl).
   - The incoming water valve needs to be shut off to stop contaminated water from entering your home, especially if there are reports about water or sewage lines. To use the water in your pipes, let air into the plumbing by turning on the faucet in your house at the highest level. A small amount of water will trickle out. Then obtain water from the lowest faucet in the house.
   - To use the water in pipes, let air into the plumbing by turning on the faucet in your house at the highest level. A small

amount of water will trickle out. Then obtain water from the lowest faucet in the house.

- To use the water in your hot-water tank, be sure the electricity or gas is off, and open the drain at the bottom of the tank. Start the water flow by turning off the water intake valve and turning on a hot-water faucet. Do not turn on the gas or electricity when the tank is empty.

5.2 Emergency Treatment Process[16]

In addition to having a bad odor and taste, contaminated water can contain microorganisms that cause diseases such as dysentery, typhoid, and hepatitis. Water of uncertain purity should be treated before using it for drinking, food preparation, or hygiene.

There are many ways to treat water. None is perfect. Often the best solution is a combination of methods.

1. *Boiling.* It is the safest method of purifying water. Bring water to a rolling boil for 2 to 3 minutes. Let the water cool before drinking.
2. *Disinfection.* Use only regular household liquid bleach that contains 5.25 percent sodium hypochlorite. Do not use scented bleaches, color safe bleacher or bleaches with added cleaners. Add 16 drops of bleach per gallon of water, stir and let stand for 30 minutes. If the water does not have a slight bleach odor, repeat the dosage and let stand another 15 minutes.
3. *Distillation.* It involves boiling water and then collecting the vapor that condenses back to water. The condensed vapor will not include salt and other impurities. To distill, fill a pot halfway with water. Tie a cup to the handle on the pot's lid so that the cup will hang right side up when the lid is upside-down and boil the water for 20 minutes. The water that drips from the lid into the cup is distilled.

5.3 Water Safety Testing

There are laboratories specializing in water safety testing, including quantitative and qualitative analysis of microbial and chemical contaminants. Details of these are discussed in Chapter 2.

5.4 Storage[16]

Water should be stored in thoroughly washed plastic, glass, fiberglass or enamel-lined metal containers. Never use a container that has held toxic substances. Plastic containers, such as soft drink bottles, are best. You can also purchase food-grade plastic buckets or drums. Seal water containers tightly, label them and store in a cool, dark place. Rotate water every six months.

6.0 FOOD SUPPLIES IN EMERGENCIES

Preparing an emergency food stockpile will help you during emergencies. You are less likely to forget important items especially the special need of a family member during emergency period.

6.1 Preparing an Emergency Food Stockpile

It may be necessary to designate a special set of food as part of the emergency food stockpile and in fact place them in special

Table 13.6
SAMPLE OF GENERAL CHECKLIST FOR AN EMERGENCY FOOD STOCKPILE

- ❑ High energy foods such as peanut butter, jelly, cracker, unsalted nuts, health food bars, trail mixes
- ❑ Canned meat and fish
- ❑ Canned fruits and vegetables
- ❑ Powdered milk properly stored or canned liquid milk
- ❑ Canned, powdered, or crystallized juices
- ❑ Staples, such as rice, flour, corn
- ❑ Long shelf-life root crops such as potatoes
- ❑ Stress foods like sugar cookies, hard candies, sweetened cereals
- ❑ Seasonings such as sugar, salt, pepper

ready-to-carry containers such as duffle bags or sacks that can stand any vagaries of the weather. The food to be included will vary from family to family. In general, you would like to have shelf stable foods that will give you the necessary nutrients for at least one week. Table 13.6 gives the sample list of foods that you might like to consider for the family. The amount and the specifications for each will likewise differ with your family preferences.

6.1.1 Short-term Food Supplies for People with Special Needs

Besides the general needs of the family, it may be necessary to prepare for the family members with special needs, such as infants and elderly or disabled persons. Table 13.7 gives the checklist for special needs.

6.1.2 How to Store Short-term Stock Pile[16]

To store short-term stockpile, the following are recommended:

1. Avoid foods that are high in fat and protein, and don't stock salty foods, since they will make you thirsty.
2. Familiar foods can lift morale and give a feeling of security in time of stress.
3. Canned foods won't require cooking, water, or special attention.
4. Try to include foods that people will enjoy and that are also high in calories and nutrition.
5. Store supplies of non-perishable foods and water in a handy place. You need to have these items packed and ready in case there is no time to gather food from the kitchen when a disaster strikes.
6. Select foods that require no refrigeration, preparation, or cooking, and little or no water. Foods that are compact and lightweight are easy to store and carry.

Recommended foods include:

1. Ready-to-eat canned meats, fruits, and vegetables
2. Canned juices, milk, and soup
3. High energy foods, such as peanut butter, jelly, crackers, granola bars and cookies
4. Instant coffee, tea bags
5. Foods for infants, elderly persons or persons on special diets, if necessary

Table 13.7
CHECKLIST FOR SPECIAL NEEDS

For babies	❑ Formula
	❑ Powdered milk in airtight containers
	❑ Medications
For adults, elderly, children and the sick:	❑ Heart and high blood pressure medication
	❑ Insulin
	❑ Prescription drugs
	❑ Vitamins

6. Compressed food bars. They store well, are lightweight, tasty and are nutritious.
7. Trail mix. It is available as a prepackaged product or you can assemble it on your own.
8. Dried foods. They can be nutritious and satisfying, but some have a lot of salt content, which promotes thirst. Read the label.
9. Freeze-dried foods. They are tasty and lightweight, but will need water for reconstitution.
10. Instant meals. Cups of noodles or cups of soup are a good addition, although they need water for reconstitution.
11. Snack-sized canned goods. Good because they generally have pull-top lids or twist-open keys.
12. Prepackaged beverages. Those in foil packers and foil-lined boxes are suitable because they are tightly sealed and will keep for a long time.

6.1.3 How to Cook if the Power Goes Out[16,18]

During a power failure, cooking and eating habits must change to fit the situation. You may have no heat, any refrigeration and limited water. In addition, there are greater health risks from eating contaminated or spoiled food. When preparing food during a power outrage, conserve fuel, conserve water and take health precautions.

In emergency cooking, consider the amount of cooking time needed for each food. If you have limited heat for cooking choose food that cook quickly. Alternate cooking methods are:

1. Propane camp stoves or grills (for outside cooking only). These can be used any time of the year. Use foil to wrap a variety of foods, including vegetables, for easy cooking and cleanup. Grill and toast other foods as you would for a barbeque. Make sure you close the propane tank when you're done cooking to prevent gas from escaping during cold weather.
2. Fireplace. Many foods can be skewed, grilled, or wrapped in foil and cooked in a fireplace.
3. Candle warmers and fondue pots. These may be used if no other heat sources are available. Use safety precautions with these devices.
4. Wood stove. Cooking on top of the wood stove may be an option. Depending on the amount of heat you have available, preparing one-dish meals, breads, and soups may be possible.

Do not cook frozen foods unless you have ample heat for cooking. Most frozen foods need a lot more cooking time than fresh or canned foods. Also, if the power is off, it is best to leave the freezer door closed to keep food from thawing

6.1.3.1 Ensuring Health During Power Outage.[18] Here are some useful tips to ensure the health of your family during power outage:

- Bring all water used in food preparation to a hard boil for 2 to 3 minutes, covered with a lid to prevent evaporation.
- If you are without refrigeration, open only enough food for one meal. Some foods can be kept a short time without refrigeration. In an emergency, cooked vegetables, cooked meats and meat dishes can be kept unrefrigerated for two hours. Do not keep these dishes overnight without refrigeration.
- Do not serve foods that spoil easily, such as ground meats, creamed foods, hash, custards, meat pies, and any food containing mayonnaise (contains raw eggs). These are potential source of botulism poisoning and other foodborne pathogens.
- When feeding babies and toddlers, open fresh foods for each meal. There may be waste, but safety is important.
- If necessary, substitute canned and powdered milk for fresh milk. Canned milk will keep safely for a few hours after you open the can. Use only boiled or disinfected water to mix powdered milk. Use powdered milk immediately after it is mixed. If you are using canned formula to feed your baby, use ready-to-use or mix only enough for one feeding. Never use formula that is stored cooled and refrigerated.
- If safe water or water disinfecting material is not available, use canned or bottled fruit juices instead of water.
- Prepare and eat foods in their original containers, if possible. This will help if dishwashing is not possible.

6.1.4 Long-term Food Supplies[17]

There are many foods that can be stored at room temperature in kitchen cabinets, in a pantry or in a dry basement. On-the-shelf foods generally have a relatively long storage life; many will keep for a year or more. In hot moist climates, some packaged foods require special attention to avoid damage by insects and mold. You should keep most foods stored on the shelf tightly sealed and in a dry place, preferably away from light and heat.

Several things can happen to foods you store in the cupboard for too long or under poor conditions.

1. Nutrient loss, such as vitamin loss.
2. Spoilage by microorganisms, enzymatic action, or insect infestation.
3. Quality loss, such as loss of flavor, aroma, texture, or general appearance. Bread and bakery goods may become stale, oils may become rancid, spices lose flavor.
4. Loss of functional properties such as leavening activity in baking powder and thickening power in sauce mixes. This can happen if moisture affects the food. Shelf-life foods are considered "non-perishable" at room temperature.

Many unprocessed foods fall into this category and are unaffected by microorganisms because of their low water content. Included are such foods as pastas, cereal grains, or nuts. Processed food products can be shelf-stable if they are preserved by heat (such as canning), dry formulation (cake mixes) and reduced water content (dried foods, raisins, or crackers).

6.1.5 Nutrition Tips[16]

During and after a disaster, it is vital that you maintain your strength. So, remember:

1. Eat at least one well-balanced meal each day
2. Drink enough liquid to enable your body to function properly (2 quarts a day)
3. Take enough calories to enable you to do any necessary work.
4. Include vitamin, mineral and protein supplements in your stockpile to assure adequate nutrition.

6.1.6 Shelf-life of Foods for Storage[16]

Here are some general guidelines for rotating common emergency foods.

1. Use within six months:
   - powdered milk (boxed)
   - dried fruit (in metal container)
   - dry, crisp crackers (in metal container)
   - potatoes
2. Use within one year:
   - Canned condensed meat and vegetable soups
   - Canned fruits, fruit juices and vegetables
   - Ready-to-eat cereals and uncooked instant cereals (in metal containers)
   - Peanut butter
   - Jelly
   - Hard candy and canned nuts
3. May be stored indefinitely:
   - Wheat
   - Vegetable oils
   - Dried corn
   - Baking powder
   - Soybeans
   - Instant coffee, tea and cocoa
   - Salt
   - Non-carbonated soft drinks
   - White rice
   - Bouillon products
   - Dry pasta
   - Powdered milk (in nitrogen-packed cans)

6.1.7 Ways to Supplement Your Long-term Stockpile[16]

To supplement your long-term stockpile, change stored water supply every six months so it stays fresh. Replace your stored food every six months. Re-think your kit and family needs at least once a year. Replace batteries, update clothes, etc.

If your family finds it helpful to pull food products for your regular meals from your disaster supplies kit, replace them immediately on an ongoing basis, so the food supplies are always fresh.

7.0 SOURCING OF FOOD AND WATER DURING OUTDOOR SURVIVAL SITUATIONS

Reality TV programs have made us realize the challenges that come with outdoor "survival" situations. A lack of water may make it necessary for us to look for unconventional sources such as collected rainwater, rivers, and other moving bodies of water, ponds and lakes, and natural springs. It is wise to follow these guidelines:

- Avoid water with floating material, an odor, or dark color,
- Use saltwater only if you distill it first.
- Do not drink floodwater.
- Remember that contaminated water may contain microorganisms that may cause dysentery, typhoid, and hepatitis.
- Purify water of uncertain purity before using it for drinking, food preparation, or hygiene–the usual ways of purifying

water are by boiling, disinfecting, and distillation.

Sourcing of food, if there are no emergency food supplies at hand, or if the emergency food supplies have run out, can be very challenging. For those in tropical forests, you can try relatively unconventional sources that the natives or those familiar with the territory may be eating themselves. They may take a little getting used to!

8.0 SAFETY GUIDELINES AFTER A DISASTER

8.1 Water Safety

After a flood, drink only approved or chlorinated water. Consider all water from wells, cisterns and other delivery systems in the disaster area unsafe until tested. Purchase bottled water, if necessary, until you are certain that your water supply is safe. Keep a five day-supply of water or a minimum of five gallons per person.

8.2 Food Safety

8.2.1 After a Brown-out

When the power is out, an appliance thermometer will always indicate the temperature in the refrigerator and freezer no matter how long the power has been out. The refrigerator temperature should be 40°F or below, the freezer, 0°F or lower. If you are not sure if a particular food is cold enough, take its temperature.

8.2.2 After a Fire

It may be best to discard food that has been near a fire. Food exposed to fire can be damaged by heat of the fire, smoke fumes, and chemicals used to fight the fire.

8.2.3 Kitchen Utensils

Disasters such as floods, tornadoes, or fire may leave kitchen items contaminated. Floodwaters may contain silt, raw sewage, oil or chemical wastes, while fires may leave residues from toxic fumes or fire-fighting chemicals.

For those without dishwashers, the steps for disinfecting dishes, cookware and utensils are as follows:[6]

- Wash all items in a strong detergent solution. Use a brush to remove dirt. Rinse in hot water.
- Immerse glass, porcelain, china, plastic dinnerware and enamelware for 2 to 3 minutes in a disinfecting solution of 2 tablespoons chlorine bleach per gallon of hot water.
- Disinfect silverware, metal utensils, and pots and pans by boiling in water for 10 minutes. Chlorine bleach should not be used in this case because it reacts with many metals and cause them to darken.
- Air-dry dishes. Do not use towels.
- Discard and replace soft, porous plastic or wood items saturated by floodwaters since they cannot be sanitized. These include baby bottles, nipples and pacifiers.
- If cupboards and counters come in contact with floodwater, clean and rinse them with a chlorine bleach solution before storing dishes.

For those with dishwashers and the hot water temperature at least 140°F–use a long wash cycle and heater drying cycle to clean and disinfect dishwasher-safe items.

9.0 WATER SAFETY SYSTEMS IN INSTITUTIONS FOR EMERGENCIES

It is more challenging to prepare for water safety systems in institutions for emergencies. Hospitals may be given priority over other institutions in terms of water use during emergencies for obvious reasons. In developing countries water tanks have been used to safeguard water until needed. The size and number of water tanks have to be planned by the institutions early enough during its construction period. In addition, it is necessary to make sure that the water tanks have no leakages and that safeguards are made to prevent contamination. Restaurants and other institutions have sources of bottled water from commercial water dealers. Many of the large establishments have their own water purification systems, which will hopefully remain active during emergencies.

10.0 EMERGENCY PLANNING AND PREPAREDNESS

10.1 Community and National Coverage[19]

The Lutheran Congregation has a very good example of emergency planning for a disaster. Here is an example of their plan:

10.2 International Coverage[11]

The Pan American Health Organization (PAHO) helps in food aid programs during disasters by collaborating with national and local authorities in priority activities with relevant agencies and organizations, and organizes a coordinating group, if there is none, identifying sources of supplies and providing experienced personnel.

Food aid programs aim to prevent malnutrition in populations affected by a disaster. It is necessary, however, to plan for the treatment and management of cases of malnutrition that existed prior to the disaster, or which have become acute and will become evident during aid operations.

In ensuring an effective food aid program, the following should be adhered to:

1. Estimate the quantity of food available
2. Calculate the dietary needs of the affected population; and
   - As an immediate measure, provide any population group that is or appears to be at high nutritional risk with 3 or 4 kg of food per person per week. The important thing at this stage is to provide a sufficient quantity of energy, even if it is not a balanced diet. For a short period of time, 1700 Kcals daily will prevent severe deterioration of the nutritional status, and famine.
3. Determine the food rations in accordance with the characteristics of the population and estimated operations.
   - Food rations can be calculated by taking into account the approximate number and composition of the affected population. Composition of a food ration that can provide approximately 1700 Kcals: basic

Preparing your congregation for a disaster
Before a disaster strikes

I. Prepare a plan to respond to a disaster

1. Survey facilities, members, programs to identify special concerns to deal with during and following a disaster.
2. Arrange to use your resources by encouraging an agreement with the Red Cross, other emergency-management agencies and your closest Lutheran social-ministry organization.
3. Know resources, identify functions.
4. Develop processes for raising funds for disaster response or receiving them from outside sources.

II. Prepare your facility for a disaster

1. Post an emergency number by each phone. Include 911, the poison control center, law enforcement and the fire department. Make sure a phone is accessible in each are of the building at all hours.
2. Identify the nearest storm shelter.
3. Post clear directions on what to do and where to go in case of severe storm/tornado warning.
4. Practice evacuation/fire drills.
5. Have a working weather radio or battery-operated radio in an accessible location in the church. Ensure that someone is listening during watches while church functions are in progress.
6. Maintain a list of who is assigned to cut off facilities, cover windows and secure loose items inside/outside the building.
7. Collect emergency/disaster-preparedness needs such as emergency lights, flashlights, first-aid kits, and blankets.
8. Check exits: make sure they are marked and/or lit, free of obstruction, locked doors have crash bats; establish evacuation routes on upper floors, have a plan to evacuate handicapped persons.
9. Check electrical equipment, mark circuit breakers, cover switches and outlet boxes, ground electrical units, do not overload circuits.
10. Check gas equipment, know where gas main is, and know where meter-shut-off valve and gas wrench is.

Figure 13.2. Disaster Preparedness Guidelines

grain (i.e., rice) = 400g, fat (i.e., oil) = 15g, and protein-rich food (i.e., dried fish) = 45g.

11.0 VIGILANCE FOR VICTORY

11.1 Individuals

When our guards are down, then the enemy strikes! By emergency planning and preparedness, and through constant vigilance, food and water safety can be better assured. All these steps for preparation need not be crammed in one day. Planning can be done on a regular basis, methodically, but vigilance has to be a habit and a frame of mind. We must be ever watchful of hazards, and find ways of controlling them as they come.

11.2 Food Security Measures for Food Producers, Processors, Transporters, and Retailers

Very specific guidelines[10] have been provided to assist the food industry operators in connection with food security measure by the USFDA Center for Food Safety and Applied Nutrition.[13] The topics include:

1. Security procedures–investigation of suspicious activity, mail/packages, physical facility, visitors, physical security, laboratory safety, storage and use of hazardous chemicals
2. Employees–pre-hiring screening, daily work assignment, identification, restricted access, personal items, training in food security measures, unusual behavior
3. Computer system–access
4. Raw materials and packaging–supplies
5. Operations–security of water, security of plant facilities
6. Security strategies–response to tampering or criminal or terrorist activities, recall strategy, additional steps
7. Evaluation program.

11.3 Food Security Measures for Importers and Exporters

The USFDA Center has provided specific guidelines for Food Safety and Applied Nutrition that can be used as a guide by importers and exporters. The guidelines include:[10]

1. Establishment operation and practices–management of food security, security procedures, investigation of suspicious activity, mail/packages
2. Employees–pre-hiring screening, daily work assignments, identification, restricted access, personal items, training in security procedures, unusual behavior, data systems
3. Data system
4. Physical security–visitors, physical facility, storage of hazardous chemicals, products and shipments, suppliers, security of products
5. Security strategy–response to tampering or criminal or terrorist act, recall strategy; and
6. Evaluation program.

REVIEW QUESTIONS

1. Define important terms: (See text or Glossary)
   a. Anthrax
   b. Botulism
   c. Cholera
   d. Bioterrorism
2. What steps can families take to prepare for emergencies?
3. Which agencies can assist families during times of emergencies?
4. What numbers should be contained in the family emergency directory?
5. Why should families hold emergency council meetings?
6. What are the usual protective devices that families should have to prepare for food and water safety in emergencies?
7. What should be included in a family's emergency food supply? What should be included in a family's emergency kit?
8. What are some food security measures for importers and exporters?
9. What are some food security measures for producers, processors, transporters, and retailers? Research your country's national preparedness plan.

REFERENCES

1. North Carolina State University AT&T Cooperative Extension Family Disaster Kit. Available at http://www.cex.ncsu.edu/handbook/disaster2.html. Accessed May 21, 2002.
2. North Carolina State A&T State University Cooperative Extension.2002. Preparing your

family for a disaster. Available at http://www.ces.ncsu.ed/disaster/handbook/disaster2.html. Accessed May 21, 2002.

3. Federal Emergency Management Agency. 2002. Preparedness Training and Exercises-Emergency Food and Water Supplies. Available at http://www.fema.gov/pte/emfdwtr.html. Accessed May 21, 2002.
4. Btox Analytical Laboratories, Poster on Biological Warfare Agents, Aerotech Laboratories, 2001.
5. Tierno, P. M. *Protect Yourself Against Terrorism,* New York, Pocket Books, 2002.
6. Prescott, L. M., Harley J. P., and Klein, D. A. *Microbiology,* Iowa, Wm C Brown, 1993.
7. USFDA Centre for Food Safety and Applied Nutrition Food Safety and Security Operational Risk Management System. Available at http://www.fda/gov/orra/insptrefion/iomoradiv.html. Accessed May 23, 2002.
8. Clark County Health District. *Your Family Disaster Plan.* Las Vegas, October 2001.
9. American Red Cross. *Family Disaster Planning.* 2001. Available at http://www.nyredcross.org.health_safety/healthsaffety_disasterplan.html. Accessed May 21, 2002.
10. University of Maine Cooperative Extension. Preparing Food During a Power Failure, #9001. Available at http://www.umext.maine.edu/emergency/9001.htm. Accessed May 23, 2002.
11. NSDU Extension Nutrition Specialists. April 1995. *On the Shelf-Storage.* Available at http://www.ag/nsdu.nodak.edu/drought/drought.htm. Accessed May 23, 2002.
12. National AG. Safety Information, University of Wisconsin Cooperative Extension. Michigan State University Cooperative Extension Service, University of Florida Cooperative Extension Service, Illinois Cooperative Extension Service.
13. Preparing your Congregation for a Disaster. Available at http://www.elca.org/dcs/disaster/during.htm. Accessed May 23, 2002.
14. Food and Nutrition in Disasters. Available at http://www.paho.org/english/pcd/te_nutr.htm. Accessed May 21, 2002.
15. US Department of Health and Human Resources: Biological and Chemical Terrorism: Strategic Plan for Preparedness and Response, *Morbidity and Mortality Weekly Report,* Vol. 49: No RR-4, (1–13) Center for Disease Control and Response, Georgia, April 21, 2000.

Chapter 14

CHALLENGES OF FOOD AND WATER SAFETY FOR THE FUTURE

1.0 THE CHANGING SCENARIO

1.1 Forces Driving Change

The path towards food safety is unending. The method in which food is produced, distributed, and consumed not only presents many challenges for ensuring food safety but also increases the diversity of foodborne illness. Many forces are responsible for driving change in food safety. These include the following:

1.1.1 Globalization of Trade and Food Supply

People from many parts of the world are eating a variety of foods, in which supplies are available year round. The globalization of trade and the continuous import and export of food supplies around the globe increases the introduction of risks and hazards associated with imported foods in the local markets. In 1996 and 1997 alone, the outbreak of *cyclosporiasis* in North America was traced back to contaminated raspberries imported from South America.[1] The globalization of trade and food supplies entails globalization of food safety.

1.1.2 Introduction of Pathogens into New Territories

Food and waterborne pathogens advance with the food across borders. A number of food borne outbreaks have been related to globalization of the food supply.[2] Increasing trade traffic and migration of people carry many possible pathogens in and out of the country. In 1991, *Vibrio cholerae* was introduced into the waters of the United States via contaminated ballast water discharged from a cargo ship.[1]

Many countries are enforcing stringent standards and measures to control the entry of such organisms that may have contaminated susceptible food product

1.1.3 Changes Microorganisms

Through the years, microorganisms have evolved and developed into more virulent and resistant strains. One good example is *Escherichia coli,* an organism commonly found in the gastrointestinal microflora of humans. Its serotype, E.coli O157:H7 has been the cause of many food borne disease outbreaks during the past years.

Outbreaks associated with this virulent bacterium, are mainly due to contaminated beef, as reported in Australia, Canada, Japan, United States, in various European countries, and in Southern Africa. In 1996 alone, an outbreak of *E. coli* O157:H7 in Japan affected over 6,300 school children, and even the death of two.[1]

1.1.4 Change in Human Demographics

According to the WHO (1999), one out of every four people is at risk to foodborne diseases in most countries. They also added that more than 1,000 million people would be over 60 years of age by the year 2005, two-thirds of them from the developing countries. The emergence of AIDS and other deadly diseases have increased the population of highly susceptible persons. In addition to this, malnutrition, increasing population of elderly people, and reduced immunity due to underlying environmental and economic factors increases the demographics of susceptibility to food and waterborne infections.

1.1.5 Changes in Lifestyle

The advent of the new century brought about a more convenient lifestyle for many. Changes in the technology of food preparation have influenced the eating habits of people. More people are eating a variety of foods. Aside from this, an increasing number of women are working away from home; thus, more and more people are eating their meals away from home in restaurants, canteens, fast food outlets, street food vendors and many other food establishments. As the task of preparing large numbers of meals for the public becomes more and more popular, the incidence of food and waterborne diseases increases.

1.1.6 Biotechnology and Development of Genetically Modified Organisms (GMOs)

Traditional plant breeding has been around for centuries. Recent advances in agricultural biotechnology and the development of Genetically Modified Organisms are currently redesigning the trend of the future of the food industry. However, it is actually difficult (in practice) to draw a distinct line between the traditional plant breeding techniques and biotechnology.[3]

Genetic engineering and biotechnology is still a fresh industry. Unprecedented risks due to the capacity of genetic engineering to move genes across generations and families have sprouted fears among many. It is necessary that we proceed through it cautiously as we try to gain more experience in the field.[3]

1.1.7 Bioterrorism

The dream of tranquility and peace in the world by the twenty-first century has been shattered by ongoing conflicts in different areas, including the September 11 attack in the United States last 2001. Now the world is gearing itself for possible biological and chemical terrorism. There have been incidents like the sarin gas attack in the Tokyo subway on March 1995, the discovery of military bio-weapons programs in Iraq, and the former Soviet Union have alerted national and international agencies to this imminent danger. "Preparing the nation to address this threat is a formidable challenge, but the consequences of being unprepared could be devastating" is true not only for the United States but for every nation in the world as well.

1.2 Trends Shaping the Future

1.2.1 Megatrends in the Food Industry

"Megatrends" are currently affecting the food industry. These trends are events whose beginnings are difficult to predict, have effects that are difficult to evade, and whose progress is hard to stop. Trends that might affect the exports of food products are the following:[4]

- Consolidation-integration of food chains–the "take over or be taken over" trend and a "survival of the fittest" attitude is becoming a popular approach towards meeting global competitiveness in the food industry.
- Worldwide distribution of food products–this emerging trend offers many possibilities such as: commerce without borders, diversity of cultures and values, varied regulatory frameworks/ equivalency, more documentation, economies of scale, and seasonal advantages
- New products–continual advances in technology brought about ready-to-eat foods, convenience-driven changes in lifestyle and eating habits, the urgency to innovate, larger margins, and implications for sanitation/safety.
- Microbiological sensitivity–science and technological advancements gave rise to the "sterile consumer" and increasing consumer sensitivity, urging more innovations in medicine, detection and diagnostics.
- Allergenic sensitivity–at the same time as the developments in the methods of identification and detection have improved, an increasing number of people suffer from allergenic reactions. Currently, more than 160 allergens have been detected.[4] Among these are the "Big Eight": peanuts, tree nuts, milk, eggs, wheat, soy, shellfish, and fish, responsible for 90 percent of the food allergies in individuals.[5,6]
- Biogenetic engineering–advances in biotechnology offers a number of benefits for the consumers such as increased food supply and availability. However, these advances should be backed up by many other studies in order to assure the consumers about the short and long-term soundness of the food that they are eating.
- Pesticide restrictions–reduction or elimination, lack of substitutes, higher costs, higher infestation problems, non-traditional controls, sanitation programs, and customer/supplier coordination are the most emergent issues needed to be answered by the food and agricultural community.
- Regulatory environments–trends concerning increases in processing costs, reduced water resources, increased cost of food, automation in the workplace, and other socio-economic issues influence and will continue to affect the food industry in the future.
- Food safety–beyond quality and price, the safety of foods is considered a global concern.
- The Internet–rethinking of purchasing function, time compressions, democratization of information, productivity and competitiveness are just a few of the impacts that the Worldwide Web has effected in the food industry.

1.2.2 Reliance on Food Safety Systems

The popularity of the Hazard Analysis and Critical Control points (HACCP) system is greatly increasing. A growing number of companies are relying on their HACCP plan to monitor, maintain and ensure food safety at all parts of their process. According to Dr. Michael Taylor,[7] HACCP is not only an overall process that correlates food safety in process point, but also an effective risk based process control that searches for farm-to-table solutions to food safety problems.

The HACCP plan could be applied in the plant or company, farm-to-table and government/national level. This food safety system extends beyond the processing plant and also tackles risks and hazards during travel and storage. It also clarifies the role of the government as the body responsible for verifying that every company designed HACCP plan is suitable in meeting food safety standards.[7]

1.2.3 Proliferation of Standards

International trade plays an important role in driving the generation of standards. Aside from individual countries that are enforcing their own standards on food, the Codex Alimentarius Commission of the WHO/FAO Food Standards Program has been tasked to harmonize international standards of food and agricultural products.

Food companies also effect changes in the proliferation of standards. Product specific HACCP plans and CCPs serve as a kind of standard. It also serves as a tool for achieving a level of food safety performance in producing sound food.[7]

1.2.4 Greater Role of Science and Technological Solutions

A huge chunk of the improvement of food safety is dependent on science and technological solutions. Advances in HACCP provided the industry an "analytical framework for gauging where technological control measures can best be applied to control hazards."[7] Aside from this, improvements in data collection and information dissemination also serve a great role in shaping and ensuring food safety in the future.

2.0 WORKING TOWARDS THE FUTURE

2.1 WHO Activities

The World Health Organization (WHO) has made food safety a global priority. It has and continues to work on increasing awareness and other advocacy training programs in countries such as Cambodia, Fiji, and Papua New Guinea. Follow-up work in the operational plans of action for food safety in the Western Pacific Region was also conducted in November 2000, and brought together health and non-health officials from 14 member countries in the region.[8]

In conformance to resolution WHA53.15 of the World Health Assembly, the WHO is also tasked to continue to promote the adoption of modern food laws, regulations and standards, as well as strengthening the participation of its member in the work of the Codex.[9]

2.2 WTO/SPS Agreement

The World Trade Organization has also implemented measures in monitoring the safety and quality of the goods available for trade. Through the Sanitary and Phytosanitary measures agreement, trading countries are required to develop food control and safety programs to ensure consumer protection and well-being.

2.3 Activities for Addressing Food and Water Diseases[10]

The National Center for Infectious Diseases (NCID) of the Centers for Disease Control and Prevention in the United States has come up with definite public health activities to address the problem of food and waterborne diseases. These include the following:

2.3.1 *Surveillance and Response*

- Assess the burden of sporadic and outbreak related non-gastrointestinal food borne diseases in the United States.
- Transfer standardized molecular methods for sub-typing foodborne pathogens to state health department laboratories and link the laboratories into a national electronic network.
- Monitor the incidence of, and complications caused by gastrointestinal food and waterborne illnesses that are not identified by laboratory examination of diarrheal stools.
- Enhance rapid detection and coordinated response to multistate and multinational foodborne outbreaks.
- Monitor the levels of antibiotic resistance in foodborne pathogens.

2.3.2 *Applied Research*

- Develop assays for detecting and subtyping food and waterborne pathogens for which adequate testing methods do not currently exist.
- Evaluate food production and distribution practices, as well as behavioral risk factors associated with food- and waterborne diseases, both in the United States and internationally.
- Identify the causative agents for food- and waterborne outbreaks of unknown etiology, as well as pathogens responsible for sporadic cases of food- and waterborne illness.
- Evaluate the public health significance of chlorine resistant organisms in municipal drinking water distribution systems.
- Evaluate new strategies for reducing contamination of food and water, including irradiation of solid foods and ultraviolet disinfection of water.

2.3.3 *Infrastructure and Training*

- Provide state and local public health facilities with computer equipment, software, and training for conducting laboratory-based electronic surveillance of food- and waterborne pathogens.
- Train state and local health departments to use new surveillance methods for detecting food and waterborne microorganisms, including the techniques of molecular epidemiology, so that broadly distributed outbreaks can be detected more rapidly.
- Provide epidemiologists at state and local health departments with the resources and training to respond to outbreaks of food- and waterborne diseases.

2.3.4 *Prevention and Control*

- Conduct and evaluate educational campaigns to change food-handling behaviors.
- Promote disease prevention strategies in food and animal production and processing to reduce pathogen contamination and antibiotic resistance.

- Evaluate the impact of changes in the meat inspection, egg refrigeration, irradiation, and other food industry practices on food safety.
- Evaluate the impact of improved water filtration methods and new water disinfectants such as ozone and ultraviolet light irradiation.
- Ensure that people at particular risk for food and waterborne diseases have access to information that can help them make informed choices on how to reduce their risks.
- Work with public and private partners to implement sustainable food- and waterborne disease intervention programs in developing countries throughout the world.
- Develop and evaluate strategies for reducing outbreaks from exposure to contaminated recreational water.

2.4 Food Safety Strategic Act

In 1998, the Clinton administration created a Council on Food Safety tasked "to develop a comprehensive strategic plan for Federal food safety activities that would establish a seamless, science-based food safety system."[11] The President's Council on Food Safety (Executive Order 13100) has established several interrelated guiding themes. These include the following:

2.4.1 Public Health Protection

Improvements in public health serve as the number one guiding theme for the council. Increased consumer awareness, followed by a subsequent decrease in the incidence of foodborne diseases and outbreaks, and the reduction in pesticide residues are targeted by the federal government. Table 14.1 shows the tabulated performance measures that the Council on Food Safety wishes to accomplish.

2.4.2 Science-Based System

An objective and scientific approach on the collection, analysis, and dissemination of important information is one of the goals of the Council. The capacity of the national food safety programs depends on how much they are founded on sound sciences, such as risk assessment, HACCP-based programs, surveillance and analytical capacity.[8]

2.4.3 Priorities Based on Risks

Efficient use of resources based on scientific risk-based analysis is an important part of the program. A thorough understanding of food safety and its risks is essential in the success of the program. This procedure determines and sets the target areas and priorities on the zone that shows the greatest hazard.

2.4.4 Prevention Emphasis

"An ounce of prevention is worth a pound of cure." A proactive and vigilant approach towards food safety is the fourth guiding theme of the Council. It has also been proven to be more effective and less expensive than on-the-spot responses to food safety issues as they happen.

2.4.5 Responsible Government Oversight

The fifth goal of the Council is to strengthen and clearly define the government's role, however limited its resources may be, in harmonizing and increasing collaboration among agencies. It should also monitor and affect

Table 14.1
FOOD SAFETY STRATEGIC PLAN

Performance Measures	*Baseline*	*Target*
25% Reduction of infection from *Campylobacter* species (Cases/100,000)	24.6 (1997)	18.5 (2005)
25% Reduction of infection from *Escherichia coli* O157:H7 (Cases/100,000)	2.1 (1997)	1.6 (2005)
50% Reduction of infection from *Listeria monocytogenes* (Cases/100,000)	0.5 (1997)	0.25 (2005)
50% Reduction in illness from *Salmonella enteriditis* in eggs (Cases/100,000)	1.9 (1998)	0.95 (2005)
Prevention of an increase in proportion of isolates of *Salmonella* species from humans that are resistant to fluoroquinolones (Percent increase over baseline)	0% (1997)	0% (2005)
Increase in proportion of consumers who follow key food safety practices	72% (1998)	75% (2005)
50% reduction in detection of residues of choline-esterase inhibiting pesticides on the foods most frequently eaten by children	33.5% (1994–1996)	16.8% (2006)
50% reduction in detection of residues of carcinogenic pesticides on the foods most frequently eaten by children	25% (1994–1996)	12.5% (2006)
130% increase in agricultural acre treatments of "reduced risk" pesticides (percent acres)	3% (1997)	7% (2006)

Source: President's Council on Food Safety. *Food Safety Strategic Plan.* January 19, 2001. Available at: www.foodsafety.gov. Accessed June 23, 2002.

police power on those who do not observe federal laws on food safety in general.

2.4.6 Everyone Has a Role

Lastly, the Council foresees that partnerships from the different sectors are essential in the success of the program. Amid conflicting interests and differences, everyone has a need for ensuring food safety and the development of an efficient and effective food safety system that really works.

2.5 Strategic Plan for Preparedness and Response

The CDC held a Strategic Planning Workshop in 2000 which resulted in the Strategic Plan for Preparedness and Response.[12] It marked the first time that the CDC joined with law enforcement, intelligence and defense agencies, in addition to traditional CDC partners, to address a national security threat. The inputs were obtained from the National Center for Infectious Diseases, the National Center for Environmental Health, the Public Health Practice Program Office, the National Institute for Occupational Safety and Health, Office of Health and Safety, the National Immunization Program, the National Center for Injury Prevention Control, and the Agency for Toxic Substances and Disease Registry (ATSDR).

Large-scale outbreaks caused by highly dangerous agents such as the varioa virus will require rapid mobilization of public health workers, emergency responders, and private health care providers. These outbreaks will also require rapid procurement and distribution of large quantities of drugs and vaccines, which must be available quickly.

The implementation priorities of focus areas from 2000–2002 included the following five major areas:[13]

2.5.1 Preparedness and Prevention

- Maintain public health preparedness and a response cooperative agreement that provides support to state health agencies that are working with local agencies in developing coordinated bioterrorism plans and protocols.
- Establish a national public health distance learning system that provides biological and chemical terrorism preparedness training to health care workers and to state and local public health workers.
- Disseminate public health guidelines and performance standards on biological and chemical terrorism preparedness for use by state and local health agencies.

2.5.2 Detection and Surveillance

- Strengthen state and local surveillance systems for illness and injury resulting from pathogens and chemical substances that are on the CDC's critical agents list.
- Develop new algorithms and statistical methods for searching medical databases on a real-time basis for evidence of suspicious events.
- Establish criteria for investigating and evaluating suspicious clusters of human or animal disease or injury and instruments for notifying law enforcement of suspected acts of biological or chemical terrorism.

2.5.3 Diagnosis and Characterization of Biological and Chemical Weapons

- Establish a multilevel laboratory response network for bioterrorism that links public health agencies to advanced capacity and facilities for the identification and reporting of critical biological agents.
- Establish regional chemical terrorism laboratories that will provide for diagnostic capacity during terrorist attacks involving chemical agents.
- Establish a rapid-response and advanced technology laboratory within the CDC to provide around the clock diagnostic support to bioterrorism response teams, and expedite molecular characterization of critical biological agents.

2.5.4 Response

- Assist state and local health agencies in organizing response capacities to rapidly deploy in the event of an overt attack or a suspicious outbreak that might be the result of a covert attack.
- Ensure that procedures are in place for rapid mobilization of CDC terrorism response teams that will provide on-site

assistance to local health workers, security agents, and law enforcement officers.

- Establish a national pharmaceutical stockpile to provide medical supplies in the event of a terrorist attack that involves biological or chemical agents.

2.5.5 Communication

- Establish a national electronic infrastructure to improve the exchange of emergency health information among local, state, and federal health agencies.
- Implement an emergency communication plan that ensures rapid dissemination of health information to the public during actual, threatened, or suspected acts of biological or chemical terrorism.
- Create a web site that disseminates bioterrorism preparedness and training information, as well as other bioterrorism-related emergency information, to public health and health care workers and the public.

3.0 MANAGEMENT OF PROTECTIVE RESPONSE STRATEGIES

3.1 By Nations and Governments

National governments should be able to create a food safety program whose goal is to ensure consumer health. Priority should also be given in updating food laws and legislation; and follow up and proper enforcement of these laws should be well monitored.

In addition, countries have to invest in systems to be able to mitigate illness and injuries that result from acts of biological and chemical terrorism. The government first has to realize the need, and then the responsible agencies can have a strategic planning workshop to map out protective response strategies.

3.2 By Civil Society

Voluntary non-government organizations (NGOs) can work as partners of the public health agencies in their campaign against biological and chemical agents. Now, while it is still possible to access information through the Internet anywhere in the world, it might be advisable for NGOs to be part of food and water safety networks. Thus, they can be part of a country's risk communication system, and be aware of the current developments in combating biological and chemical terrorism.

Since many of the governments of developing countries cannot finance the entire physical and human infrastructure necessary for warding off the ill effects of chemicals and biological terrorism, non-government agencies may partner with the government agencies in some selected geographical or medical areas.

3.3 By Individuals

It is important that we learn to work closely with the healthcare and public health workers in our locality. One of the greatest weapons of the bioterrorists is fear–psychological warfare is part of the enemy's total plan. An informed public will be less prone to fear if the citizens are duly informed. They can also inform the authorities of any suspicious activities that may be related to terrorist attacks.

4.0 MEETING THE CHALLENGES OF THE FUTURE

4.1 Education and Training

Food safety can only be a way of life and culture if there is proper education and training. The simple matter of washing hands has not yet become a habit among food handlers. The campaign should include children as soon as they go to school; in fact it would be best that this training begin at home by example of the parents and the caregivers. It is encouraging to note that the media has assisted in the food campaign through the various soap commercials to make bacteria more real to TV viewers. Voluntary and broad-based media campaigns all over the world, like the FIGHT BAC!® in the United States has improved food safety in these countries.

An informed public can be a powerful force for food safety. As consumers, we must continue to support and patronize the clean establishments that serve good food. In addition we must try to educate these eateries that we do care when we tell them "there is a fly in my soup." If they do not pay attention, then discontinue going to that establishment.

Schools are powerful catalysts for change in any country. The curriculum of health-related courses should include one or more subjects in food safety. Schools can likewise offer adult education courses in conjunction with the industry on food safety systems. Developed areas like the United States, Canada, Europe, Japan, and Australia have many such formal and continuing education courses offered on a regular basis for the industry. It is notable to also see the progress that has been done in developing countries like Malaysia, Indonesia, Thailand and the Philippines on food safety training and education. Much has been done, but more education and training is definitely still needed all over the world. Food safety systems, food regulations, food control are known, but does everyone in the food chain practice these?

4.2 Research

An intensive statistical database relating food and water safety to consumer health and the decline of diseases, as well as other essential information should be established. Moreover, a complete understanding of the strength, weaknesses, opportunities and threats that the food industry is facing should be undertaken. These steps serve as the basis for the pursuit of science and technological solutions on ensuring food safety for the future. Serious brainstorming by the different scientific and responsible communities on the aspects that the studies should focus on and determination of problem areas is crucial.

4.3 Communication and Linkages

Collaboration among agencies, as well as thorough information dissemination campaigns on the strength, weaknesses, opportunities and threats of food and water safety, should be the primary concern of all those involved. An expansive network of responsible agencies resolved to harmonize and solve the inconsistency and fragmentation of the different sectors should be assembled.

4.4 High Level of Leadership from the Food Industry

The food industry should assume leadership in establishing, strengthening, enforcing, and educating the rest of the world on food safety and its challenges. Day-to-day operations give them product-specific experience and expertise. A proactive and aggressive approach by the industry is necessary in facing emerging food issues.

REVIEW QUESTIONS

1. Define important terms:
   - GMOs
   - Megatrends
   - Protective Response strategy
   - Irradiation
   - Sanitary and Phytosanitary (SPS) Agreement
2. What are some of the forces driving change in terms of food and water safety?
3. What are some of the trends shaping the future and how will these trends affect food and water safety?
4. What are the developments in biotechnology and what are their effects on the safety of food?
5. What are your country's regulations regarding irradiated food?
6. What are your country's regulations regarding genetically modified organisms?
7. What are some of the important areas of research on food and water safety for the future? How can individuals prepare for food and water safety for the future?
8. How can companies prepare for food and water safety for the future?
9. What do governments have to do to prepare for food and water safety for the future?
10. What are international organizations doing to ensure food and water safety in the future?

REFERENCES

1. WHO. Emerging Food Borne Diseases. *WHO Fact Sheet 124.* Geneva, WHO, 2002. Available at http://www.who.int. Accessed June 23, 2002.
2. Merican, Z. Food Safety in Malaysia. Regional Consultative Workshop on Food Safety Research and Development Proceedings. Los Banos, SEAMO SEARCA. (23–33). 2001.
3. Conway, G. R. *The Doubly Green Revolution: Food for All in the 21st Century.* New York, Cornell University Press, 1998.
4. Peterson, N. *American Institute of Baking Official Outlines Megatrends in Food.* K-State Research and Extension News. Kansas, June 4, 2002.
5. Chavez, L. L. Food allergy: What we need to know and what we have to do if we have it. *Food Safety Bulletin.* 9:4. FAFST, Quezon City. 2001.
6. White, L. GMPs plus allergen labeling equals safe product. *Food Quality,* November–December 2001, 7:6 (32).
7. Taylor, M. *Food safety 1997–driving forces and emerging trends.* A paper presented at the food Safety, Sufficiency and Security Conference sponsored by the Council for Agricultural Science and Technology, November 2–4, 1997. Available at: www.cast-science.org/fsss/fsss_c03.htm. Accessed June 14, 2002.
8. WHO. Report of the Regional Director of the Work of WHO in the Western Pacific Region: July 1, 2000–June 30, 2001. (85-90). WHO, Philippines, 2001.
9. World Health Organization. *Food Safety.* World Health Assembly, Eighth Plenary Meeting on May 20, 2000. Geneva, WHO, 2000.
10. CDC/NCID. *Preventing Emerging Infectious Diseases: A Strategy for the 21st Century.* Available at: www.cdc.gov/ncidod/emergplan/index.htm. Accessed January 20, 2002.
11. President's Council on Food Safety. *Food Safety Strategic Plan.* January 19, 2001. Available at: www.foodsafety.gov. Accessed June 23, 2002.

12. *Food Producers, Processors, Transporters, and Retailers: Food Security Preventive Measures Guidance.* Available at www.cfsan.fda.gove/~dms/secquid2html. Accessed November 12, 2001.

13. *Importers and Filers: Food Security Preventive Measures Guidance.* Available at: www.cfsan.fda.gov/~dms/secquid2.html. Accessed May 23, 2002.

Chapter 15

INTRODUCTION TO FOODBORNE DISEASE OUTBREAK

A foodborne disease outbreak (FBDO) is used by the US Centers for Disease Control and Prevention (CDC), as "an incident in which (1) two or more persons experience the same illness after ingestion of a common food, and (2) epidemiologic analysis implicates the food as the source of illness." A few exceptions are: ONE CASE OF BOTULISM OR ONE CASE OF CHEMICAL POISONING constitutes an outbreak.[4]

Due to space limitation, 50 FBDOs are presented. Care was taken in selecting the topics, so that classical cases of historic significance are included. For recent reports, the criteria for choosing these reports are:

- Location of outbreaks (representing different countries)
- Variety of etiological agents that cause the foodborne and waterborne diseases
- Vehicles and vectors of transmitting the disease (humans, animals, insects, rodents, food, water, air, soil, etc.)
- Impact on people's health and life

Hopefully, these reports are "FOOD FOR THOUGHT" for everyone. In our shared responsibility to avoid, or at least, reduce the incidence of FBDOs, a knowledge of these reports will instill in our minds to be serious about safety and consider sanitation a way of life.

The sequencing of the reports may not follow the order of the chapter topics in the text. More important is to refer the reader to the right number corresponding to the intended report when citing it in the text.

Most of the cases are from documents or literature from North America. We hope other nations have agencies or organizations, similar to the Centers of Disease Control and Prevention that regularly publish FBDO reports.

The reader is encouraged to look up the original references for more details about the outbreak.

For future revisions, we appreciate your feedback and please call our attention to other FBDOs, especially from developing countries that should receive priority in this chapter.

FBDO # 1 Cholera Epidemic in Peru

The 1991 cholera outbreak in Peru was the first South American epidemic to occur in the twentieth century. It was part of the epidemic involving over half a million cases with 4,700 fatalities that spread through nineteen countries. The outbreak was attributed to the water supply that was untreated, and sewage contamination. Human waste infected with the cholera bacterium was used as fertilizer. Other modes of transmission were eating raw seafood and other food items served at a fiesta, and dipping contaminated hands into water vessels that contained drinking water. The authors remarked that the hands factor is almost unbelievable to many people, but this is a major problem in undeveloped countries of the world.

- Swerdlow, D., Mintz, E, and M. Rodriguez. Waterborne transmission of epidemic cholera in Peru. The Lancet: 340: 28–32, 1992.

FBDO #2 Outbreak of Giardiasis in New Mexico, 1989

This is a case of cross-contamination between water and sewer systems. Investigations showed that the lettuce and tomatoes used in preparing homemade tacos for a church event of an Albuquerque youth group were rinsed in the kitchen sink, whose water came from the municipal system.

Many of the persons who ate the tacos that contained *Giardia lamblia* came down with long-term diarrhea. They experienced symptoms like abdominal cramps, fatigue and weight loss. More than 70 percent of stool specimens were positive for cysts of the parasite.

Investigations revealed several possible connections resulting in potential cross contamination between the water system and the sewer system. The plumbing was quickly fixed.

- Epidemiologic notes and reports: outbreak of giardiasis–New Mexico. CDC *MMWR 33* (13), 173, 1984

FBDO #3 Drinking Water Contaminated with High Levels of Industrial Solvent

This happened at Reese Air Force Base in Lubbock, Texas. Seven families who reside at the base got their drinking water from a well which later was found to contain high levels of trichloroethylene (TCE), an industrial solvent. The Environmental Protection Agency (EPA) has set standards for TCE at five parts per billion (ppb). The measured level in the well was as high as 70 ppb. The EPA then issued a citation of "imminent and substantial endangerment" against the base. The families received bottled drinking water and were cautioned that the use of tap water still posed a health threat for bathing and washing dishes.

- *Indoor Pollution News,* July 9, 1993.

FBDO #4 Shigellosis Outbreak Associated with an Unchlorinated Wading Pool

On June 15, 2001, local physicians in Iowa reported 11 cases of diarrhea to their county health department. Stool samples from two of the affected persons were confirmed to have *Shigella sonnei.* A preliminary investigation found nine of these persons had recently visited a city park with a fill-and-drain wading pool.

The Iowa Department of Health assisted in the investigation and summarized their results, implicating the inadequately disinfected wading pool as the source of the outbreak. The pool did not have a recirculation and disinfection system. Chlorine was not added to the pool water after replacing the water. At the end of the day used water was drained and the following day the pool was filled with potable city water through a direct inlet pipe. However, it was not treated with chlorine and the chlorine levels were not monitored on a regular basis.

- CDC *MMWR 50* (37): 797–800, 2001.

FBDO #5 Bacillus cereus–Maine, USA, 1985

On September 22, 1985, several customers who ate at a Japanese restaurant in Maine complained of severe gastrointestinal illness. The owner immediately closed the restaurant and cooperated with the health department officials who interviewed the customers. Other customers complained of nausea, vomiting, diarrhea, abdominal cramps, and headache. The onset of symptoms was rapid with one person experiencing symptoms within half an hour after eating. Although most symptoms were gone within several days for most of the victims, some had to be hospitalized and placed on oral rehydration therapy.

In the final analysis, two samples of stool specimens and one sample of vomit confirmed the presence of *Bacillus cereus*. Many dishes served that day were analyzed, but the only food found to be *B. cereus* positive was Hibachi steak, which is unlikely to harbor this pathogen. It was believed that the steak was contaminated with B. cereus from fried rice by cross-contamination.

- CDC *MMWR 23:* 405, 1989.

FBDO #6 Foodborne Botulism Associated with Home-canned Bamboo Shoots–Thailand, 1998

On April 13, 1998, the Thailand Ministry of Public Health was informed of six persons with sudden onset of cranial nerve palsies, suggestive of botulism. They were admitted to a provincial hospital. The six patients lived in a village where further investigation in the community revealed 11 more case-patients. The source of *Clostridium botulinum* was home-canned bamboo shoots. The patients all ate from one 20-L can. No other common food eaten by the stricken persons was identified.

- CDC *MMWR 21:* 437, 1999.

FBDO #7 Type B Botulism Associated with Roasted Eggplant in Oil–Italy, 1993

On October 5–6, four of nine members of an extended family who had dined together on October 2 were hospitalized in Naples with suspected botulism. The meal consisted of green olives, proscuitto, bean salad, green salad, mozzarella cheese, sausages, and commercially prepared eggplant in oil. Based on an investigation and past histories, the eggplant was implicated as the probable source. All the patients were treated with trivalent botulism antitoxin and gradually improved. On September 27, investigators indicated that another family member had opened and dipped a fork into the implicated jar of eggplant. Although he did not eat any eggplant, he used the fork for other food items. The following day, he developed vomiting, dysphagia, and double vision. His symptoms resolved; he was treated with trivalent botulism antitoxin after botulism was diagnosed in other family members.

The commercially prepared eggplant suspected of causing both outbreaks was produced by one company and sold only in Italy. Public health officials issued a national warning and recalled the product.

- CDC *MMWR 44:* 33, 1995.

FBDO #8 Cryptosporidiosis Outbreak in Ireland Linked to Public Water Supply

The Department of Health in the Republic of Ireland noted increases of outbreaks from *Cryptosporidium* during April–May, 2002. Thirteen of these cases were found to be linked to the same water supply. Epidemiological and environmental investigations were conducted. The water source was a spring-fed lake, which was chlorinated but not filtered. Microbiological tests were also done and 24 stools samples were positive for *Cryptosporidium parvum*. The difficult detection of *C. parvum* oocysts is due to their small size (4 to 6 mm) and their low concentration in the polluted water.

- *Eurosurveillance Weekly 22*, May 30, 2002.

FBDO #9 Cholera Associated with International Travel, 1992

Approximately one case of cholera per week is reported in the United States. Most of these cases have been acquired during international travel and involve persons who return to their homelands to visit their family or foreign nationals visiting relatives in the United States. The following are some examples of such cases:

A mother and her two daughters, residing in Connecticut, visited relatives in Ecuador during the Christmas holidays. The mother ate cooked crab and lobster, and the 16-year-old daughter ate cooked crab. The 13-year-old did not eat any seafood. Sixteen hours after eating the seafood meal, the mother had vomited, suffered abdominal cramps and diarrhea. The 16-year-old also developed similar symptoms. Both sick persons got hospitalized and given IV fluids and oral antimicrobials. Toxigenic *Vibrio cholerae* was recovered from their stool cultures. The 13-year-old daughter remained well.

In 1991, 26 cases of cholera were reported in the United States. Eighteen of them were associated with travel to Latin America of which eleven were related to crabs brought back in their suitcases.

Although the spread of cholera on an aircraft is unlikely, if routine sanitary measures are observed, crew members of commercial aircraft for international travel should be prepared to treat passengers who develop symptoms of cholera. Packets of oral rehydration solution (ORS) should be available on board.

- CDC *MMWR 4*. Sept. 11, 1992.

FBDO #10 Escherichia coli *O157:H7 Infections Associated with Eating a Nationally Distributed Commercial Brand of Frozen Beef Patties and Burgers–Colorado, 1997*

The Colorado Department of Public Health identified an outbreak of *E. coli* O157:H7 infections associated with consumption of a nationally distributed brand of frozen beef patties and burgers. Subsequently after laboratory tests and investigations, the products were recalled.

In cooperation with the USDA and CDC, continuing efforts were carried out to determine potential contamination points during meat processing. The investigation of this outbreak illustrates the value of molecular sub-typing in the surveillance for E. coli O157:H7 infections.

- CDC *MMWR 46* (33): 778, August 22, 1997.

FBDO #11 Outbreak of Escherichia coli *O157:H7 and* Campylobacter *Among Attendees of the Washington County Fair–New York, 1999*

Ten children were hospitalized suffering from bloody diarrhea in counties near Albany, New York. They had attended the Washington County Fair. Subsequently, some attendees during the week of August 23–29, 1999 were found to be in infected with *Campylobacter jejuni*. Further investigations and laboratory tests by the New York State Department of Health (NYSDOH) confirmed the presence of *E. coli* and *Campylobacter* spp. One source of the pathogens came from the water supply of a shallow well, which was not chlorinated. Several street vendors used this water for making beverages and ice.

- CDC *MMWR 48* (36): 803, September 17, 1999.

FBDO #12 E. Coli *Outbreak in a Popular UK Holiday Spot*

Twelve people were believed to have been affected by an *E. coli* O157 outbreak, which hit a popular UK holiday spot. Three cases, all of them children, have so far been confirmed, and health officials say they fear the numbers will rise. Tests carried out confirmed the presence of the bacterium in the water supply to the Rothiemurchus Camp and Caravan Park at Coylumbridge, near Inverness. A number of houses in the area also use the same private water supply.

- MacNeill, Fergus. *PA News,* August 2002.

FBDO #13 Outbreaks of Escherichia coli *O157:H7 Infections Among Children Associated with Farm Visits–Pennsylvania and Washington, 2000*

These outbreaks happened during spring and fall, 2000 involving 56 illnesses and 19 hospitalizations of children in Pennsylvania and Washington who visited farm animals. All of the children had direct contact with farm animals. They were allowed to touch cattle and calves, sheep, goats, chickens, and a pig. Handwashing was not supervised and the facilities lacked soap.

Investigators from the CDC and State Departments of Health from Maryland and Pennsylvania identified the risk factors and confirmed findings from stool specimens. Fifteen persons in the Pennsylvania had either *E. coli* O157 symptoms or hemolytic uremic syndrome (HUS). In the Washington area, five persons ages 2 to 14 years old, had diarrhea, abdominal cramps and three were hospitalized.

- CDC *MMWR 50* (15) 293–397. April 20, 2001.

FBDO # 14 Outbreaks of Cyclosporiasis–*United States and Canada, 1997*

Since April1997, CDC received reports of cyclosporiasis involving twenty-one clusters of cases from eight states across the US and one province from Canada. They were associated with events like banquets, receptions, or meals eaten in the same restaurant on the same day. Other events occurred on a cruise ship that departed from Florida.

Fresh raspberries were served at nineteen of the twenty-one events. The berries reportedly had been rinsed in water at ten of the nineteen events for which such information was available. Another cluster of events in Florida were traced to eating fresh greens, called mesclun, which is a spring mix of field baby greens.

After these outbreaks, the FDA and CDC helped the berry industry in Guatemala to implement a Hazard Analysis and Critical Control Point (HACCP) system.

- CDC *MMWR 46* (23), 521–523. June 13, 1997.

FBDO #15 Clostridium perfringens *Gastroenteritis Associated with Corned Beef–Ohio and Virginia, 1993*

The Cleveland City Health Department (CCHD) received telephone calls from 15 persons who became ill after eating corned beef purchased from one delicatessen. Investigations revealed that the outbreaks were caused by *Clostridium perfringens* following the consumption of the infected corned beef on St. Patrick's Day. Improper cooling after cooking a big batch of the meat by the same delicatessen was the main cause of the outbreak. CCHD therefore recommended proper handling of the cooked corned beef and reheating immediately before serving to an internal temperature of 165°F (74°C). Similar situations happened in Virginia. Health officials recommended that meat after cooking be cooled rapidly to 40°F (4.4°C or less).

- CDC *MMWR 43* (08) 137–138. March 4, 1994.

FBDO #16 Foodborne Outbreak of Cryptosporidiosis in Washington, 1997

On December 29, 1997, the Spokane Regional Health District received reports of acute gastroenteritis among persons who ate a dinner banquet at a Spokane restaurant. The buffet included eighteen different food and beverage items, seven of which had uncooked produce. Investigations revealed that fifty-one guests who suffered symptoms characteristic of cryptosporidiosis consumed menu items that contained fresh green onions. The green onions were not washed before delivery to the restaurant and the food workers at the restaurant did not consistently wash them before preparing and serving.

- CDC *MMWR 47* (27) 565. July 17, 1998.

FBDO #17 Salmonella typhimurium *Found in Foods Served at a Buffet*

This happened in the City of Cardiff, the capital of Wales where some 260 delegates attended a medical conference. They ate a luncheon buffet that included baked chicken, breads, and beef. About 75 percent of the physicians who ate breaded baked chicken got sick with symptoms of diarrhea, vomiting, fever, and abdominal cramps. Some of the doctors had as many as fifteen watery stools a day. The source of the food poisoning was traced to *S. typhimurium,* which was found in many items in the kitchen, including liver pate, cooked beef, and bread crumbs.

- Palmer, S. R. et al. Outbreak of salmonella food poisoning amongst delegates at a medical conference in London. *J. Royal College of Physicians of London. 24* (1): 26–29. 1990.

FBDO # 18 Outbreak of Salmonella Kottbus *Infections Associated with Alfalfa Sprouts, February to April, 2001*

The California Department of Health Services identified a cluster of *Salmonella Kottbus,* which affected twenty-three persons, implicating alfalfa sprouts produced by a single facility. Twenty-one of the patients developed acute diarrheal illness and three had urinary tract infections. A trace back investigation identified a single alfalfa sprout producer as the source of the contamination. Consequently, the US FDA recommended decontamination of seeds with an approved treatment (e.g., soaking the seeds in a 20,000 ppm calcium hypochlorite for 15 minutes).

- CDC *MMWR 51* (01): 7–9. January 11, 2002.

FBDO #19 Salmonellosis due to Raw Eggs in Homemade Ice Cream

About 50 percent of the students in a Fort Monmouth, New Jersey College preparatory school suffered severe gastroenteritis. They had severe diarrhea, abdominal cramps, headaches, and fever. One-third of them had to be hospitalized. Fortunately, all of them recovered. Each of the patients was tested positive for *Salmonella enteriditis* that they ingested from homemade ice cream made with Grade A raw eggs.

- CDC *MMWR 34* (15) 215, 1985.

FBDO #20 Salmonellosis from Belgian Chocolate

About forty cases of salmonellosis were confirmed as reported in Canada and the United States. The victims, who were mostly children, ate the familiar gold foil-wrapped chocolate coins. Fortunately, the symptoms were mild.

Normally, cocoa, a very low-moisture product, will not be suspected to support salmonella growth, but the contamination could happen during the processing of cocoa beans to the finished powdery product.

- Hocken, J. C. et al. *J Food Protection 52* (1), 51–54, 1989.

FBDO # 21 Salmonellosis from Hot Pink Paprika

This is another unusual food vehicle for salmonella: a dry spice or seasoning. Between April to September 1993, there was a national outbreak of salmonellosis in Germany that was traced to potato chips seasoned with paprika powder, called Hot Pink Paprika. An estimated 1000 cases, mostly children under fourteen years old, were affected. More than 3,000 tons of snack products seasoned with the contaminated paprika were recalled

- Paprika recall. *International Safety News 2:* (9) 99, 1993

FBDO #22 Outbreak of Salmonella Muenchen *Infections Associated with Unpasteurized Orange Juice*

During June 1999, the Washington State Health Department and the Oregon Health Divisions independently investigated clusters of diarrheal illnesses caused by salmonella serotype Muenchen. The source of both outbreaks was traced to a single processor, who distributed the unpasteurized orange juice nationally. All these products were recalled.

- CDC *MMWR. 48* (27): 582, July 16, 1999.

FBDO #23 Selected Outbreaks of Shigellosis with Various Associated Foods

A huge outbreak of shigellosis occurred in Midland-Odessa, Texas in 1985 involving as many as 5,000 people. The implicated food was chopped bagged lettuce prepared in a central location for a Mexican restaurant chain. FDA investigation subsequently showed that *Shigella sonnei* was isolated from the lettuce. This pathogen can survive in refrigerated lettuce.

In 1985–86, several shigellosis outbreaks in college campuses were associated with fresh vegetables from the salad bar. *S. sonnei* has been found to be the leading species that cause shigellosis found in foods. The other species are more closely associated with contaminated water. An example of such case happened in Guatemala involving *Shigella dysenteriae* Type 1. For details, read *MMWR* report vol. 40, June 28, 1991.

- Matthews, D., *Food Safety Sourcebook.* (114–115) Detroit, Omnigraphics, 1999.

FBDO #24 Staphylococcal Food Poisoning Associated with Precooked Ham

Several persons were treated in a community hospital in northeastern Florida because of gastroenteritis. Investigations showed that staphylococcal intoxication was the cause of the illness among guests of a retirement party on September 26, 1997. Ninety-eight attendees filled out questionnaires and eighteen of them had symptoms that met the case definition. Onset of the illness occurred at a mean of 3.4 hours after eating the precooked ham. The food worker had baked the 16-pound ham at home for 1.5 hours, at 400°F in a conventional oven; then transported it to her workplace to slice in a meat slicer of a large institutional kitchen. All 15 pounds of sliced ham were stored in a walk-in cooler for six hours, covered with foil. Then, the worker transported the ham back to her home, refrigerated overnight, and served cold the following day. The meat slicer was not sanitized before using and a probable cause also is not washing the hands before handling the meat.

- CDC *MMWR 46* (50), 1189–91. Dec. 19, 1997.

FBDO # 25 Outbreak of Vibrio parahaemolyticus *Infections Associated with Eating Raw Oysters, Pacific Northwest, 1997*

The largest reported outbreak in North America of culture-confirmed *Vibrio parahaemolyticus* infections occurred in July–August, 1997. Illness in 209 persons was associated with eating raw oysters harvested from California, Oregon, and Washington (US) and from British Columbia (Canada). While the contributing factor that brought about the illness was elevated water temperatures, the main reason for the outbreaks was that the victims did not cook the oysters.

On August 19, the Federal Department of Fisheries and Oceans closed all BC coastal waters to the harvesting of oysters. On August 20, members of the Pacific Coast Oyster Growers Association voluntarily halted shipments of shell oysters harvested in Washington. On August 23, the USFDA issued procedures for cooking oysters. The oysters' beds were reopened on September 15 and no additional illnesses were reported.

- CDC *MMWR 47* (22): June 12, 1998.

FBDO# 26 Yersinia enterocolitica *Outbreaks in Tennessee*

A large interstate outbreak of gastroenteritis occurred in the summer 1982 and tests by the Health Department zeroed in on the milk pasteurized at a plant in Memphis, Tennessee. It contained *Yersinia enterocolitica* as the responsible pathogen.

About 200 people in the states of Arkansas, Tennessee, and Mississippi were positive for *Y. enterocolitica*. Most of the patients suffered from diarrhea, abdominal pains, and fever. Many had secondary infections of the throat, blood, urinary tract, and even the central nervous system. More than 40 percent were children under five years of age. Most of them had to be hospitalized.

Although the milk from the Tennessee plant was pasteurized, it could have been recontaminated. Yersinia can grow at refrigerator temperatures.

- CDC. *MMWR 31* (37) 505, 1982.

FBDO # 27 Trichinellosis Outbreaks in Germany, 1998–1999

From November 1998 to January 1999, fifty-two cases of trichinellosis were identified by the public health surveillance systems in eleven cities in the state of Northine-Westfalia, Germany. Investigation of the cases revealed that one outbreak was caused by contaminated ground meat. The other was due to a commercially prepared raw smoked sausage. A case of trichinellosis was defined as a positive serologic test for Trichenella antibodies (IgG and/or IgM). Symptoms seen with case-patients included: myalgia, fever, headache, diarrhea, and facial edema. Seven patients ate ground pork or mixed ground meat (beef and pork) and all obtained the meat from one supermarket.

In Germany, trichinellosis screening of all pork has been mandatory since 1937. The extremely low prevalence of *Trichinella* in pigs has led to the debate about the need for continued routine testing of all slaughtered pigs after the 1998–99 outbreaks.

- CDC *MMWR 48* (23) 488, June 18, 1999.

FBDO # 28 Horsemeat-Associated Trichinosis

In August and October 1985, two outbreaks of trichinosis associated with the consumption of horsemeat occurred in France. The first outbreak involved several cases in Melun, a town located 30 miles southeast of Paris. Several cases were diagnosed later from a southern district of Paris. Cases of trichinosis were identified through a review of medical records from private and public laboratories. Three hundred twenty-five individuals met the case definition for trichinosis. Of the symptoms compatible with trichinosis, myalgia was reported among 94 percent of the cases; fever among 90 percent, facial edema among 58 percent, and diarrhea among 52 percent. The investigation implicated horsemeat as the source of the parasite and all 325 patients had consumed horsemeat. Ninety-nine percent ate it raw or rare.

The second outbreak implicated horsemeat again as the source of infection. All patients purchased the meat from one shop where five of nine butchers were also infected. This is an interesting case and the reader can read more about it from the reference below.

- CDC *MMWR 35* (18) 291, May 09, 1986.

FBDO #29 Trichinosis in Hawaii Associated with Wild Boar

Three cases of trichinosis were reported to the Hawaii Department of Health in January 1986. The victims ate wild boar meat from a local Hawaiian who slaughtered the animal. Because the meat was given to several families and friends of the hunter, an investigation was conducted to determine the extent of the outbreak. Twenty-eight persons ate the meat, and seven of them met the standard case-definition for trichinosis. They showed symptoms like malaise, myalgia, fever, headache, diarrhea, vomiting, and trunk/limb edema. Four cases ate meat after it had been microwaved at high heat for two minutes only; the rest fried the meat. The two persons with the most severe illness had eaten the most meat. Subsequently, the community was instructed on the proper handling and cooking of pork and pork products.

- CDC. *MMWR 36* (2) 14, Jan. 23, 1987.

FBDO #30 Trichinosis Outbreaks in the US–1990

Two outbreaks of trichinosis in 1990 were investigated to be caused by eating undercooked infested pork. The US CDC in Atlanta warned in its February 1991 MMWR that the risk is particularly high among Southeast Asian immigrants who eat undercooked pork. One outbreak involved 250 people who attended a wedding reception of Southeast Asians in Des Moines, Iowa. Ninety guests developed trichinosis. The food implicated was raw pork sausage.

In November–December 1990, four Virginia counties reported outbreaks of fifteen sausage-related cases. Fortunately, no deaths were reported.

The CDC noted that the proportion of cases from commercial pork has declined since 1975, probably due to laws prohibiting feeding raw garbage to pigs, the use of home freezers, and consumer education about cooking pork thoroughly.

- *FDA Consumer,* May 1991.

FBDO #31 Intestinal Parasitism Study in a Cohort of Peace Corps Volunteers in Guatemala

A prospective longitudinal study was conducted in a cohort of 36 Peace Corps volunteers in Guatemala to study the incidence and natural history of intestinal parasitism in their more than two years of stay. Stool specimens were collected at least monthly when they were taken ill with gastrointestinal symptoms. The volunteers had 116 episodes of infection, with eleven parasites identified. The highest was for *B. hominis,* followed by *Entamoeba coli* and *Cryptosporidium parvum.* For more details, readers can access this interesting study available as a microfilm in some libraries.

- Herwaldt, B. et al. Multiyear prospective study of intestinal parasitism of Peace Corps volunteers in Guatemala. *J Clin Microbiology* (34) Jan. 2001.

FBDO #32 Norwalk Virus among British Military Personnel in Afghanistan, May 2002

Outbreaks of acute gastroenteritis were traced to Norwalk-like viruses (NLVs) that occurred among twenty-nine British soldiers and staff of a field hospital in Afghanistan during May 2002. Fecal specimens were tested for NLVs by electron microscopy and by biochemical assays. The results confirmed the presence of small, round-structured viruses considered consistent with NLVs.

In the United States, NLVs cause an estimated 23 million episodes, 50,000 hospitalizations, and about 300 deaths each year. NLVs can be transmitted by fecally contaminated food and water, or by direct person-to-person contact. Outbreaks of NLV-associated gastroenteritis illnesses are common among military settings.

- CDC *MMWR 51* (22) 477, June 7, 2002.

FBDO #33 Gastrointestinal Disease Outbreak Traced to Faulty Cross-Connection

At a convention attended by 1200 individuals, 123 suffered from gastrointestinal disease. Upon investigation, the two microorganisms suspected to be the etiologic agents were *Guardia lamblia* and Norwalk-like virus. Because these are both waterborne, investigators turned their attention to the water supply at the convention center. The ice machine, which supplied the needs for portable bars was found to have a flexible tube inserted into a floor drain. When the machine's filters were serviced, the tube formed a connection between the ice machine's water supply and the raw sewage.

- McSwane, D., Rue, N., and Linton, R. *Essentials of Food Safety and Sanitation,* 2nd ed. Upper Saddle River, Prentice Hall, 2000.

FBDO #34 DDT (chlorophenothane): Dilemmas with Exportation, Storage, and Disposal in the Americas

International concerns over DDT continue to pose a public health hazard as the situation in Belize demonstrates. The United States and Mexico are two countries that still allow companies to export DDT. In 1997 sacks, approximately five tons, of unused DDT were discovered in a dilapidated, leaky wooden building, with unsecured windows, no security, one door, and located only 30 feet from the sea shore in an area prone to flooding. Belize officials have struggled with the responsibility for disposing of this persistent organic pollutant (POP). The material has been temporarily relocated until a method for disposal can be found. The recommended method for disposal is incineration. However, there is no incinerator or hazardous waste landfill facility in Belize. The Belize Ministry of Health and the Department of the Environment (DOE) contacted the United States Environmental Protection Agency for assistance in disposing of the unused DDT. The DDT is still under temporary storage in Belmopan, Belize.

- Alegria, M. *Problems with Final Disposal of DDT in Belize.* United Nations Environmental Programme. Available at http://www.chem.unep.ch/pops/POPs_Inc/proceedings/cartagena/ALEGRIA.html. Accessed March 21, 2002.

FBDO #35 Dioxins Travel Internationally, Belgium's Dioxin-Containing Products Were Banned from the US and Asian Markets

In Belgium, dioxins found their way into the food supply, suspecting the improper disposal of industrial oil containing dioxin and PCBs in January of 1999. These substances were placed into a container meant for recycled frying fats, which were sold to feed mills supplying European farms. A Dutch laboratory determined that a chicken from a Belgian farm in April 1999 had 400 ppm of PCBs in its fatty tissue, 400 times the accepted limit in Holland. Dioxins, at 781 pp trillion, 1,5000 times higher than the Dutch safe level were also detected. And PCB levels 65 times greater than the countries limit were detected in eggs exported to Germany from Belgium. In Asia, health regulators from Bangkok to Taipei banned food imports from

Europe and recalled products suspect of contamination.

In June, in the United States the FDA issued an Import Bulletins and Import Alerts directing numerous animal products, animal feeds and animal by-products and egg-containing products be held at the port of entry. The import ban was extended to all European countries for animal feed and pet foods because of the uncertainty of the extent of the contamination and the lack of measures to prevent exposed animals from being recycled into the feed supply. The FDA is tracking and sampling products already imported during January to June 1999. In Asia, authorities are next puzzled about how to dispose of potentially contaminated foods. Burial in landfills is a common choice. Danger may well return in another form if the chemicals leach into the groundwater.

Source:

1. *WSWS: News & Analysis: Medicine & Health.* Available at http://www.wsws.org/articles/1999/jun1999/diox-j01.shtml. Accessed March 22, 2002.
2. The Great Dioxin Scare. Asia Week. Available at http://www.pathfinder.com/asiaweek/99/0625/feat6.html. Accessed March 25, 2002.
3. CVM and International Dioxin Concerns. Available at http://www.fda.gov/cvm/index/dioxin/dioxin_intl.html. Accessed March 25, 2002.

FBDO # 36 Kepone's Long-term Monitoring Program Tracks Pesticide Residue in Plant Workers, in Fishing Waters, and Dietary Supplements

Another pesticide, kepone (chlordecone), detected in plant workers in Hopewell, Virginia has been shown to cause cancer, neurological diseases and sterility. The employees had been exposed to kepone through inhalation, ingestion, and skin absorption. Hopewell, Virginia is located on the James River that flows into the Chesapeake Bay opening into the Atlantic Ocean. During production from 1966 to 1975 an estimated 90,720 kg of kepone was released to the environment through atmospheric emissions, wastewater discharges, and bulk-disposal of off-specification batches. In 1975 the entire James River was closed to the taking of any shellfish and/or finfish because of kepone, with various bans in place thereafter until 1988. In 1988 all James River fishing restrictions due to kepone were allowed to expire as kepone levels in fish remained below the US Food and Drug Administration (FDA) action level of 0.30ppm. The area is currently under a contaminant advisory, which states, "Kepone may be hazardous to your health. A fish-eating advisory exists for those who consume fish from these waters on a daily basis." (Department of Environmental Quality, http://www.deq.state.va.us./water/reports.html). The human health concerns extend to oysters and oyster shells harvested and used in natural calcium supplements.

- Fishing Restrictions and Health Advisories in Effect for Virginia Rivers. Available at http://www.vdh.state.va.us/HHControl/fishing_advisories.htm. Accessed March 21, 2002.

FBDO #37 Fixed Obstructive Lung Disease in Workers at Microwave Popcorn Factory in Missouri, 2000–2002

In May 2000, an occupational medicine physician contacted the Missouri Department of Health and Senior Services to report eight cases of fixed obstructive lung disease in former workers of a microwave popcorn factory.

All eight had a respiratory illness with symptoms of cough and dyspnea on exertion, had reduced lung capacity, and had worked from eight months to nine years in the factory. At the factory soybean oil, salt and flavorings had been mixed into a large heated tank in a process that produced dust, aerosols and buttery smelling odors. FDA regulates flavorings based on the safety of the amounts consumed, not the safety of prolonged worker inhalation of high concentrations. CDC has no evidence to suggest that consumers are at risk from the heating and consuming of the purchased product.

CDC is conducting repeated air sampling and medical surveillance at four-month intervals. One factory worker in another factory in Nebraska has reported similar symptoms. Preliminary animal studies suggest severe damage to airway passages after inhalation exposure to high air concentrations of butter flavorings.

- CDC *MMWR* April 26, 2002/51(16); 345–347. Available at http://www.cdc.gov/mmwr/preview/mmwrhtml/mm5116a2.htm. Accessed April 26, 2002.

FBDO #38 Scombroid Fish Poisoning

On December 3, 1998, four adults became ill after eating tuna-spinach salad at a restaurant in Pennsylvania. Their symptoms included: burning sensation in the mouth, metallic taste, facial flushing, nausea, diarrhea, and headache with an onset of five minutes to two hours. A presumptive diagnosis of scombroid fish poisoning was made based on clinical and epidemiologic features of the outbreak.

Fish samples were found positive for histamine levels above 50 ppm, versus normal levels of below 10 ppm.

- *MMWR 49* (18): 399. May 20, 2000.

FBDO #39 Neurologic Illness Associated with Eating Pufferfish, 2002

As of May 15, 2002, a total of 13 presumptive cases of saxitoxin poisoning were reported in Florida. Victims ate pufferfish caught in waters near Titusville, Florida. Investigators reported that the persons who ate pufferfish experienced numbness of the mouth and lips (all 13 patients), face (8 persons), arms (10 persons), and legs (7 persons). Four had vomited before presenting to a hospital. Onset of symptoms occurred from thirty minutes to eight hours after ingesting the Florida pufferfish. They were treated in the hospital and fortunately the cases were all resolved.

- CDC. *MMWR 51*(19): 314, May 17, 2002.

FBDO #40 Amanita phalloides Mushroom Poisoning in California

From December 28, 1996 to January 6, 1997, nine persons in northern California required hospitalization after eating Amanita phalloides ("death cap") mushrooms. Two died and the others had to undergo intensive medical treatment. These wild mushrooms contain a potent hepatotoxin. Worldwide ingestion of A. phalloides mushrooms account for about 90 percent of deaths attributable to the ingestion of these mushroom species. The principal toxins (amatoxins) are taken up by hepatocytes and interfere with messenger RNA synthesis, thus suppressing protein synthesis in the liver and resulting in acute hepatitis with possible liver failure. Some cases develop renal failure. Toxicity symptoms develop rapidly: the first stage, which occurs within six to twenty-four hours after ingestion, include: abdominal pain, nausea and vomiting, fever, hyperglycemia, hypotension, and electrolyte imbalance. The second stage, which occurs after twenty-four to forty-eight hours, shows initial stages of liver and renal malfunctions.

The last stage, which may occur four to seven days after ingestion, includes cardiomyopathy, coagulopathy, seizures, and eventually death from hepatic and/or renal failure.

- CDC. *MMWR 46*(22): 489, June 6, 1997.

FBDO # 41 Outbreak of Salmonella enteriditis *in Denmark, January 2000*

The Office of Public Health in Vejle County, Denmark received a report on January 2, 2000 about the death of two people within the same family. On December 28, the first victim was taken ill from gastroenteritis with severe diarrhea, abdominal pains and fever. The 44-year-old victim died on December 31 from cardiac arrest. The 18-year-old son of the first victim also fell ill on New Year's Eve. He also experienced vomiting, diarrhea, and fever. The boy lost consciousness and died on New Year's Day.

Forensic autopsy isolated *Salmonella enteriditis* phage type (PT) 6. Further investigations revealed that the culprit was a cake, prepared on December 23 and eaten by the family on December 27, 1999, containing a cream made from cocoa powder, vegetable fat and raw egg. The cake had *Salmonella* concentrations ranging from 10,000 to 100,000 per gram.

- WHO Global Salmonella-Survey List, Server Message #2000-05. Reported by K. Molbak, Statens Serum Institute, Copenhagen, Denmark. Available at http://www.who.int/emc/diseases/zoo/SALM-SURV/server messages/message5.html. Accessed July 30, 2002.

FBDO # 42 Outbreak of E. coli *0157:H7 in Radish Sprouts, Sakai City, Japan*

Nine thousand people were affected by the *E. coli* O157:H7 outbreak in Sakai City, Japan in July 1996. The main culprit was found to be contaminated radish sprouts served in school lunches. According to investigations, the large concentration E. coli 0157:H7 in the edible parts of the plant may have grown at the time of germination of the radish that were soaked in contaminated water.

- Medical News Service: *Sugarcane, Chicken and Radish Sprouts: A Sampling of Country Food Safety Experiences.* January 28, 2002. Available at http://www.medicalnewsservice.com/fullstory.cfm. Accessed July 30, 2002.

FBDO # 43 Salmonellosis Outbreak in Rockhampton, Australia

Salmonella heidelberg PT 1 were found to have caused an outbreak involving a number of residents in a nursing home. The residents of the home were fed with a pureed diet, and evidence revealed that raw egg might have been added to some of the foods.

Similarly, this salmonella subtype has been linked to the outbreak in another nursing home near Rockhampton in 1998. The culprit was eggnog fed to the patients.

- WHO Global Salmonella-Survey Electronic Discussion Group, Message # 2001-11: *Recent Salmonella Outbreaks in Central Queensland, Australia.* Submitted by J. Bates, Chief Scientist, and Public Health Microbiology, Queensland Scientific Services. Available at http//www.who.int/emc/diseases/zoo/

SALM-SURV/server mesages 2001/ message11.html. Accessed July 30, 2002.

FBDO # 44 Outbreak of Salmonellosis Associated with Fried Ice Cream, Australia, June 2001

Thirty persons were reported being ill after eating fried ice cream. This food product is usually prepared by coating the ice cream with a layer of sponge cake, dipped in egg mixture, frozen, and deep-fried for a short-period, when required. Investigations revealed that the culprit was *Salmonella typhimurium* PT64, and that the food product was heavily contaminated, as observed by the short incubation period and hospitalization of some of the victims.

- Communicable Diseases Network Australia: *Australian Disease Outbreaks,* June 2001. Reported by G. Dowse, Medical Epidemiologist from the Communicable Disease Control Branch, Health Department of Western Australia. Available at http://www.health.gov.au/pubhlth/cdi/ausbreak.htm. Accessed June 30, 2002.

FBDO # 45 E. coli *O157 Outbreak at Campsite in Scotland*

Health officials in Scotland were cited as confirming an outbreak of *E. coli* O157. One child was in the hospital and all those affected were staying at a campsite at Coylumbridge, Scotland.

- Macneill, F. Available at http://www.plant.uoguelph.ca/safefood/archives/fsnet-archives.htm. Accessed August 2, 2002

FBDO #46 Alaska Cruise Cancelled After Second Virus Outbreak

Hundreds of travelers on a Holland America Lines Alaskan cruise on the Rydam were sickened because of a second outbreak of a Norwalk-type virus. The bug, which causes 24 to 48 hours of diarrhea, vomiting, stomach pains, and fever hit 189 of the 1,318 passengers, and 29 of the 564 crew, according to Health Canada. This second sailing was launched just nine hours after the Ryndam had a first incident affecting 170 passengers and crew who caught the virus. After the first incident, the ship's water and food supply was investigated and the surfaces were cleaned with a bleach solution. Apparently these safeguards were not enough, thus the company had to notify passengers of the cancellation of the cruise.

- Reported by Lazaruk, S. Times Colonist, Victoria. Available at http://www.plant.uoguelph.ca/safefood/archives/fsnet-archives.htm. Accessed August 2, 2002

FBDO # 47 Bacterial Infection Outbreak at Prison

From Walla Walla, the State Health Department is investigating an outbreak of bacterial infection during the third week of March, 2002, at the Washington State Penitentiary. There were an estimated forty-four people reported feeling ill. There have been twelve confirmed cases of camphobacter infection–eleven inmates and one staff member. One of the primary sources of bacterium is raw poultry, and turkey was on the prison menu the week of the infection.

- Available at http://seattlepi,nwsource.com/local/64521 walla 29.shtml. Archived at http:www.plant.uoguelph.ca/safefood/archives/fsnet-archives.htm. Accessed on August 2, 2002.

FBDO #48 Virus Strikes Rail Passengers

There was a "rash of illness" aboard the VIA Rail Canadian train in Toronto in July affecting passengers and crew who had the following symptoms: nausea, vomiting, diarrhea, abdominal pains, muscle aches, headaches, fatigue, and fever. These symptoms are consistent with those of Norwalk-like viruses. The viruses are spread when food that is not cooked is handled by infected people who did not wash their hands after using the washroom; by consuming water contaminated by sewage; by consuming ice made from contaminated water; and from shellfish harvested from sewage-contaminated water.

- Reported by J. Kennedy, The Vancouver Sun. Available at http://www.plant.uoguelph.ca/safefood/archives/fsnet-archives.htm. Accessed August 2, 2002

FBDO # 49 Food Poisoning in Australia

Health authorities have confirmed the number of people affected by Victoria's worst food poisoning in five years. Affected were 256 people, including children as young as one year old who were taken to Melbourne hospitals suffering from acute stomach pains, vomiting and nausea. Bacterial infection was the most likely cause of the food poisoning that affected people after a function at the Imam Ali Islamic Centre. A meal of rice, lamb, and potatoes was served at the function that attracted about 600 people. Part of the food was cooked the day before and reheated for the function. This outbreak is believed to be the biggest since the pork roll food poisoning in 1997.

- Reported by L. Gooch. *The Age,* Tuesday 26 Mar 2002 [edited]. http://www.theage.com.au/articles/2002/03/26/1017089530996.html A ProMED-mail post. Available at http://www.promed-mail.org. International Society for Infectious Diseases. Available at http://www.isid.org Archived at: http://www.plant.uoguelph.ca/safefood/archives/fsnet-archives.htm

FBDO #50 Twenty-eight Fatalities from Listeriosis

This was reported in 1985 from California when 86 cases of *Listeria monocytogenes* infection were identified in Los Angeles and Orange Counties. It was a needless tragedy of eight neonatal deaths, 13 stillbirths, and 8 other deaths, classified as non-neonatal. The mothers involved ranged in age from 15 to 43 years and were all of Hispanic origin. The sources of *Listeria* were Mexican-style cheeses from local producers. For details about this outbreak, read the *MMWR* report listed below.

- CDC *MMWR 34* (24): 357, 1985. Epidemiologic notes and reports: Listeriosis outbreak associated with Mexican-style Cheese–California.

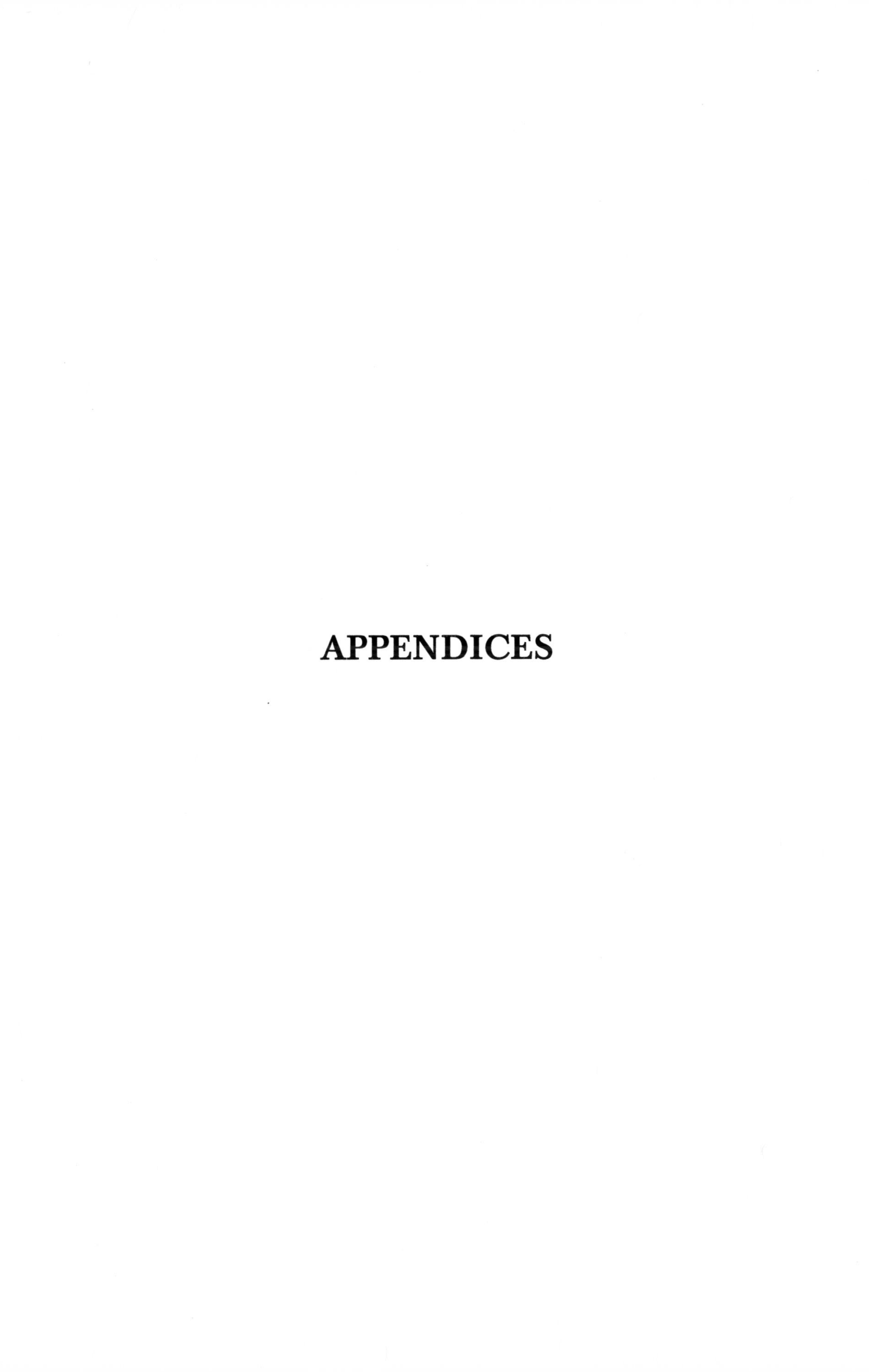

APPENDICES

Appendix A

CONVERSION TABLE FOR FAHRENHEIT AND CELSIUS FOR COMMON TEMPERATURES USED FOR FOODS

Formula:

Centigrade (Celsius) to Fahrenheit		5/9 times (°F minus 32°)
	Or	(°F minus 32°) times 5 divided by 9
Fahrenheit to Centigrade (Celsius):		(9/5 times °C) plus 32°
	Or	(1.8 times °C) plus 32°

EXAMPLES OF EQUIVALENTS FOR COMMONLY USED VALUES IN FOODS

°F	°C	°F	°C
–31	–35	80	27
–4	–20	85	30
0	–18	90	32
29	–2	100	38
30	–1	110	43
32	0	120	49
33	1	130	54
36	2	150	66
38	3	160	71
41	5	165	74
45	7	180	82
50	10	190	88
55	13	194	90
60	16	200	93
65	18	212	100
70	21	240	116
75	24	250	121

Appendix B

A TYPICAL FOOD FLOWCHART

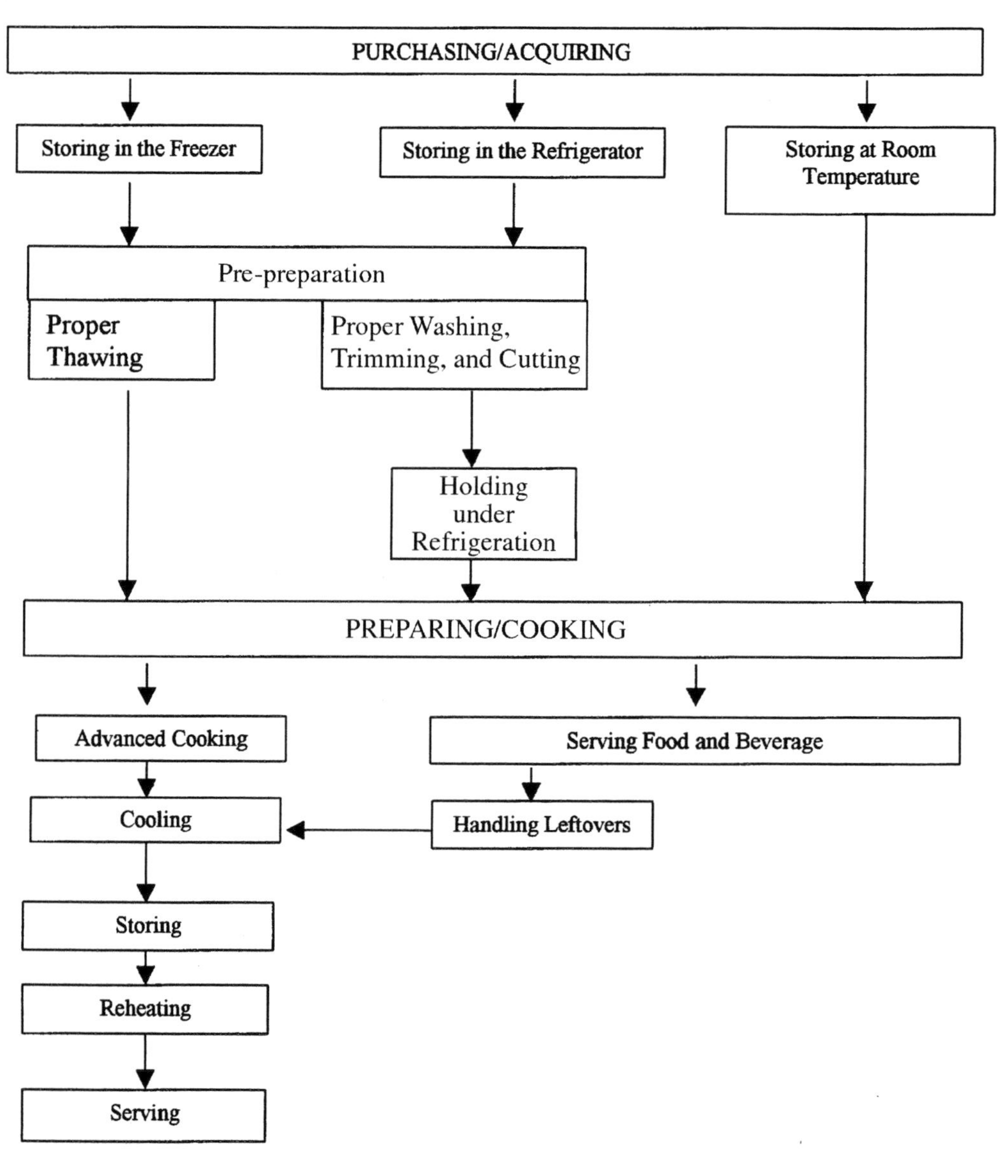

Appendix C

SAMPLE MATERIAL SAFETY DATA SHEET (MSDS)
MATERIAL SAFETY DATA SHEET
(Prepared according to OSHA 29CFR 1010, 1200)

Product Name ______________________________

Section 1. Manufacturer/Distributor Information

Prepared by:____________ On Date: ________ For (Company Name): __________

Address:______________________________ Emergency Phone: ____________

____

____

Section 2. Ingredient Information

____

Section 3. Physical and Chemical Characteristics

Boiling Point: ________ Specific Gravity: __________ Vapor Pressure: __________

Solubility in Water: __________ Appearance:__________ Odor: __________

Section 4. Fire and Explosion Hazard Data

Flash Point: ______________ Flammable Limits: ______________

Extinguishing Media: ______________________________

Special Fire Fighting Procedures: ______________________________

____

Unusual Fire and Explosion Hazards: ______________________________

____

D.O.T. Classification: ______________________________

Section 5. Reactivity Data

Stability: __________ Incompatibility (Materials to avoid): __________________________

____

Hazardous Products of Decomposition: ____

Hazardous Polymerization: ____

Section 6. Hazard Data

Primary Routes of Entry: (Inhalation, Skin Absorption, Etc.)_______________________

____

Health Hazards: _________Oral Toxicity: ____________ Inhalation: ________________

Eye Irritation: __________________ Primary Skin Irritation: ______________________

Carcinogenicity: ______________Signs and Symptoms of Exposure: ________________

____

Emergency and First Aid Procedures: Eyes____________ Skin_______________________

Ingestion: ____

Section 7. Special Protection Information

Respiratory Protection: ______________ Protective Gloves: ______________________

Eye Protection: ________________ Protective Clothing: _________________________

Ventilation: ____

Section 8. Special Precautions and Spill/Leak Procedures

Steps to be Taken if Spilled or Released: _____________________________________

Waste Disposal: ____

Precautions to be Taken in Handling and Storage: _____________________________

____

Appendix D

APPLICANT AND FOOD EMPLOYEE INTERVIEW*

Preventing transmission of diseases through food by infected food employees with emphasis on illness due to *Salmonella typhi, Shigella* spp., *Shiga* toxin-producing *Escherichia coli,* and Hepatitis A virus.

THE PURPOSE OF THIS FORM IS TO ENSURE THAT APPLICANTS TO WHOM A CONDITIONAL OFFER HAS BEEN MADE, AND FOOD EMPLOYEES ADVISE THE PERSON IN CHARGE OF PAST AND CURRENT CONDITIONS DESCRIBED, SO THAT THE PERSON IN CHARGE CAN TAKE APPROPRIATE STEPS TO PRECLUDE THE TRANSMISSION OF FOODBORNE ILLNESS.

Name of Applicant or Employee
(PRINT)____

ADDRESS ____

Tel. No. (DAYTIME) ____________________

Tel. No. (EVENING)____________________

TODAY

Are you suffering from any of the following:

1. Symptoms
   Diarrhea? YES NO
   Vomiting? YES NO
   Jaundice? YES NO
   Sore throat with fever? YES NO
2. Lesions (such as boils and infected wounds however small) containing pus on the hand, wrist, or an exposed body part? YES NO

PAST:

1. Have you ever been diagnosed as being ill with typhoid fever (*Salmonella typhi*), shigellosis (*Shigella* spp.), *Shiga* toxin-producing *Escherichia coli* infection (*E. coli* 157:H7), or Hepatitis A virus? YES NO

HIGH-RISK CONDITIONS

1. Have you been exposed to or suspected of causing a confirmed outbreak of typhoid fever, shigellosis, *Shiga* toxin-producing *Escherichia coli* infection, or Hepatitis A? YES NO
2. Do you live in the same household as a person diagnosed with typhoid fever, shigellosis, Hepatitis A, or illness due to *Shiga* toxin-producing *Escherichia coli?* YES NO
3. Do you have a household member attending or working in a setting where there is a confirmed outbreak of typhoid fever, shigellosis, *Shiga* toxin-producing *Escherichia coli* infection, or Hepatitis A? YES NO

Name, address, and telephone number of your doctor:

Name: ____________________

Address ____________________

Telephone Daytime: ____________ Evening: ____________

Signature of Applicant or Food Employee ____________ Date ________

Signature of Permit Holder's Representative ____________ Date ________

Source: Food and Drug Administration (FDA), US Department of Health and Human Services, *2001 Food Code.*

Appendix E

PROPER STORAGE OF REFRIGERATED FOODS

Foods	*Recommended Temperatures (°F/°C)*	*Maximum Storage Periods*	*Remarks*
Meat			
Roasts, steaks, chops	32–36/0–2.2	3 to 5 days	Wrap loosely
Ground and stewing	32–36/0–2.2	1 to 2 days	Wrap loosely
Variety meats	32–36/0–2.2	1 to 2 days	Wrap loosely
Whole ham	32–36/0–2.2	7 days	May wrap tightly
Half ham/ham slices Luncheon meats	32–36/0–2.2	3 to 5 days	May wrap tightly
Canned ham	32–36/0–2.2	1 year	Keep in can
Frankfurters	32–36/0–2.2	1 week	Original wrapping
Bacon	32–36/0–2.2	1 week	Original wrapping
Leftover cooked meats	32–36/0–2.2	1 to 2 days	Wrap or cover tightly
Gravy, broth	32–36/0–2.2	1 day	Highly perishable
Poultry: Chicken, turkey, duck, goose, giblets	32–36/0–2.2	1 to 2 days	Wrap loosely, Wrap giblets separately
Stuffing	32–36/0–2.2	1 to 2 days	Covered container separate from bird
Fish: Fatty or lean; Not iced	30–34/–1.1 to 1.1	1 to 2 days	Wrap loosely
Iced	32/0	3 days	Don't bruise with ice
Shellfish	30–34/–1.1 to 1.1.	1 to 2 days	Covered container

Continued on next page

Foods	*Recommended Temperatures (°F/°C)*	*Maximum Storage Periods*	*Remarks*
Eggs, in shell	40/4.4	1 week	Do not wash, or remove from container
Eggs, leftover yolks/whites	40–45/4.4–7.2	2 days	Cover yolks with water
Dried eggs	40–45/4.4–7.2	1 year	Cover tightly
Reconstituted eggs	40–45/4.4–7.2	1 week	Same treatment as eggs in shell
Cooked dishes: eggs, meat, milk, fish, poultry, cream-filled pastries	32–36/0–2.2	Serve day prepared	Highly perishable
Dairy Products:			
Fluid milk	38–39/3.3–3.9	5 to 7 days after date on carton	Keep covered and in original container
Butter	38–40/3.3–4.4	2 weeks	Waxed cartons, once opened wrap in tight container
Hard cheese (cheddar, parmesan, romano)	38–40/3.3–4.4	6 months	Cover tightly to preserve moisture
Soft cheese, cottage cheese	38–40/3.3–4.4	3 days	Cover tightly
Evaporated milk, canned, Dry milk	50–70/10–21.1	1 year unopened	Refrigerate after opening
Reconstituted dry milk (liquid)	38–40/3.3–4.4	1 week	Treat as fluid milk
Fruit:			
Apples	40–45/4.4–7.2	2 weeks	Room temp. until ripe
Avocados, bananas	40–45/4.4–7.2	3 to 5 days	Room temp. until ripe
Berries, cherries, grapes	40–45/4.4–7.2	3 to 5 days	Do not wash before refrigerating
Citrus juice	40–45/4.4–7.2	1 month	Original container
Cranberries	40–45/4.4–7.2	1 week	Do not wash before refrigerating

Foods	*Recommended Temperatures (°F/°C)*	*Maximum Storage Periods*	*Remarks*
Pears, pineapples, citrus fruit	40–45/4.4–7.2	3 to 5 days	Room temp. until ripe; then refrigerate
Plums	40–45/4.4–7.2	1 week	Do not wash before refrigerating
Vegetables:			
Sweet potatoes, mature onions, hard rind squashes	60/15.6	1 to 2 weeks at room temp.	Ventilated containers
Potatoes	45–50/7.2–10	30 days	Ventilated containers
All other vegetables	40–45/4.4–7.2	5 days max. for most; 2 weeks for cabbage, root vegetables	Unwashed for storage

Source: (1) University of Florida, Institute of Food and Agriculture Science (UF/IFAS). Fact Sheet HE 8490, Series Prepared by the Home Economics Department, Florida Cooperative Extension Service, February, 1994. (2) Food Safety and Inspection Service (FSIS), USDA. Refrigeration and Safety, www.fsis.usda.gov. Accessed on 3/9/03.

Appendix F

PROPER FREEZER STORAGE OF FOODS

Food	*Freezer Temperature (0°F/–18°C)*	*Maximum Storage Periods*	*Remarks: Proper Handling*
Eggs: fresh, in shell	0°F/–18°C		Don't freeze
Raw yolks, whites		1 year	
Hard cooked			Don't freeze
Liquid pasteurized eggs or egg substitutes opened			Don't freeze
Liquid pasteurized eggs or egg substitutes unopened		1 year	
Mayonnaise, commercial			Don't freeze refrigerate after opening
TV dinners, frozen casseroles		3 to 4 months	
Deli & vacuum-packed products; store-prepared (or homemade) egg, chicken, tuna, ham, macaroni salads			Don't freeze
Pre-stuffed pork & lamb chops, chicken breasts stuffed with dressing, store-cooked convenience meals, commercial brand vacuum-packed dinners with USDA seal			If you are going to freeze these foods, do so as soon as you get them home, not after they've sat in the refrigerator
Soups, stews, and vegetable or meat-added		2 to 3 months	
Hamburger and stew meals, ground turkey, veal, pork, lamb and mixtures of them		3 to 4 months	

Food	*Freezer Temperature (0°F/−18°C)*	*Maximum Storage Periods*	*Remarks: Proper Handling*
Hot dogs and lunch meats opened/ unopened package		1 to 2 months	Freezer wrap
Bacon and sausage breakfast links, patties, pepperoni, jerky sticks		1 month	
Ham and corned beef fully cooked		1 month	
Fresh meat; beef steaks, roasts, lamb roast, chops		6 to 9 months	
Pork chops and roasts, veal, chop and roasts		4 to 6 months	
Leftover meats, gravy, broth		2 to 3 months	
Fresh poultry		9 months	
Giblets		3 to 4 months	
Cooked poultry		4 months	
Chicken nuggets, patties		1 to 3 months	
Smoked fish (salmon, cod, whiting)			Freezing not recommended. After 6 months loses quality
Pasteurized fresh whole or skimmed milk, sweet cream, flavored milk drinks			Do not freeze (change of texture, body appearance). Fat separates
Dairy products; whipped topping, opened sweetened and condensed milk, custards, puddings			Do not freeze
Natural hard cheese and semi-hard cheese and processed (cheddar, Swiss, parmesan, brick, bleu, etc.)			Preferably, do not freeze. Freezing affects texture. Still suitable for cooking.
Soft cheese (cream, cottage, limburger, camembert), cheese spreads			Do not freeze. (can freeze cream cheese, but texture may change).

Source: Bellenir, K., and Dresser, P. D. *Food and Animal Borne Diseases Sourcebook.* Detroit, Omnigraphics, Inc., 1995.
University of Florida, Institute of Food and Agricultural Sciences (UF/IFAS). Fact Sheet HE 8490, Series Prepared by the Home Economics Department, Florida Cooperative Extension Service. February, 1994.

Appendix G

PROPER HANDLING OF GOODS IN DRY STORAGE

Food	*Recommended Maximum Storage (at 70°F/21° C)*	*Remarks*
Baking powder	18 months or expiration date on can	Keep dry and covered
Baking soda, bouillon cubes or granules	2 years	Keep dry and covered
Cereals, ready to eat unopened	6 to 12 months*	Refold package tightly after opening. Keep cool
Opened	2 to 3 months	
Chocolate, premelted; semi-sweet;	12 months	Keep cool and well-wrapped
Unsweetened	18 months	
Chocolate syrup, unopened	2 years*	Cover tightly. Refrigerate after opening. Label and date.
Opened	6 months	
Cocoa mixes	8 months*	Cover tightly
Coffee in cans, unopened	2 years*	
Opened	2 weeks	Refrigerate after opening
Coffee, instant dry, unopened	1 to 2 years	Keep tightly closed
Opened	2 weeks	Keep tightly closed. Use dry spoon
Cornmeal, cornstarch	12 months	Keep tightly closed
Flour, white or whole wheat	6 to 8 months	Keep tightly closed
Gelatin, all types	18 months	Keep in original container
Grits	12 months	Store in airtight container
Honey	12 months	Cover tightly; if crystallized, warm jar in a pan of hot water
Jellies, jams	12 months	Cover tightly. Refrigerate after opening. Remove any light mold on surface and use.

Food	*Recommended Maximum Storage (at 70°F/21° C)*	*Remarks*
Marshmallow crème, unopened	3 to 4 months	Cover tightly and refrigerate after opening.
Marshmallows	2 to 3 months	Keep in airtight container
Milk, condensed or evaporated unopened;	12 months	Invert can every 2 months
dry nonfat milk unopened	6 months*	Put in airtight container
opened	3 months	
Pasta (dry noodles)	2 years	Once opened, store in airtight container
Rice, white	2 years*	Keep tightly closed
Rice, flavored or herb	6 months	Keep tightly closed
Salad dressings, unopened bottles;	10 to 12 months	Refrigerate after opening
opened	3 months	
Salad oil, unopened	6 months*	Refrigerate after opening
Shortenings, solid, unopened	8 months	Refrigeration not needed
Opened	6 months	Refrigeration not needed
Sugar, brown	4 months	Put in airtight container
Sugar, confectioners	18 months	Put in airtight container
Sugar, granulated; artificial	2 years	Cover tightly
Tea bags, instant; Loose tea	18 months to 3 years; 2 years.	Put in airtight containers; cover tightly
Vinegar, unopened	2 years*	Keep tightly closed;
Opened	12 months	Slight cloudiness does not affect vinegar
Nondairy creamer, dry unopened	12 months	Keep lid tightly closed
Opened	6 months	Keep lid tightly closed
Canned Goods, unopened	12 months*	Keep cool
Canned Fruit Juices, Unopened		Keep cool
Canned Foods, Opened	2 days	All opened cans: Remove from can and transfer to glass or plastic container; label and date
Fruits, dried; vegetables, dried	6 months to 1 year	Keep cool in airtight container; refrigerate, if possible
Catsup, chili sauce, unopened	12 months*	Keep cool
Opened	1 month	Refrigerate tightly closed
Mustard, prepared unopened	2 years	May be refrigerated; stir
Opened	6 months	before using
Spices, herbs, blends, whole	1 to 2 years	Store in airtight containers in
Ground	6 months	a dry place away from sunlight and heat. If aroma has faded, replace.

Continued on next page

Food	Recommended Maximum Storage (at 70°F/21°C)	Remarks
Vanilla, unopened; opened	2 years*; 12 months	Keep tightly closed
Other extracts	12 months	Keep tightly closed, volatile oils escape.
Cake mixes and other packaged foods		Keep cool and dry
Biscuit, brownie, muffin mixes	9 months	
Cake mixes	9 months	Keep cool and dry
Casserole mixes	9 to 12 months	Keep cool and dry
Cookies, homemade or packaged	2 to 3 weeks	Put in airtight container
Crackers, unopened	8 months*	Keep box tightly closed
Frosting, canned	3 months*	Store leftovers in refrigerator
Pancake mix; pie crust mix	8 months*	Keep cool and dry
Potato, instant unopened	6 to 9 months	Keep in airtight package
Pudding mixes, unopened	12 months*	Keep cool and dry
Sauces and gravy mix, unopened	6 to 12 months	Keep cool and dry
Soup mixes, unopened	12 months*	Keep cool and dry

*Total time "unopened" product can be stored at home. If recommendation is for "opened" product, subtract this time from the total or storage "unopened" time.

Source: University of Florida, Institute of Food and Agricultural Sciences (UF/IFAS). Fact Sheet HE 8490, Series Prepared by the Home Economics Department, Florida Cooperative Extension Service. February, 1994.

Appendix H

FDA SANITARY INSPECTION FORM*

DEPARTMENT OF HEALTH, EDUCATION AND WELFARE PUBLIC HEALTH SERVICE – FOOD AND DRUG ADMINISTRATION FOOD SERVICE ESTABLISHMENT INSPECTION REPORT	
Based on an inspection this day, the items circled below identify the violation in operations or facilities which must be corrected by the next routine inspection or such shorter period of time as may be specified in writing by the regulatory authority. Failure to comply with any time limits for corrections specified in this notice may result in cessation of your Food Service operations.	
OWNER NAME: ADDRESS:	BUSINESS NAME: PHONE NUMBER:

FOOD

*01 SOURCE: SOUND CONDITION, NO SPOILAGE (5)

02 ORIGINAL CONTAINER, PROPERLY LABELED (1)

FOOD PROTECTION

*03 POTENTIALLY HAZARDOUS FOOD MEETS TEMPERATURE REQUIREMENTS DURING STORAGE, PREPARATION, DISPLAY, SERVICE, TRANSPORTATION (5)

PERSONNEL

*11 PERSONNEL WITH INFECTIONS RESTRICTED (5)

*12 HANDS WASHED AND CLEAN, GOOD HYGIENIC PRACTICES(5)

13 CLEAN CLOTHES, HAIR RESTRAINTS (1)

21 WIPING CLOTHS CLEAN, STORED, RESTRICTED (1)

22 FOOD CONTACT SURFACES OF EQUIPMENT AND UTENSILS CLEAN, FREE OF ABRASIVES, DETERGENTS (2)

23 NON-FOOD CONTACT SURFACES OF EQUIPMENT AND UTENSILS CLEAN (1)

*04 FACILITIES TO MAINTAIN PRODUCT TEMPERATURE (4)

05 THERMOMETERS PROVIDED AND CONSPICUOUS (1)

06 POTENTIALLY HAZARDOUS FOOD PROPERLY THAWED (2)

*07 UNWRAPPED AND POTENTIALLY HAZARDOUS FOOD NOT RE-SERVED (4)

08 FOOD PROTECTION DURING STORAGE, PREPARATION, DISPLAY, SERVICE, TRANSPORTATION (2)

09 HANDLING OF FOOD (ICE) MINIMIZED (2)

10 IN USE, FOOD (ICE) DISPENSING UTENSILS PROPERLY STORED (1)

FOOD EQUIPMENT AND UTENSILS

14 FOOD (ICE) CONTACT SURFACES DESIGNED, CONSTRUCTED, MAINTAINED, INSTALLED, LOCATED (2)

15 NON-FOOD CONTACT SURFACES, DESIGNED, CONSTRUCTED, MAINTAINED, INSTALLED, LOCATED (1)

16 DISHWASHING FACILITIES DESIGNED, CONSTRUCTED, MAINTAINED, INSTALLED, LOCATED, OPERATED (2)

17 ACCURATE THERMOMETERS, CHEMICAL TEST KITS PROVIDED, GAUGE COCK (1/4 IPS VALVE) (1)

18 PRE-FLUSHED, SCRAPED, SOAKED (1)

19 WASH, RINSE WATER CLEAN, PROPER TEMPERATURE (2)

*20 SANITIZATION RINSE, CLEAN, TEMPERATURE, CONCENTRATION, EXPOSURE TIME, EQUIPMENT, UTENSILS SANITIZED (4)

24 STORAGE, HANDLING OF CLEAN EQUIPMENT/ UTENSILS (1)

25 SINGLE-SERVICE ARTICLES, STORAGE, DISPENSING USED (1)

26 ON RE-USE OF SINGLE SERVICE ARTICLES (2)

WATER

*27 WATER SOURCE, SAFE, HOT AND COLD UNDER PRESSURE (5)

SEWAGE

*28 SEWAGE AND WASTE WATER DISPOSAL (4)

PLUMBING

29 INSTALLED MAINTAINED (1)

*30 CROSS-CONNECTION, BACK SIPHONAGE, BACKFLOW (5)

TOILET AND HANDWASHING FACILITIES
*31 NUMBER, CONVENIENT, ACCESSIBLE, DESIGNED, INSTALLED (4)
32 TOILET ROOMS ENCLOSED, SELF CLOSING DOORS, FIXTURES, GOOD REPAIR, CLEAN HAND CLEANSER SANITARY TOWELS/ TISSUE/HAND-DRYING DEVICES, PROPER WASTE RECEPTACLES (2)

GARBAGE AND REFUSE DISPOSAL
33 CONTAINERS OR RECEPTACLES, COVERED ADEQUATE NUMBER, INSECT/RODENT-PROOF, FREQUENCY, CLEAN (2)

34 OUTSIDE STORAGE AREA ENCLOSURES PROPERLY CONSTRUCTED, CLEAN, CONTROLLED INCINERATION (1)

INSECT, RODENT, ANIMAL CONTROL
*35 PRESENCE OF INSECT/RODENTS - OUTER OPENINGS PROTECTED, NO BIRDS, TURTLES, OTHER ANIMALS (4)

FLOORS, WALLS AND CEILING
36 FLOORS CONSTRUCTED, DRAINED, CLEAN, GOOD REPAIR, COVERING INSTALLATION, DUSTLESS CLEANING METHODS (1)

37 WALLS, CEILING, ATTACHED EQUIPMENT CONSTRUCTED, GOOD REPAIR, CLEAN SURFACES, DUSTLESS CLEANING METHODS (1)

LIGHTING
38 LIGHTING PROVIDED AS REQUIRED, FIXTURES SHIELDED (1)

VENTILATION
39 ROOMS AND EQUIPMENT VENTED AS REQUIRED (1)

DRESSING ROOMS
40 ROOMS CLEAN, LOCKERS PROVIDED, FACILITIES CLEAN, LOCATED, USED (1)

OTHER OPERATIONS
*41 NECESSARY TOXIC ITEMS PROPERLY STORED, LABELED, USED (5)

42 PREMISES MAINTAINED, FREE OF LITTER, UNNECESSARY ARTICLES, CLEANING MAINTENANCE EQUIPMENT PROPERLY STORED AUTHORIZED PERSONNEL (1)

43 COMPLETE SEPARATION FROM LIVING/SLEEPING QUARTERS LAUNDRY (1)

44 CLEAN, SOILED LINEN PROPERLY STORED (1)

RATING SCORE:
(100) LESS WEIGHT OF ITEMS VIOLATED →

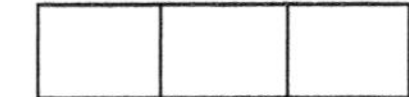

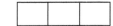

*Form is modified to highlight the criteria or items inspected.
Figures enclosed in parentheses ( ) are the weights.

Appendix I

FOOD CODE 2001 (USA) *

The Food Code 2001 by the United States Public Health Service, Food and Drug Administration (FDA), is a model for safeguarding public health and ensuring that food is unadulterated and honestly presented when offered to the consumer. "It represents FDA's best advice for a uniform system of provisions that address the safety and protection of food offered at retail and in food service."

"This model is offered for adoption by local, state, and federal governmental jurisdictions for administration by the various departments, agencies, bureaus, divisions, and other units within each jurisdiction that have been delegated compliance responsibilities for food service, retail food stores, or food vending operations. Alternatives that offer an equivalent level of public health protection to ensure that food at retail and food service is safe are recognized by this model."

"This guidance represents FDA's current thinking on safeguarding public health and ensuring food is unadulterated and honestly presented when offered to the consumer. It does not create or confer any rights for or on any person and does not operate to bind FDA or the public. This guidance is being issued in accordance with FDA's Good Guidance Practices regulations (21 CFR 10.115, 65 FR 56468: September 19, 2000)."

For Public Sale by:
US Department of Commerce
Technology Administration
National Technical Information Service
5285 Port Royal Road, Springfield, VA 22161
(703) 605-6000 (Refer to report No. PB 2002100819)

CONTENTS OF THE US FOOD CODE 2001

*The contents of 2001 Food Code may be viewed also from the web site using FDA/CFSAN FDA 2001 Food Code.

Appendix J

SELECTED FOOD SAFETY WEB SITES

Americas

Agriculture and Agri-food Canada Online
http://www.agr.gc.ca/

Health Canada
http://www.hc-sc.gc.ca/

Canadian Food Inspection Agency
http://www.inspection.gc.ca/english/toce.shtml

Centers for Disease Control and Prevention (US) (CDC)
http://www.cdc.gov

Food Safety Consortium, USA
http://www.uark.edu/depts/fsc/

National Food Safety Database, USA
http://www.foodsafety.org/

Food and Drug Administration, USA
http://vm.cfsan.fda.gov/

Food Safety and Inspection Service, USA
http://www.fsis.usda.gov/

Food Safety Research Information Office, National Agricultural Library, USA
http://www.nal.usda.gov/fsrio/

Asia-Australia-Pacific

Asia-Pacific Economic Cooperation (APEC)
http://www.apecsec.org.sg/

Food Standards, Australia and New Zealand
http://www.anzfa.gov.au/

National Institute of Animal Health, Japan
http://ss.niah.affrc.go.jp/

CSIRO Division of Food Science and Technology, Australia
http://www.dfst.csiro.au/

Food Quality Control Division, Ministry of Health, Malaysia
http://dph.gov.my/division/fqc/

Europe

European Union Food Safety Authority
http://www.efsa.eu.int/

The European Commission
http://www.apecsec.org.sg/

National Public Health Institute, Finland
http://www.ktl.fi/nutrition/food_safety.html

Food Safety Authority of Ireland
http://www.fsai.ie/

Food Standards Agency, UK
http://tnsis.private.tnsofres.com/eSampler/foodstandards_int.htm

Department for Environment, Food and Rural Affaires, UK
http://www.defra.gov.uk/

The Danish Veterinary and Food Administration Home Page
http://dph.gov.my/division/fqc/

Consumer Policy and Consumer Health Protection, European Union
http://europa.eu.int/comm/dgs/health_consumer/index_en.htm

World

International Association for Food Protection (IAFP)
http://www.foodprotection.org

International Food Information Council (IFIC)
http://www.ificinfo.health.org

International Organizations and Foreign Government Agencies
http://www.fda.gov/ioa/agencies.htm

Organization for Economic Cooperation and Development
http://www.oecd.org/EN/home/0,EN-home-0-nodirectorate-no-no-no-0,FF.html

United Nations Organization (UNO)
http://www.un.org/

Food and Agriculture Organization (FAO) of the United Nations
http://www.fao.org/

World Health Organization (WHO)
http://www.who.int/en/
http://www.who.int/fsf/

Selected Professional Organizations/Associations

American Dietetic Association (ADA)
http://www.eatright.org

Institute of Food Technologists (IFT)
http://www.ift.org

Food Safety Organization
http://www.food safety.org

National Restaurant Association (NRA)
http://www.nra.com

Food Marketing Institute (FMI)
http://www.fmi.org

GLOSSARY

A

Abrasive cleaner: Cleaners that contain a scouring agent (finely ground minerals) that help scrub off hard-to-remove soils. They may scratch some surfaces.
Acceptable level: Within an established range of safety.
Accredited program: The certification process with an independent evaluation of factors such as the sponsor's mission, organizational scope, eligibility requirements, recertification, discipline and grievance procedures; and test development and administration; also, a food protection manager certification program that has been evaluated and listed by an accrediting agency as conforming to national standards for organizations that certify individuals.
Acid: A substance with a pH of less than 7.0. An exception is fresh milk which has a pH of 8.0 but it is not an acid.
Acid cleaner: Acid cleaners (pH below 7.0) are used on mineral deposits and other soils that alkaline cleaners can't remove, such as scale, rust, and tarnish.
Acids, strong: Acids that release high concentrations of hydrogen ions in a solution giving a low pH; examples are muriatic and sulfuric acids.
Acids, weak: Acids with a moderately low pH. Examples are organic acids, such as acetic and hydroxyacetic acids.
Acidity: An acidic substance has a pH below 7.0. Foods with a pH range from 5.0 to 7.0 (slightly acidic) are called potentially hazardous foods. *See* **High-acid foods.**
ADA (Americans with Disabilities Act): Federal law which requires reasonable accommodation for access to a facility by both patrons and employees with disabilities.
Additives: Natural and manmade substances added to a food for an intended purpose (such as preservatives and colors) or unintentionally (such as pesticides and lubricants).
Adulterated: The deliberate addition of undesirable, inferior or cheaper material to a supposedly pure food product in order to stretch out supplies and increase profits. Also cited in the Federal Food, Drug, and Cosmetic Act, § 402.
Aerobic: The ability to live and reproduce only in the presence of oxygen, such as aerobic microorganisms, or aerobes.
Air curtain: A ventilation unit that blows a steady stream of air across an open door (or outward) to discourage flying insects from entering. Also called air doors or fly fans.
Air dry: To dry in room air after cleaning, washing, or sanitizing.
Air gap: A device to prevent water backflow to a potable water supply. It is an unobstructed open space that separates an outlet of the potable water supply (for example, a faucet) from any potentially contaminated source like a drain.

Air screen: A unit that provides a strong downward air movement of air at doors to prevent refrigeration loss and insect entry.
Alkali: An alkali with a pH of more than 7.0.
Alkalis, strong: Substances that release high concentrations of hydroxyl ions in a solution giving a high pH; examples are sodium hydroxide and potassium hydroxide.
Alkalis, weak: Substances that release moderate to low concentrations of hydroxyl ions in a solution giving a moderately high pH; examples are sodium bicarbonate and sodium tetraphosphate.
Alkaline cleaner: All detergents are mildly alkaline (pH above 7.0) and are used to clean fresh soil from floors, walls, ceilings, prep surfaces, and most equipment and utensils.
Alkalinity: An alkaline substance has a pH above 7.0. Most foods are not alkaline.
Americans with Disabilities Act: *See* **ADA.**
Anaerobic: The ability to live and reproduce in the absence of oxygen, such as anaerobic microorganisms or anaerobes.
Antibiotic: A compound produced by a microorganism that inhibits or kills another microbe.
Anisakiasis: A disease caused by the anisakis parasite, which is a roundworm parasite found in fish.
Antiseptic: A chemical substance used to interfere with or inhibit the growth of harmful microorganisms.
Antimicrobial agent: A substance or compound that inhibits or kills microbes.
Antioxidant: Any substance that protects other substances or compounds from the effects of oxygen by reacting itself with oxygen first, thereby protecting the others from oxidation. Vitamin E and beta-carotene are antioxidants.
Application: A key element of training practice by the learner.
Approved: Acceptable to the Regulatory Authority based on a determination of conformity with principles, practices, and generally recognized standards that protect public health.
Approved suppliers: *See* **Suppliers.**
Aseptis packaging: A method in which food is sterilized or commercially sterilized outside the can and then aseptically placed in previously sterilized containers which are then sealed in an aseptic environment. This method may be used for liquid foods such as concentrated milk and soups.
At risk: The term used to describe individuals such as infants, children, pregnant women, and those with weakened immune systems for whom foodborne illnesses can be very severe, even life threatening.
a_w: Means water activity that is a measure of the free moisture in a food, is the quotient of the water vapor pressure of the substance divided by the vapor pressure of pure water at the same temperature, and is indicated by this symbol. Sometimes called available water, which microorganisms can utilize.

B

Bacilli: Rod-shaped bacteria
Backflow: A type of cross-connection that can occur in a potable water system. Backflow is the unwanted reverse flow of contaminated water, caused by backpressure, through a cross-connection into a potable water system. *See* **Air gap.**
Backsiphonage: A form of backflow that can occur when pressure in the potable water supply drops below pressure in the flow of contaminated water.
Bacteria: The most common foodborne microbial contaminants. Bacteria are living, single-celled microorganisms that decompose matter, resulting in subsequent product spoilage and/or foodborne illness. *See* Chapter 2 for details.
Bacterial growth: Bacteria reproduce (or grow) by splitting into two. *See* **Vegetative microorganisms.** When conditions are

favorable, bacteria can grow and multiply very rapidly, doubling the population as often as every twenty minutes, in some cases. Three phases of bacterial growth are the lag phase (slow growth), log phase (rapid growth), and death phase (decrease in population). *See* the acronym **FAT-TOM,** which lists the conditions conductive to bacterial growth.

Bactericide: A chemical substance that will kill certain bacterial cells. Sanitizers are examples.

Bacteriostat: An agent that inhibits the growth of bacteria but does not necessarily kill them.

Bacterium: One microorganism. Singular for bacteria.

Behavioral objectives: Specific sections a learner will be able to perform upon completion of training.

Beverage: A liquid for drinking, including water.

Bi-metallic stemmed thermometer: Food thermometer used to measure product temperatures. The most common and versatile type of thermometer, it measures temperature through a metal probe with a sensor in the end. Easily recalibrated. Most can measure temperatures from 0° to 220°F (–18°C to 104°C); accurate to within +/–2°F or =/–1°C.

Binary fission: The process by which bacteria grow. One cell divides to form two new cells; two divide to form four, etc.

Bioaccumulation: The accumulation of a contaminant in the tissues of living organisms in the food chain. For example, a toxic substance could accumulate or increase in amount as it flows from the producer-organism like plantons, to the next higher level (e.g. plankton-eating fish) then passed on to the next (e.g. small fish are eaten by big fish). Finally, man eats the fish with the toxin, receiving all of what was accumulated in the food chain.

Biofilm: A thin layer of microbial growth on surfaces that are improperly cleaned (table tops or equipment surfaces), or sanitized.

Biological contamination: Presence of microorganisms in food. Biological contamination from microorganisms, or microbial contamination, is the leading cause of foodborne illness throughout the world *See* **Contaminants.**

Biological toxin: A poisonous substance produced by a living organism. Many biological poisons or toxins occur naturally (in some fish, plants, mushrooms). Some toxins cannot be destroyed by heating.

Biological, chemical, and physical hazards: *See* **Hazards, biological; Hazards, chemical; Hazards, physical.**

Blast chiller: A special refrigerated unit that quickly freezes food items. Blast chillers can move food through the temperature danger zone quickly. Most cool foods from 140°F to 37°F within 90 minutes.

Bodily fluids: Fluid secretions of the human body, such as mucus, saliva, feces, perspiration, and oily secretions in skin and hair. Microorganisms in those fluids can be transmitted to customers via food if employees do not practice good personal hygiene.

Booster heater: An extra water heater attached to hot-water lines leading to warewashing machines or sinks; it raises water to temperatures required for heat sanitizing of tableware and utensils (180°F [82°C]). Many warewashing machines have internal booster heaters.

Bottled drinking water: Water that is sealed in bottles, packages, or other containers and offered for sale for human consumption, including bottled mineral water.

Botulism: A type of food intoxication resulting from consumption of food containing a toxin produced by *Clostridium botulinum.*

Buffer: A material that moderates the intensity of an acid or alkali in solution without reducing the quantity of acidity or alkalinity.
Builder(s): An adjunct added to cleaning compounds to control properties that tend to reduce the surfactant's effectiveness.

C

Calibrate: To determine and verify the scale of a measuring instrument with a standard. Thermometers used in food establishments are commonly calibrated using an ice slush method (32°F or 0°C) or a boiling point method (212°F or 100°C).
Campylobacter jejuni: A microaerophilic non-spore forming bacterium that causes a foodborne illness called Campylobacteriosis. *See* Chapter 2 for more details.
Canning: A process of preserving food by heating the food under pressure (as in retorts) and packing them in cans or bottles that are hermetically sealed. *See* also **Hermetic.** Commercial canning destroys *C. botulinum* and its toxin. Home canned foods especially of low acidity should be avoided.
Cantilever mounted: Also wall-mounted. Equipment attached to the wall with a bracket to allow for easier cleaning behind and underneath it.
Cardiopulmonary resuscitation (CPR): First aid technique to apply to persons who have stopped breathing.
Carrier: An animal, insect, or human that carries a pathogenic microorganism, often without showing symptoms of the disease. These carriers may infect others with the disease, yet may never become ill themselves. The carrier state cannot be cured with antibiotic treatment. Carriers may not work as food handlers or as child-care attendants.
Casing: A tubular container for sausage products made of either natural or artificial (synthetic) material.
CCP: *See* **Critical Control Point, HACCP.**
CDC (Centers for Disease Control & Prevention): An agency of the U.S. Public Health Service that investigates outbreaks of foodborne illness, studies the causes and control of disease, and publishes statistical data.
Celsius: Temperature scale related to the Fahrenheit scale by the formula 5/9 (°Fahrenheit –32°) = °Celsius (centigrade).
Ceramic tile: A hard nonresilient, nonporous, porcelain-type tile, installed with grout, commonly used for floors and walls in establishments.
Certification number: A unique combination of letters and numbers assigned by a Shellfish Control Authority to a Molluscan Shellfish dealer according to the provisions of the National Shellfish Sanitation Program.
Chemical agent: Chemical agents often used in establishments include cleaning products, polishes, lubricants, sanitizing chemicals, and pesticides. All can be dangerous to customers and employees if not properly used or stored.
Chemical contaminant: One type of contamination that causes foodborne illness, food can become contaminated by chemical substances normally found in establishments, including cleaning chemicals; utensils and equipment that leach toxic metals into foods; pesticides; and food additives and food preservatives, even those generally regarded as safe (GRAS), if not used correctly.
Chemical hazard: *See* **Hazard, chemical.**
Chemical sanitizing: A method of reducing the number of microorganisms on a surface by exposing an object to a sanitizing solution for a specific period of time. Common sanitizing chemicals are chlorine, iodine, and quaternary ammonia. *See* **Heat sanitizing.**
Chlorine: Most commonly used chemical sanitizer.
Cholera: A bacterial infection caused by a *Vibrio* spp. Foods commonly implicated are raw or undercooked fish and shellfish. It is also transmitted via polluted waters. *See* **Vibrio.**

Ciguatera Food Poisoning: A foodborne illness caused by a biological toxin. Ciguatera occurs when a person eats certain predatory fish (finfish like mackerel, groupers, barracuda, and snappers) that eat smaller fish that have eaten a certain species of toxic algae. The toxins in the algae accumulate in the tissues of the larger fish. Cooking does not inactivate the toxin.

"CIP": Cleaned in place by the circulation or flowing by mechanical means through a piping system of a detergent solution, water rinse, and sanitizing solution onto or over equipment surfaces that require cleaning, such as the method used, in part, to clean and sanitize a frozen dessert machine. Also, does not include the cleaning of equipment such as band saws, slicers, or mixers that are subjected to in-place manual cleaning without the use of a CIP system.

"CFR": *See* **Code of Federal Regulations.**

Clean: Free of visible soil but not necessarily sanitized; surface must be clean before it can be sanitized. *See* **Soil.**

Cleaning: The process of removing visible food and other types of soil from a surface. Surfaces must first be cleaned and rinsed before being sanitized.

Cleaning agent: Chemical compounds that remove food, soil, rust, stains, minerals, or other deposits from surfaces.

Clean-in-Place (CIP): Equipment designed to be cleaned without moving, usually large or very heavy.

Clostridium botulinum: An anaerobic bacterium that forms spores. It produces a deadly toxin that attacks the nervous system (i.e. a neurotoxin). Fortunately, the toxin is destroyed by boiling the food for a few minutes or by proper canning. *See* Chapters 2 and 13 for more details.

Clostridium perfringens: An anaerobic bacterium that forms spores. Unlike *C. botulinum* described above, its toxin is produced by surviving bacteria inside the human gut. For more details, *see* Chapter 2.

Cocci: Spherically shaped bacteria.

Code: A systemic collection of regulations, or statutes, and procedures designed to protect the public.

Code of Federal Regulations: The compilation of the general and permanent rules published in the US *Federal Register* by the executive departments and agencies of the federal government which (1) is published annually by the US Government Printing Office, and (2) contains FDA rules in 21 CFR, USDA rules in 7 CFR and 9 CFR, EPA rules in 40 CFR, and Wildlife and fisheries rules in 50 CFR.

Cold-holding: Refers to the safe temperature range (less than 41°F or 5°C) for maintaining foods cold prior to service for consumption.

Cold paddles: Utensils that can be filled with water and frozen. Stirring food products with them chills food very quickly.

Communicable disease: Infectious illness transmittable to others.

Commingle: (1) To combine shellstock harvested on different days or from different growing areas as identified on the tag or label, or (2) To combine shucked shellfish from containers with different container codes or different shucking dates.

Comminuted: (1) Reduced in size by methods including chopping, flaking, grinding or mincing. (2) Fish or meat products that are reduced in size and restructured or reformulated such as gefilte fish, gyros, ground beef, and sausage; and a mixture of two or more types of meat that have been reduced in size and combined, such as sausages made from two or more meats.

Competency-based training: A job is analyzed and broken down into steps that must be learned to gain mastery of the task; training should focus on those steps.

Confirmed disease outbreak: A foodborne disease outbreak in which laboratory analysis of appropriate specimens identifies a causative agent and epidemiological analysis implicates the food as the source of the illness.

Consumer: A person who is a member of the public, takes possession of food, is not functioning in the capacity of an operator of a food establishment or food processing plant, and does not offer the food for resale.

Contact spray: A liquid or powder insecticide that must come into direct contact with insects to kill them.

Contaminate: To add foreign and unwanted matter to an object or environment.

Contaminants, contamination: Presence of harmful substances not originally present in the food. Three types of contaminants are biological hazards, chemical hazards, and physical hazards. Although most food-safety hazards are contaminants introduced by humans, some food hazards occur naturally, such as toxins in certain fish, mushrooms, or plants.

Contamination: The unintended presence of harmful substances or conditions in food that can cause illness or injury to people who eat the infected food.

Control measures (versus preventive measures): Steps taken, usually by a PCO, to control or eliminate pests that have infested buildings. These include chemical and nonchemical treatment methods. Preventive measures include steps that can be taken to prevent pests from entering a building, such as keeping the facility clean and sanitary and maintaining the building properly.

Control point: Any step or procedure where biological, physical, or chemical hazards can be controlled. *See* **HACCP.**

Cooking: The act of providing sufficient heat and time to a given food to effect a change in food texture, aroma, and appearance, color, flavor, sanitary quality. More importantly, cooking ensures the destruction of foodborne pathogens inherent to that food.

Cooling: the act of reducing the temperature of properly cooked food to 41°F (5°C) or below.

Corrective action: A predetermined action taken when food doesn't meet a critical limit. For example, when the temperature of a hot food falls below 140°F (60°C), the proper corrective action is reheat the food to 165°F (74°C) for fifteen seconds within two hours. *See* **Critical limit, HACCP.**

Corrosion resistant materials: Materials that maintain their original surface characteristics under continuous use in food service with normal use of cleaning compounds and sanitizing solutions.

Coving: A curved, sealed edge between the floor and walls that makes cleaning easier and eliminates hiding places for insects.

Critical Control Point (CCP): A point or procedure in a food system where loss of control may result in an unacceptable health risk; the last step where you can intervene to prevent, control, or eliminate the growth of microorganisms in food. *See* **HACCP.**

Critical item: A provision of the FDA Food Code that, if in noncompliance, is more likely than other violations to contribute to food contamination, illness, or environmental health hazard; an item that is denoted in the FDA Food Code with an asterisk (*).

Critical limits: The maximum or minimum value to which a physical, biological, or chemical parameter must be controlled at a critical control point to minimize the risk that the identified food safety hazard may occur.

Critical zone (*See* **Danger zone**): The range of temperatures at which microbes grow fastest, 36–140°F (2–60°C).

Cross-connection: Any physical link through which contaminants from drains, sewers, or waste pipes can enter a potable water supply.

Cross-contamination: Transfer of harmful substances (soil, other particles, or disease-causing microorganisms) from one food product to another through direct contact, or contact with a nonfood surface, such as utensils, equipment, air, work surfaces, or employees' hands or clothing.

Cumulative: Increasing in effect by successive additions. For example, hot food must be cooled from 140°F (60°C) to 70°F (21°C)) within 2 hours; it must reach 41°F (5°C) within an additional 4 hours to prevent bacterial growth. Therefore, the *cumulative time the food is in this danger zone equals a total of 6 hours or less.*

Curing: Preserving foods, notably meats, by the addition of nitrate/nitrite. Nitrate salt (saltpeter) becomes nitrite, which is the final curing agent. Examples of cured meats are ham, bacon, bologna, hotdogs, salami, and *longganisa* (Philippine sausage).

D

Danger zone (*See* **Critical zone**): The range of temperatures at which microbes grow fastest, 36–140°F (2–60°C).

Dead man's switch: Activates equipment when depressed and stops if pressure is relieved.

Death phase: The period of bacterial growth when the number of microorganisms dying exceeds the number of microorganisms being produced and the number declines.

Deep-chill storage: Deep-chill units hold foods at near-freezing temperatures, between 26°F and 32°F (–3°C to 0°C), for short periods of time. Poultry, meat, seafood, and *sous vide* products stored at these temperatures have a longer shelf life, but deep-chill temperatures may freeze and damage other foods.

Deflocculation (dispersion): The action of breaking up aggregates into individual parts.

Detergent: A water-soluble preparation, chemically different from soap, used in cleaning to break down oils, hold dirt in suspensions, and act as a wetting agent. General-purpose detergents are mildly alkaline.

Diarrhea: Loose and frequent bowel movement, hence sometimes referred to as LBM (loose bowel movement). Stools or feces are unformed and watery. Could be bloody, depending on causative factor. *See also* **Traveler's Diarrhea.**

Digital thermometer: A battery-powered thermometer that reveals temperature in a digital numerical display.

Disinfect: To remove potentially pathogenic microorganisms from an object or environment.

Disinfectant: A chemical used to destroy the growing forms, but not necessarily the spores, of potentially pathogenic microorganisms (harmful bacteria).

Disinfection: Killing harmful microorganisms using disinfectants.

Dispersion: Deflocculation; breaking up of a mass into fine particles that are suspended in solution.

Drinking water: A water that meets 40 CFR 141 National Primary Drinking Water Regulations; traditionally known as potable water; includes the term "water" except where the term used connotes that the water is not potable, such as "boiler water," "mop water," "rainwater," "wastewater," and "nondrinking" water.

Droppings: The feces of insects, birds or animals.

Dry storage: The holding of nonperishable food items, such as rice, flour, crackers, and canned goods, at 50 to 60 percent humidity and between 50°F and 70°F (10°C and 21°C).

Dysentery: A bacterial infection due to a bacillus (bacillary dysentery) characterized by diarrhea, abdominal pain. There is also amebic dysentery.

E

Easy-to-clean: Materials and designs that facilitate cleaning; varies with the likelihood

of the surface's role in introducing pathogenic or toxigenic agents or other contaminants into food based on the surface's approved placement, purpose, and use.
Easy-to-move: Portable, mounted on casters, gliders, wheels, raised on legs, or provided with a mechanical means to safely tilt a unit of equipment for cleaning.
Electrocutor trap ("zapper"): A mechanical devise that attracts flying insects to a light. Insects flying inside are then killed by electricity.
Employee: Person working in or for a food establishment who engages in food preparation, service, or other assigned activity.
Endotoxin: A toxin produced within a microorganism and liberated when the microorganism disintegrates.
Enterotoxin: A toxin produced by an organism that harms the gastrointestinal tract of animals and man.
Enzyme: A biocatalyst that speeds up chemical reactions.
EPA (US Environmental Protection Agency): A government agency that sets standards for environmental quality, to include air and water quality, and regulates the use of pesticides and the handling of wastes.
Equipment: The appliances; stoves, ovens, etc.; and storage, such as refrigerated units used in food establishments.
Escherichia coli (E.coli): Coliform bacterium transmitted via feces, sewage, polluted water and some foods. Recently discovered is a particular strain identified as O157:H7 which was observed in undercooked hamburgers in 1982. *See* Chapter 2 for more details.
Evaluation: Judging the performance of training participants against the learning objectives.
Evaluation procedures: Systematically checking progress to determine if goals have been met.
Exclude: To prevent a person from working as a food employee or entering a food establishment except for those areas open to the general public.
Exotoxin: A toxin excreted by a microbe into the surrounding medium.

F

Facultative: Facultative microorganisms grow in the presence or absence of free oxygen. Most bacteria that cause foodborne illness are facultative. *See* **Aerobic, anaerobic.**
Fahrenheit: A temperature scale related to Celsius (centigrade) by the formula 9/5 (°Celsius + 32°) = °Fahrenheit.
FATTOM: An acronym that lists the six conditions bacteria need for growth. The conditions are Food, Acid, Time, Temperature, Oxygen, and Moisture. On the other hand, adverse conditions of these factors will slow down growth or even destroy bacteria. Some bacteria form spores to protect them from adverse conditions to a certain limit.
FDA (US Food and Drug Administration): An agency of the US Department of Health and Human Services that regulates food and drug safety: also responsible for developing the Model Food Code.
Feedback: Evaluation given to employees about their performance. This may be constructive criticism given to an individual to correct a mistake, or praise given to reinforce proper performance of a skill or procedure.
FIFO (first in, first out): A method of stock rotation in which supplies with earliest expiration date are shelved in front of supplies with later dates, so the old are used first. All inventory is marked with the expiration date, when it was received, or when it was stored after preparation.
Finger cot: A protective covering, similar to a glove, for one finger.
Fish: Fresh or saltwater finfish, crustaceans and other forms of aquatic life, including alligator, frog, aquatic turtle, jellyfish, sea cucumber, and sea urchin and the roe of such

animals, other than birds or mammals, and all mollusks, if such animal life is intended for human consumption. An edible human food product derived in whole or in part from fish, including fish that have been processed in any manner.

Flocculation: Agglomeration or building of a macrofloc resulting from coagulation into larger particles until the sheer force of water movement prevents further building or until it settles out.

Flood rim: Spillover point on a sink. An air gap exists between the top of the flood rim and the sink faucet.

Flow of food: The path of food through an establishment, from receiving through storing, preparing, cooking, holding, serving, cooling, and reheating. Food-safety hazards can occur at every stage in the flow of food. *See* Appendix B for a sample food flow chart.

Food: A raw, cooked, or processed edible substance, ice, beverage, or ingredient used or intended for use or for sale in whole or in part for human consumption, or chewing gum. Any organic or inorganic compound that supports growth, maintains and regulates life processes because of its nutrient content. Water and ice are considered inorganic foods. Sugars, starches, protein foods, fats, and oils are organic compounds, e.g. they contain carbon in their chemical composition. *See also* **Organic food** that has a different meaning in terms of food technology and agriculture.

Food additive, food preservative: Common food additives and preservatives include sulfites, nitrites, and sorbates. Most are generally regarded as safe (GRAS) but excessive amounts of certain food preservatives have caused illness or allergic reactions.

Food allergy: The body's negative reaction to a particular food or foods.

Food and Drug Administration (FDA): *See* **FDA.**

Food bar: Also called a self-service bar or self-service buffet where patrons can choose what they want to eat and serve themselves. Self-serve areas should be monitored by employees trained in food-safety procedures to prevent contamination of food by customers.

Food Code, The US: (Also referred to as the FDA Model Food Code.) The set of science-based guidelines for food safety for restaurants and establishments. Local, state, and federal regulators use the Food Code as a model to help develop or update their own food-safety rules.

Food-contact surface: A surface or utensil that normally touches food. *See* **Non-food-contact surface.**

Food contaminant: *See* **Contamination** and **Chemical contaminant.**

Food employee: An individual working with unpackaged food, food equipment or utensils, or food-contact surfaces.

Food establishment: An operation that stores, prepares, packages, serves, vends, or otherwise provides food for human consumption such as a restaurant, food market, institutional feeding location, or vending location.

Food-grade sealant: A lubricant or oil rated safe for use on kitchen equipment or utensils.

Food infections: Illnesses caused by ingesting pathogenic (infectious) microorganisms (with food or drink), such as bacteria, viruses, or parasites.

Food poisoning: an illness caused by eating food that contains certain toxins made by microbes or chemical poisons.

Food quality: Proper appearance, flavor, texture, consistency, and nutritional value in food. Food that is stored, prepared, and served properly is more likely to have high quality.

Food processing plant: A commercial operation that manufactures, packages, labels, or stores food for human consumption and does not provide food directly to a consumer.

Food safety: Unsafe food usually results from contamination due to biological hazards, chemical hazards, or physical hazards. To ensure food safety, establish standards that focus on controlling time and temperature, practicing good personal hygiene, maintaining a sanitary facility, preventing cross-contamination, and purchasing food supplies from approved suppliers.

Food spoilage: Changes in the color, flavor, or texture of foods due to prolonged changes.

Foodborne illness: A disorder or sickness caused by either foodborne infection or foodborne intoxication. Foodborne diseases are classified as infections, intoxications, or toxin-mediated infections.

Foodborne-disease outbreak (FBDO): The Centers for Disease Control and Prevention (CDC) defines a foodborne disease outbreak as an incident in which two or more people experience the same illness after eating the same food. Epidemiological analysis identifies the food as the source of the illness.

Foodborne infection: A foodborne illness that results when live, pathogenic microorganisms ingested in food grow in the intestines. Symptoms typically do not appear immediately.

Foodborne intoxication: An illness caused by eating food-containing toxins produced by pathogens (microorganisms). A person does not need to ingest live microorganisms to become ill, just the toxins, many of which are not destroyed by cooking. Symptoms of foodborne intoxication typically appear within a few hours.

Freezing: A preservation method by subjecting the food to temperatures below 0°F (–18°C) to change the water or fluids into ice or solid crystals. Remember that freezing does not destroy bacteria, but stops their growth, because the available water or water activity (A_w) is zero.

Frozen storage: The holding of frozen perishable food items at freezing temperatures, typically 0°F (–18°C) or lower. Frozen storage extends the shelf life of food. Freezers should not be used to freeze refrigerated or room-temperature foods. Also, freezing does not kill most microorganisms.

FSIS (Food Safety and Inspection Service): An agency of the USDA that deals with all food-safety issues concerning meat and poultry, their products, and produce shipped across state boundaries.

Fumigant: A gas or vapor mixture used to destroy pests.

Fumigate: Using a gas or vapor to destroy pests. A bomb that releases gas is placed in the room, and the room is closed up for several hours to allow the gas to work. The area is well ventilated before people go in again.

Fungi: Collective term for molds, yeasts and mushrooms, some of which can cause illness. *See* Chapter 2 for more details.

G

Game animal: An animal, the products of which are food, which is not classified as cattle, sheep, swine, goat, horse, mule, or other equine in 9 CFR. Includes mammals such as reindeer, elk, deer, antelope, water buffalo, bison, rabbit, squirrel, opossum, raccoon, nutria, or muskrat, and non-aquatic reptiles such as land snakes. Does not include ratites such as ostrich, emu, and rhea.

Garbage (or refuse): Wet waste matter, usually containing foods that cannot be recycled.

Gastroenteritis: Inflammation of the linings of the stomach and intestines that can cause nausea, vomiting, diarrhea, and cramping. Common occurrence with Traveler's diarrhea.

Gastrointestinal illness: An illness relating to the stomach or intestine.
General use pesticide: A pesticide that is not classified by EPA for restricted use as specified in 40 CFR 152.175.
Germicide: A chemical substance that kills harmful microbes.
Germs: General layman's term for microorganisms, including bacteria and viruses.
Glue board: Mice are trapped by the glue on these pest control devices, and then die from exhaustion or lack of water or air.
Grade A standards: The requirements of the United States Public Health Service/FDA "Grade A Pasteurized Milk Ordinance" and "Grade A Condensed and Dry Milk Ordinance" with which certain fluid and dry milk and milk products comply.
Grade standards: Primarily standards of quality to help producers, wholesalers, retailers, and consumers in marketing and purchasing food products. The grade standards are not aimed at protecting the health of the consumer, but rather at ensuring value received according to uniform quality standards.
GRAS (Generally Regarded As Safe): (also Generally Recognized As Safe). Food additives that are designated as "Generally Regarded As Safe" for use based on a long history of common usage in food. These are therefore permitted to be used without undergoing the policies and procedures required by law for approval.

H

HACCP (Hazard Analysis Critical Control Point): A dynamic system that uses a combination of proper food handling procedures, monitoring techniques, and record keeping to help ensure the consistent safety of food.
HACCP Plan: A written document based on HACCP principles, which describes the procedures a particular establishment will follow to ensure the safety of the food served.
Haff disease: A disease caused by eating certain fish (buffalo fish in the United States) that results in an unexplained destruction of skeletal muscle cells.
Hair restraint: A cap, net, hat, or other device used to cover the hair and/or beard.
Hand sanitizer: A liquid used to lower the number of microorganisms on the surface of the skin.
Hand washing: The proper cleaning of hands with soap and warm water from 20 to 30 seconds to remove dirt, filth, and disease germs. A very important sanitary practice to be done properly and frequently by food handlers. Soap and water will kill most bacteria.
Handwashing station: A sink set aside for handwashing only, never used for mixing cleaning chemicals or for washing food or utensils. Handwashing stations must be located in restrooms, and must be located in other convenient locations throughout the food-preparation and warewashing areas as well.
Hard water: Water that contains minerals such as calcium, magnesium and iron in concentrations of more than 120 parts per million (ppm). Concentrations of 61 to 120 ppm are considered moderately hard.
Hazard Analysis Critical Control Point: *See* **HACCP.**
Hazard analysis: Determining where hazards may occur in the flow of food if care is not taken to prevent or control them.
Hazards: Biological, chemical, or physical agents that may cause illness or injury if not reduced, controlled, or prevented; consumer health risks.
Hazard analysis: Identify hazards (problems) that might be introduced into food by unsafe practices or the intended use of the product.
Hazards, biological: Pathogenic microorganisms that contaminate food, such as certain bacteria, viruses, parasites, and fungi.

Biological hazards also exist in certain plants, mushrooms, and fish in the form of harmful toxins. *See* **Contaminants.**

Hazards, chemical: Chemical substances that may contaminate food, such as pesticides, food additives, preservatives, cleaning supplies, and toxic metals that leach from worn cookware and equipment. *See* **Chemical contamination.**

Hazards, physical: Foreign objects that accidentally get into food and contaminate it, such as dirt, metal staples, and broken glass.

HCS: (Hazard Communication Standard) of OSHA. Also known as Right-to-Know or HAZCOM. Standard that requires employers to inform employees of chemical hazards that they may be exposed to in the workplace. *See* **OSHA.**

Health inspector: City, county, or state employees who conduct inspections in most states. They generally are trained in food safety, sanitation, and in public health principles and methods. Also called sanitarians, health officials, or environmental health specialists.

Heat sanitizing: Raising the temperature of a food-contact surface to 165°F (74°C) or above to kill microorganisms. The most common way to heat sanitize tableware, utensils, or equipment is to submerge or spray items with hot water.

Heat-treated: Plant foods that have been cooked, partially cooked, or warmed, and have thereby become potentially hazardous foods.

Heavy metals: Minerals like lead, mercury, and cadmium that have high atomic weights. Many of them are toxic beyond tolerable limits. They are usually accidental contaminants in food or drink.

Heimlich maneuver: A method used to expel a foreign body caught in someone's throat.

Hepatitis A: A viral disease that causes inflammation of the liver. Sources of the virus can be from blood, urine and feces of infected people and animals; polluted water, infected rodents, and insects, contaminated food like milk, meat, shellfish, fruits or juices and hands of infected food handlers. *See* Chapter 2 for more details.

Hermetic packaging (seal): A container that is sealed completely and kept intact to prevent entry/loss of gases and vapors. This seal stops the entry of microorganisms and other contaminants such as bacteria, molds, yeasts, and filth as long as it remains intact.

High-acid food: Acidic foods have a pH below 7; high-acid foods have pH values below 4.6; examples include sauerkraut, tomatoes, and citrus products.

Highly alkaline cleaner: Heavy-duty detergents that may also contain a grease-dissolving agent. Highly alkaline detergents are used to remove wax, aged or dried soils, and baked-on grease. Warewashing detergents and floor-scrubbing compounds are also highly alkaline.

Highly susceptible population: High-risk population, immunosuppressed persons, groups of people at high risk for foodborne illness due to age or health status, such as very young children, pregnant women, older people, people taking certain medications, and those with certain diseases or weakened immune systems. Establishments with a highly susceptible population may include hospitals, nursing homes, daycare centers.

High-risk population: *See* **Highly susceptible population.**

Histamine: A compound typically formed in temperature-abused scombroid fish that causes a foodborne illness, scombroid poisoning (intoxication).

Host: A food, person, animal, or plant on which another organism lives and takes nourishment. A parasite depends on a host for its survival.

Hot-holding: Refers to the safe temperature range of 140°F (60°C) and above to maintain properly cooked foods hot until consumption.

Hot-holding equipment: Equipment designed to hold hot foods for service at 140°F (60°C) or higher. Hot-holding equipment includes steam tables, *bains maries,* chafing dishes, double broilers, and heated cabinets. Hot-holding equipment should not be used to reheat foods.

Hygiene: Collective term for sanitary practices; used to maintain good health and sanitary conditions.

Hygrometer: An instrument that measures relative humidity in the air.

I

Ice-water bath: A cooling method: food is divided into small quantities in pans, and then the pans are put in ice water in a sink or large pot.

ID_{50}: *See* **Infectious dose.**

Imminent health hazard: A significant threat or danger to health that is considered to exist when there is evidence sufficient to show that a product, practice, circumstance, or event creates a situation that requires immediate correction or cessation of operation to prevent injury based on the number of potential injuries and the nature, severity, and duration of the anticipated injury.

Immune system: The bodily system that protects the body from illness. Persons with compromised immune systems are more susceptible to foodborne illness. *See* **Highly susceptible population.**

Immunocompromised/Immunosuppressed: An individual who is susceptible to becoming ill from an illness due to a weakened immune condition.

Impermeable: Does not permit passage, especially of fluids.

Incidental additives: Substances that get into the food by accident anytime during growing, harvesting, storing, transporting, manufacturing or processing, cooking and serving the food. Also called accidental food additive.

Infection: A condition caused by the invasion of the tissues of a host by living pathogenic microorganisms; illness caused by eating food that contains living disease-causing microorganisms. *See* **Foodborne infection.**

Infectious dose (ID_{50}): Number of microorganisms required to start an infection in 50 percent of a well-characterized population. After receiving this dose, half the population will exhibit disease symptoms. More susceptible individuals, such as those who are immunocompromised, will exhibit disease symptoms at lower doses.

Infestation: Occupation, invasion, or presence of animal parasites that cause disease and/or destruction, as in crops or stored grains.

Ingestion: The process of eating and digesting food.

Inherent: Being an essential part of something.

Injected: Manipulating a meat so that infections or toxigenic microorganisms may be introduced from its surface to its interior through tenderizing with deep penetration or injecting the meat, such as by processes which may be referred to as "injecting," "pinning," or "stitch pumping."

Inorganic substances: Chemicals or compounds that are not made by plants or animals and are not carbon-containing. Examples are simple elements like minerals and salts.

Inservice: A short training session held for current employees (those already "in service"). May be used to update employees on a new procedure or practice, to reinforce appropriate behaviors, or to motivate.

Integrated pest management: A system of preventative and control measures used to control or eliminate pest infestations in food establishments. *See* **IPM.**

Interstate establishments: Establishments that operate across state borders. Examples include foodservice operations on trains, planes, and ships.

Intoxication: Illness caused by consumption of poisons naturally occurring in food or produced by pathogenic microorganisms. *See* **Foodborne intoxication, Toxicity** and **Toxin.**

In vitro test: Laboratory test performed in test tubes and other glassware

In vivo test: Laboratory test performed in live animals.

Iodine sanitizer: A chemical sanitizer that is less corrosive and irritating to the skin than chlorine. One of the acceptable disinfectants for water. Extreme care is used to read instructions on the amount and concentration that is safe for water drinking. Useful to bring when traveling to places with questionable safe water supply and for camping when consumer did not pack up water bottles.

IPM (Integrated Pest Management): A system of preventative measures and control measures to prevent pests from entering your facility, and to eliminate existing pest infestations. It should be cost-effective and environmentally sound.

Irradiation: The application of ionizing rays. Ionizing radiation of foods is used to destroy microorganisms. Also known as cold pasteurization. *See* Chapter 11 for more details.

J

Jaundice: Yellow skin and eyes. A common symptom of Hepatitis A.

Job aids: Materials or visual reminders that are used to deliver training content to employees.

Juice: The aqueous liquid expressed or extracted from one or more fruits or vegetables, purees of the edible portions of one or more fruits or vegetables, or any concentrates of such liquid or puree. Juice includes juice as a whole beverage, an ingredient of a beverage and a puree as an ingredient of a beverage.

K

Kitchen sanitation: Condition of keeping all areas and surfaces of the kitchen clean and sanitized. These include: the floors, walls and ceilings, cabinets, appliances, hoods and vents, lighting fixtures and bulbs, tables, counter tops, food and kitchenware storage facilities.

Kitchenware: Utensils used to prepare, cook or store food. Surfaces must be cleaned and sanitized.

L

Lag phase: A phase in bacterial growth. When bacteria are first introduced to a new environment, they may go through an adjustment period where their numbers are stable and they are preparing for growth. To control the growth of bacteria it is important to prolong the lag phase as long as possible.

Larva: Immature stage of development of insects and parasites.

Law: Applicable local, state, and federal statutes, regulations, and ordinances.

Leach: Under some circumstances, potentially toxic metals can be leached, or drawn out of equipment, storage containers, and certain tableware, cookware, and glassware, and mixed into foods, causing chemical contamination and foodborne illness. *See* **High-acid food.**

Lecture: A prepared oral presentation used to deliver content to a group of participants.

Leftovers: Any food that is prepared for a particular meal and is held over for service at a future meal.

Linens: Fabric items such as cloth hampers, cloth napkins, tablecloths, wiping cloths, and work garments including cloth gloves.

Listeria monocytogenes: A bacterium that is widespread in nature. Causes listteriosis that is transmitted via contaminated feces and food. *See* Chapter 2 for more details.
Log phase: A phase in bacterial growth. When conditions are favorable, bacteria can multiply very rapidly. This type of population growth is called exponential growth, or the log phase of the bacterial growth curve. Foods rapidly become unsafe during the log phase.
Low-moisture foods: foods that are relatively dry. Examples are: dried beans and cereal grains, nuts, hard candies, crispy cookies, crackers, and snack chips. They are less favorable for bacterial growth, but could be infested or could support molds.

M

Mad cow disease: Also called bovine spongiform encephalopathy (BSE) that is often fatal in cattle. Caused by contaminated animal parts.
Magic apron: An ineffective type of training where employees are expected to learn proper procedures by themselves while they work on the job. A false assumption is made that employees will somehow "magically" know the job once they put on the apron.
Manager: The individual present at a food service establishment who supervises employees who are responsible for the storage, preparation, display, and service of food to the public.
MAP (modified atmosphere packaging): A sealed package in which the oxygen has been reduced, removed or replaced with other gases. This type of packaging extends the food's shelf life and reduces or prevents the growth of aerobic microorganisms. Vacuum packaging and *sous vide* foods are forms of MAP.
Master cleaning schedule: A detailed schedule that lists all cleaning tasks in an establishment, when and how they are to be cleaned, and who will do the cleaning.
Measuring device: Usually a thermometer that registers the temperature of products and water used for sanitizing.
Meat: The flesh of animals used as food including the dressed flesh of cattle, swine, sheep, or goats and other edible animals, except fish, poultry, and wild game animals as specified under the US Food Code 2001, Subparagraphs 3-201.17(A)(3) and (4).
Media: Newspapers, magazines, radio, and television; also, for growth of microbes.
Mesophiles: Microorganisms that grow best at temperatures between 20 and 45°C.
Mg/L: Milligrams per liter, which is the metric equivalent of parts per million (ppm).
Microbe: Short term for microorganisms–a microscopic organism such as a bacterium or a virus.
Microbial contamination: *See* **Biological contamination.**
Microorganisms: Also microbes. Small, living organisms that can be seen only with the aid of a microscope. While not all cause disease, some do. These are called pathogens. Four kinds of microorganisms have the potential to contaminate food and cause foodborne illness, bacteria, viruses, parasites, and fungi.
Misbranding: Falsely or misleadingly packaged or labeled food; may contain ingredients not included on label or does not meet national standards for that food.
Mobile unit: A portable foodservice facility. Mobile units range from simple vending carts that hold and display prepackaged foods to full field kitchens capable of preparing and cooking elaborate meals.
Modified atmosphere packaging: *See* **MAP.**
Molds: A filamentous fungus. Evident from its fuzzy filamentous growth on food as colored colonies (black, green, yellow). For more details, *see* Chapter 2.

Molluscan shellfish: Any edible species of fresh or frozen oysters, clams, mussels, and scallops or edible portions thereof, except when the scallop product consists only of the shucked adductor muscle.
Monitoring: A consistent procedure to observe or measure a CCP to make sure critical limits are being met and to produce a record useful for verification. *See* **HACCP.**
Monitoring procedures: A defined method of checking foods during receiving, storage, preparation, holding, and serving processes.
Monosodium glutamate: *See* **MSG.**
MSDS: Material safety data sheets that must be provided with all hazardous materials by manufacturers. These sheets list the chemical and common name of the material, potential physical and health hazards, and directions for safe handling and use.
MSG (monosodium glutamate): MSG is used as a flavor enhancer in many prepackaged foods, and is included on the federal government's GRAS (generally regarded as safe) list of chemicals that are safe to use in food. However, in some people MSG can cause illness. Only the recommended amount of MSG should be used in recipes.
Mushroom toxins: Many fungi, such as certain varieties of mushrooms, have naturally occurring toxins (poisons) that may make people ill and cause death.
Mycotoxins: Compounds or metabolites produced by a wide range of fungi that have toxic or other adverse effects on humans and animals.

N

National Marine Fisheries Service: Provides a voluntary inspection service for processed fishery products.
National Sanitation Foundation: *See* **NSF International.**
Neurotoxins: Poisons that harm the nervous system.
Nitrites: Chemicals used as flavor enhancers, curing agents, and for color stabilizers in processed red meat.
Non-food-contact surface: Surfaces that do not ordinarily come in contact with food, such as tables, walls, floors, legs of equipment, shelves, drains. *See* **Food-contact surface.**
NSF International: Agency that develops and publishes standards of equipment design. Manufacturers can request an evaluation of their equipment which, if approved, will be listed by NSF International as meeting their standards.

O

Objective: States what a learner will be able to do after training or instruction is finished.
Off-site service: Food that is delivered to people away from where it was prepared. Examples are home delivery, carryouts, or deli trays from restaurants or grocery stores; caterers; home delivery of meals to elderly or ill persons; vending machines; temporary or mobile units.
Offal: Internal organs and soft tissues removed from an animal carcass when slaughtered or butchered. Infected offal has been implicated in mad cow's disease.
Onset time: The period between eating a contaminated food and developing symptoms of a foodborne illness.
Oral Rehydration Salts (ORS): Prepared formula for replacing fluids lost from diarrhea and vomiting.
Organic foods: Foods grown and processed without the use of synthetic compounds of fertilizers, pesticides, and added preservatives.
Organism: An individual living thing.

OSHA (Occupational Safety and Health Administration): The federal agency that regulates and monitors workplace safety.

Outbreak of foodborne illness: An incident in which two or more people experience the same illness after eating the same food.

P

Packaged: Bottled, canned, cartoned, securely bagged, or securely wrapped, whether packaged in a food establishment or a food processing plant. Does not include a wrapper, carryout box, or other non-durable container used to containerize food with the purpose of facilitating food protection during service and receipt of the food by the consumer.

Palatable: Food that has an acceptable taste and flavor.

Parasite: An organism that needs to live in or on a host organism to receive nourishment and survive, but does not contribute to the host's well-being and does not necessarily cause disease. *See* Chapter 2 for more details.

Paralytic shellfish poisoning (PSP): Shellfish may contain toxins that occur because of algae upon which they feed. Generally associated with mussels, clams, cockles, and scallops.

Parts per million (ppm): Unit of measure for substances dissolved in water, water hardness and chemical sanitizing solution concentrations. An example of one ppm is 1cc in 1000 liters.

Pasteurization: A low heat treatment used to destroy disease-causing organisms and/or extend the shelf life of a product by destroying organisms and enzymes that cause spoilage. Does not sterilize or kill all germs. Therefore, pasteurized milk can spoil eventually. Pasteurization process is not limited to milk; it is also applied to fruit juices and other dairy products. Can also be achieved by irradiation.

Pathogenic bacteria: Disease-causing bacteria.

Pathogens: Another term for microorganisms that can cause disease in living organisms.

PCO (Pest Control Officer): A licensed or certified technician who implements and monitors pest-control programs for companies that contract for services.

Permit: The document issued by the regulatory authority that authorizes a person to operate a food establishment.

Permit holder: The entity that is legally responsible for the operation of the food establishment, such as the owner, the owner's agent, or other person and possesses a valid permit to operate a food establishment.

Person: An association, a corporation, individual, partnership, other legal entity, government, or governmental subdivision or agency.

Person in charge: The individual present at a food establishment who is responsible for the operation at the time of inspection.

Personal care items: Items or substances that may be poisonous, toxic, or a source of contamination and are used to maintain or enhance a person's health, hygiene, or appearance; items such as medicines, first aid supplies, and other items such as cosmetics, and toiletries such as toothpaste and mouthwash.

Personal hygiene: Sanitary health habits that include keeping body, hair, and teeth clean, maintaining good health, wearing clean clothes, and washing hands regularly, especially when handling food and beverages.

Pest control: A sanitary measure to prevent the harmful effects of pests as stated under **Pesticide.**

Pest control operator: *See* **PCO.**

Pesticide: Chemical used to control the growth of pests, usually insects, diseases, fungi, weeds, and other pests of crops and animals, like birds and rodents. Specific kinds are: Insecticides (for insects), Fungicides (for fungi), and Herbicides (for weeds). *See* **Contact spray, Residual spray.**

pH: A logarithmic measure of acidity or alkalinity of a substance due to hydrogen and hydroxyl ion concentration. Used to control the growth of microorganisms. The pH scale ranges from 0 to 14.0. A pH of 7.0 is neutral. A pH above 7.0 is alkaline. A pH below 7.0 is acidic. A value of 1.0 is a strong acid and a value of 14.0 is a strong alkali. Most potentially hazardous foods have pH values from 4.6 to 7.0, that is, they are slightly acidic.

Physical contamination: The accidental introduction of foreign particles such as dirt, hair, and glass or metal particles into food. Some physical hazards occur naturally, such as bones in fish or chicken. *See* **Contamination.**

Physical facilities: The structure and interior surfaces of a food establishment including accessories such as soap and towel dispensers and attachments, such as light fixtures and heating or air conditioning system vents.

Plant toxins: Some plants have natural toxins that may make some people ill. People may ingest plant toxins by eating toxic plants themselves, or by eating products from animals that have ingested plant toxins.

Plumbing fixture: A receptacle or device that is permanently or temporarily connected to the water distribution system of the premises and demands a supply of water from the system; discharges used water, waste materials, or sewage directly or indirectly to the drainage system of the premises.

Poisonous or toxic materials: Substances that are not intended for ingestion and are included in 4 categories: (1) sanitizers, (2) pesticides, (3) Substances necessary for the operation and maintenance of the establishment such as nonfood grade lubricants and personal care items that may be deleterious to health and (3) Substances that are not necessary for the operation and maintenance of the establishment and are on the premises for retail sale, such as petroleum products and paints.

Pollution: The accumulation of foreign, unwanted matter in an environment in which it becomes a nuisance or a danger to the health of the environment.

Pooled eggs: Eggs that have been cracked open and combined in a container for quantity cooking.

Porosity: The extent to which water and other liquids are absorbed by a substance. Term used in relation to flooring material.

Potable: Suitable or safe for drinking.

Potable water: Water that is safe for cooking and drinking, and approved water supply.

Potentially hazardous foods (PHF): Foods that require temperature control because it is in a form capable of supporting rapidly growing infectious or toxigenic microorganisms. Potentially hazardous foods often have a history of being involved in foodborne illness outbreaks, have potential for contamination due to methods used to produce and process them. They are often warm, high in protein, high moisture content, and chemically neutral or low acid. *See* Figure 5. for food examples.

Poultry: In the US Food Code 2001, any domesticated bird (chickens, turkeys, ducks, geese, or guineas), whether live or dead as defined in 9 DFR 381 Poultry Products Inspection Regulations, and any migratory waterfowl, game bird, such as pheasant, partridge, quail, grouse, or guinea, or pigeon or squab, whether live or dead and defined in 9 CFR 362 Voluntary Poultry Inspection Program.

Precipitate: A deposit of an insoluble substance resulting from chemical or physical changes in a solution.

Premises: The physical facility, its contents, and the contiguous land or property under the control of the permit holder.

Prerequisite programs: Procedures that protect food from contamination, minimize microbial growth, and ensure the proper functioning of equipment. Also called standard operating procedures (SOPs).

Presentation: A key element of training, the delivery of content to the learner through a variety of methods.

Preventative measures (versus control methods): Steps that can be taken to prevent pests from entering a building, such as keeping the facility clean and sanitary and maintaining the building properly. Control measures focus on controlling and minimizing the problems from those that do enter.

Primal cut: A basic major cut into which carcasses and sides of meat are separated, such as a beef round, pork loin, lamb flank, or veal breast.

Psychrophiles: Microorganisms that grow in cold temperatures below 15°C.

Pulper: Pulpers grind food and other waste into small parts that are flushed with water. The water is then removed so that the processed solid wastes weigh less and are more compact for easier disposal.

Q

Quarry tile: A type of stone tile, generally reddish-brown in color, often used in public restrooms or high-soil areas.

Quaternary ammonium (quats): A group of sanitizers commonly used in foodservice, all having the same basic chemical structure. Quats are generally nontoxic, noncorrosive, and stable when exposed to heat but may not kill certain types of microorganisms. *See* **Chlorine, Iodine.**

R

Ready-to-eat foods: Edible foods without additional preparation to achieve food safety; or may receive additional preparation for palatability or aesthetic, epicurean, gastronomic, or culinary purposes; properly cooked foods, and raw, washed, cut, and whole fruits and vegetables (including those that have had their rinds, peels, husks, or shells removed). The FDA identifies most ready-to-eat foods as potentially hazardous.

Reasonable care defense: A defense against a food-related lawsuit; if you can prove that your establishment did everything that could be reasonably expected to ensure that the food served was safe.

Refrigerated storage: Short-term holding of fresh, perishable, and potentially hazardous food items at internal temperatures of 41°F (5°C) or lower, but above freezing, to slow the growth of microorganisms. Refrigeration retards ripening process, but maturing enzymes continue their action. Bananas and avocados do not have to be refrigerated.

Refuse: Solid waste not carried by water through the sewage system.

Regulation: Details how a law will be put into effect by the government agency responsible for that regulation.

Regulatory authority: The local, state, or federal enforcement body or authorized representative having jurisdiction over the food establishment.

Reheating: Process of heating cooked foods and leftovers that should follow certain guidelines of time-temperature for safety.

Relative humidity (RH): The amount of water vapor in the air. An atmosphere of high RH promotes bacterial growth than a lower RH, because condensation of the water vapor can occur on food surfaces, thereby increasing available water (A_w) for microbial growth.

Residual spray: A type of pesticide spray that leaves a film behind, which eventually kills insects that walk across it. Residue sprays are typically sprayed by a PCO around the perimeter of a facility on a monthly basis to provide continuous protection against insects that might enter. *See* **Contact spray.**

Resiliency: The ability of something to react to a shock without breaking or cracking. Term usually used in relation to flooring materials.
Restrict: To limit the activities of a food employee so that there is no risk of transmitting a disease that is transmissible through food and the food employee does not work with exposed food, unclean equipment, utensils, linens, and unwrapped single service or single-use articles.
Restricted egg: Any check, dirty egg, incubator reject, inedible, leaker, or loss as defined in 9 CFR 590.
Restricted use pesticide: A pesticide product that contains the active ingredients specified in 40 CFR 152.175. Pesticides classified for restricted use, and that is limited to use by or under the direct supervision of a certified applicator.
Risk: The likelihood that an adverse health effect will occur within a population as a result of a hazard in a food.
Risk factor: A condition that predisposes an organism or human being to a disease process, but it is not necessarily the causative or etiologic factor. Malnutrition is a risk factor for foodborne illness.
Role-plays: A method in which training participants enact a situation in order to try out new skills or apply what has been learned.

S

Safe material: An article manufactured from or composed of materials that may not reasonably be expected to result, directly or indirectly, in their becoming a component or otherwise affecting the characteristics of any food.
Safety: A judgment of practical certainty that injury or harmful effects will not occur when a substance is used or a food is ingested or consumed.
***Salmonella* spp**: Bacteria that affect the intestinal tract characterized by fever, chills, headache, diarrhea, abdominal cramps and dehydration. Sources are from the GIT (gastrointestinal tract) of people and animals. Foods commonly implicated are: eggs, meats, especially poultry, meat products, fish and shellfish, raw salads, and coconut. Control points for salmonellosis (name of the infection) include: Avoiding cross-contamination, cooking meats and eggs thoroughly, chilling or cooling foods rapidly, and general hygiene, especially handwashing.
Sanitary, sanitation: A sanitary or sanitized object or surface is free from harmful levels of disease-causing organisms and other harmful contaminants. To be effective, sanitation must follow effective cleaning.
Sanitation: The creation and maintenance of conditions favorable to good health; the absence of pathogens and other harmful substances.
Sanitization: The application of cumulative heat or chemicals on cleaned food-contact surfaces that, when evaluated for efficacy, is sufficient to yield a reduction of 5 logs, which is equal to 99.999% reduction, of representative disease microorganisms of public health importance.
Sanitize: Treatment by heat or chemicals to reduce the number of microorganisms present.
Sanitizer: A compound used in the cleaning process that lowers the level of microorganisms on a surface to levels that do not cause illness. *See* **Chlorine, Iodine, Quaternary ammonium.**
Sanitizing hand lotion: A germicidal lotion or hand dip to be used after proper handwashing.
Sanitizing: The process of reducing/killing the number of microorganisms on a surface to safe levels.
Scale: The buildup of mineral deposits in pipes or equipment from water hardness. Scale is a problem for equipment that uses hot water, boiling water, or steam, for example warewashing machines and steam tables.

Scombroid poisoning (intoxication): A foodborne illness caused by histamine that is produced by bacteria growing in scombroid fish, such as tuna, mackerel, bluefish, skipjack, and bonito, are time-temperature abused, the bacteria associated with them form the toxin histamine, which causes symptoms. Scombroid intoxication has also been associated with some nonscombroid fish.

Sealed: Free of cracks or other openings that allow the entry or passage of moisture.

Service animal: An animal such as a guide dog, signal dog, or other animal individually trained to provide assistance to an individual with a disability.

Service sink: Sink used exclusively for cleaning mops and disposing of wastewater. At least one service sink or one curbed drain area is required in an establishment.

Servicing area: An operating base location to which a mobile food establishment or transportation vehicle returns regularly for such things as vehicle and equipment cleaning, discharging liquid or solid wastes, refilling water tanks and ice bins, and boarding food.

Sewage: Liquid waste containing animal or vegetable matter in suspension or solution and may include liquids containing chemicals in solution.

Shelf life: A recommended period of time that a food may be stored and remain suitable for use.

Shellfish control authority: A state, federal, foreign, tribal, or other government entity legally responsible for administering a program that includes certification of molluscan shellfish harvesters and dealers for interstate commerce.

Shellstock: Raw, in-shell molluscan shellfish.

Shellstock identification tags: The FDA requires that shipments of live molluscan shellfish carry shellstock identification tags to identify the shipper, the date of shipment, date of receipt, and other information. The tags should remain attached to the containers the shellfish came in until the container is empty. Operators then must keep the tags on file for ninety days after the shellfish has been used. Never mix shellfish from one shipment with another.

Shiga toxin-producing *Escherichia coli*: means any *E. coli* capable of producing *Shiga* toxins (also called verocytotoxins or "Shiga-like" toxins. This includes, but is not limited to, *E. coli* reported as serotype 0157:H7, 0157:NM, and 0157:H.

***Shigella* spp**: Bacteria that infect the gastrointestinal tract and the illnesses are called shigellosis. Symptoms are similar to salmonellosis, but the feces could be bloody. A known term for its infection is bacillary dysentery. Foods implicated and preventive measures are the same as for salmonella shellfish infection.

Shucked shellfish: Molluscan shellfish that have one or both shells removed.

Single-use items: (Also single-service articles) Another name for disposable eating utensils and tableware. These may be used once only. They are generally made from paper, plastic, wood, or aluminum foil.

Single-use paper towel: Paper towels designed to be used once, then discarded. Use minimizes risk of cross-contamination.

Slacking: The process of gradually thawing frozen food in preparation for deep-fat frying or to allow even heating during cooking.

Smooth: A food-contact surface having a surface free of pits and inclusions with a cleanability equal to or exceeding that of (100 grit) number 3 stainless steel; a nonfood-contact surface of equipment having a surface equal to that of commercial grade hot-rolled steel free of visible scale; and a floor, wall, or ceiling having an even or level surface with no roughness or projections that render it difficult to clean.

Sneeze guard: A food shield used to prevent contamination of food in salad bars and other self-serve food bars. It is placed fourteen to forty-eight inches above the food, in a direct line between food on display and the mouth and nose of a person of average height.

Soap: A cleaning agent used in restaurants and establishments primarily for handwashing; a compound of fatty acids and alkalis that has cleansing properties.

Soil: A general term for foreign material present on a surface that requires removal. In establishments, soil might consist of food debris on tableware, or wax, aged or dried substances; stains and baked-on grease; or scale, rust, and tarnish on other surfaces. *See* **Clean, cleaning, cleaning agent.**

Solid waste: Dry, bulky trash that can be recycled, including glass, plastic, paper, and cardboard.

Solvents: Solvent cleaners, often called degreasers, are alkaline detergents that contain a grease-dissolving agent. These cleaners work well in areas where grease has been burned on. Solvents are usually effective only at full strength.

Source: The source of a microorganism is an item or organism (often a human being) where the microorganism usually resides. Sources may be referred to as vehicles, carriers, or hosts.

Sous vide: Food processed by this method is vacuum-packed in individual pouches, partially or fully cooked, and then chilled. These foods are often heated for service in the establishment.

Spoilage: Decay or undesirable changes and damage. Food spoilage occurs when putrefaction, fermentation, changes in color, flavor, and other defects make the food unpalatable and not suitable for eating. Most molds and yeast are common food spoilage agents.

Spoilage microorganism: Foodborne microorganisms that cause food to spoil. These are microorganisms that typically do not cause foodborne illness.

Spore: Some bacteria form spores; thick-walled formations within the bacterial cell that serve as a means of protection (high or low temperatures, low moisture, high acidity, and exposure to sanitizing solutions). The spore itself does not reproduce, but it is an inactive, resistant, resting, or reproductive body that can produce another vegetative organism when conditions again become favorable. Also the reproductive cell of a fungus.

Stability: Condition of being able to resist chemical and physical breakdown.

Staphylococcus aureus: Foodborne round bacterium that causes gastroenteritis due to its heat-stable toxin. *See* Chapter 2 for more details.

Standard: A measure used as a comparison for quality to determine the degree or level that a requirement should meet.

Stationary phase: A phase of bacterial growth where just as many bacteria are growing as dying. Follows log phase of bacterial growth.

Sterile: Free from all living microorganisms.

Sterilization: Process of killing all living organisms.

Studs, joints, rafters: Internal support beams and framework for a building.

Sulfites: Preservatives added to some foods, including fruits and vegetables, to preserve freshness and color. Some people are allergic to sulfites, and some states forbid restaurants to add them to foods.

Suppliers, approved (certified): Reputable and reliable suppliers whose products and practices meet federal and local standards. Reputable suppliers deliver correctly packaged food in adequately refrigerated delivery trucks, train their employees in food-safety practices, adjust delivery schedules to meet your needs, and allow you to inspect their delivery vehicles and production facilities.

Surfactants: Agents in all detergents that reduce surface tension between soil and the item being cleaned, allowing the detergent to penetrate and soak soil loose; wetting agent.

Suspension: A temporary withdrawal of a health department permit for an establishment to operate because the health inspector determined the facility posed an immediate health hazard. Correction of all violations and a satisfactory re-inspection may be required for reinstatement of the permit.

T

Table-mounted equipment: Equipment that is not portable and is designed to be mounted off the floor on a table, counter, or shelf.

Tableware: Eating, drinking, and serving utensils for table use such as: flatware, plates, cups, bowls, etc.

Taint: To contaminate with undesirable organisms or substances.

Task analysis: Examining a job task to determine what it takes to do the job.

Technology-based training: Training programs that are delivered through a computer or other technology.

Temperature: Measurement of coldness or warmth (heat) based on a standard scale. The two systems currently used are degrees Fahrenheit (°F) and degrees Celsius (°C). The measuring device is a thermometer.

Temperature abuse: Any time potentially hazardous food is exposed to the temperature danger zone of 41°F (5°C) to 140°F (60°C) for an unacceptable period of time. Foods being prepared or cooked should pass through the temperature danger zone as quickly as possible. Temperature abuse of potentially hazardous foods can cause the rapid growth of microorganisms, potentially causing foodborne illness.

Temperature danger zone: The temperature range between 41°F and 140°F (5°C to 60°) at which bacteria grow best. Potentially hazardous foods must not be left in the temperature danger zone for more than four hours total.

Temperature measuring device: A thermometer, thermocouple, thermistor, or other device that indicates the temperature or food, air or water.

Temporary operation (unit): An establishment that operates in one location, for no more than 14 consecutive days, in conjunction with a single event or celebration. Temporary units usually serve prepackaged foods or foods that require only limited preparation.

Terrazzo: A mixture of marble chips and Portland cement used for flooring. An attractive, nonporous, non-resilient surface good for use in the back of the house, dining rooms, and restrooms.

Test kit: Device that accurately measures the concentration of sanitizing solutions to ensure that they are at proper levels.

Thermometer: A device that measures temperatures.

Thermophiles: Microorganisms that grow best at hot temperatures above 113°F (45°C).

Time-temperature indicator (TTI): Time-temperature indicators are used to determine if a product has been time-temperature abused. TTIs are most often placed on temperature-sensitive foods by packers or processors.

Time-temperature monitoring: To maximize food safety, and minimize growth of microorganisms in food, time and temperature must be controlled and monitored throughout the flow of food, including receiving, storage, preparation, cooking, holding, cooling, and reheating.

Tolerance limit: The maximum amount of a reside of substance present in the food beyond which it is no longer safe or will cause some harm.

Toxicity: The ability of a substance to cause harmful effects to an organism. Factors like the kind of toxic substance, dosage or amount, determines the potency of a toxin. A rule of thumb is to consider all substances toxic if the concentration is high enough.

Toxigenic bacteria: Bacteria that produce toxins.

Toxin: A poisonous chemical agent: may be produced by living organism, or is naturally occurring.

Toxin-mediated infection: A foodborne illness that results when a microorganism from ingested food grows in the intestinal tract and then produces toxins that cause illness.

Toxins: Some microorganisms produce toxins, or poisons, in food that is then ingested. This is called foodborne intoxication. Thus, a person does not need to ingest live organisms to become ill, just the toxins, many of which are not destroyed by cooking. Some are naturally living in plants and other organisms.

Training need: A gap between what your employees are required to know to perform their job and what they actually know.

Training program: A structured sequence of events that leads to learning.

Traveler's Diarrhea (TD): Bouts of frequent bowel movement with loose watery stools due to a number of pathogens, usually from polluted water or contaminated food as a result of poor sanitary practices. CDC (Centers for Disease Control and Prevention, USA) has a list of nations where tourists or travelers to these countries have high risk of contracting TD.

TTI: *See* **Time-temperature indicator.**

Tuberculosis (TB): An infectious disease that usually affects the lungs. It is caused by the tubercle bacillus that is transmitted from person to person via air. An infected person, who coughs, sneezes, laughs and talks could breathe out the germs and another person in close contact could breathe them in. Symptoms of active TB are: night sweats, chronic fatigue, weight loss, fever, and coughing up blood. Diagnoses include: skin test and confirmed by chest x-ray.

Tumble chiller: Equipment designed to cool food quickly. Prepackaged food is placed into a drum that rotates inside a reservoir of chilled water. The tumbling action increases the time the food is chilled.

Two-stage cooling method: Cooked foods must be cooled from 140°F (60°C) to 70°F (21°C) within two hours and from 70°F (21°C) to below 41°F (5°C in an additional four hours for a total cooling time of six hours.

U

UL (Underwriters Laboratories): An agency that lists equipment that meets NSF International's standards. UL's particular emphasis is on electrical safety requirements; it also has a sanitation mark. *See also* **NSF International**.

Ultra pasteurized foods: Foods pasteurized at a high temperature for a short time to kill pathogens; the foods are packaged aseptically and may be labeled UHT (ultrahigh temperature).

USDA (US Department of Agriculture): A government agency responsible for the inspection and grading of meats, meat products, poultry, dairy products, eggs, and egg products, and fruits and vegetables shipped across state lines.

USPHS (US Public Health Service): A federal government agency that inspects cruise ships that cross international borders.

Utensil: A food-contact implement or container used in the storage, preparation, transportation, dispensing, sale, or service of food, such as kitchenware or tableware that is multiuse, single- service, or single-use, gloves used in contact with food, temperature sensing probes of food temperature measuring devices, and probe-type price or identification tags used in contact with food.

V

Vacuum breaker: A backflow prevention device; a spring loaded device to operate after extended periods of hydrostatic pressure, designed for use under a continuous supply of pressure. *See* **Backflow.**

Vacuum packaging: Food packaging in which all of the air is removed around the product.

Variance: A written document issued by the regulatory authority that authorizes a modification or waiver of one or more requirements of the FDA Food Code if, in the opinion of the regulatory authority, a health hazard or nuisance will not result from the modification or waiver.

Vegetative cells: Active, living cells.

Vegetative microorganisms: Bacteria reproduce by splitting in tow. Vegetative microorganisms are those bacteria actively splitting in two (growing).

Vegetative state: The active state of a bacterium where the cell takes in nourishment, grows, and produces wastes.

Vehicle: Food, plant, person, or object by which pathogenic microorganisms are transferred to another food, person, plant, or object.

Vending machine: A self-service device that, upon insertion of a coin, paper currency, token, card, or key, or by optional manual operation, dispenses unit servings of food in bulk or in packages without the necessity of replenishing the device between each vending operation. Vending operators must protect foods from contamination and temperature abuse during transport, delivery, and service. Vending machines that dispense chilled or hot food must have automatic cutoff controls that prevent foods from being dispensed if the temperature stays in the danger zone for a certain amount of time.

Vending machine location: The room, enclosure, space, or area where one or more vending machines are installed and operated and includes the storage areas and areas on the premises that are used to service and maintain the vending machines.

Ventilation: Air circulation that removes smoke, odors, moisture, and grease-laden vapors from a room and replaces them with fresh air.

Verification: To prove to be true by evidence, usually a record of time and temperatures of food from receiving to serving or vending; determines whether a HACCP system is working as intended.

***Vibrio* spp**: A group of bacteria (*V. cholera, V. vulnificus,* and *V. parahaemolyticus*). *See* Chapter 2 for more details.

Virus: The smallest of all microbes. A small bundle of genes, protected by a protein coat: viruses can reproduce only by infecting a living host cell and using its genetic machinery. For more details, *see* Chapter 2.

W

Warewashing: The cleaning and sanitizing of utensils and food-contact surfaces of equipment.

Warm-air dryer: Also hot air, forced-air. An acceptable method of drying hands at a handwashing station. Some jurisdictions require the use of these machines instead of towels.

Warranty of sale: The rules stating how food must be handled in an establishment.

Water activity (a_w): A measure of the free moisture (water), in food or beverages, available for the growth of microorganisms. Pure water has a water activity of 1.0, and potentially hazardous foods have water-activity values of 0.85 or above. Raw fresh meat that has 60 percent water has a water activity (a_w) of zero when frozen. Dried pasta that is considered nonperishable has 0.5 a_w Cheddar cheese has 0.94 A_w.

Water, carbonated: Water that contains carbon dioxide gas. Sodas, seltzers, and tonic waters are legally soft drinks.

Water, distilled: Water treated by vaporizing and then recondensing. Dissolved minerals are removed. Some bottled distilled water sold states that it is "sodium-free," which is true.

Water hardness: The amount of inorganic salts (such as calcium chloride, magnesium chloride, sulfates, and bicarbonates) in water.
Water, potable: Water suitable and safe to drink or use for cooking.
Water purification: Treated water by distillation or other physical and chemical means to get rid of solid contaminants and minerals. Safe for drinking, cooking, and especially for laboratory researches.
Well water: Water drawn from ground water by tapping into an aquifer. Aquifers are underground rock formations where water is found. In artesian wells, the water is confined in an aquifer and is drawn under pressure.
Wetting agent: a substance that breaks down the soil to allow water and soap or detergent to liquefy and remove dirt and grease.
Whole-muscle, intact beef: A whole muscle beef that is not injected, mechanically tenderized, reconstructed, or scored and marinated, from which beef steaks may be cut.
Wholesome: Promoting health or well being, safe.
WHO: World Health Organization: An international organization actively involved in food and water safety, among many other global concerns related to health.

Y

Yeast: Type of fungus. These microorganisms are larger than bacteria and divide by producing buds. They grow more slowly than bacteria. For more details, *see* Chapter 5.

INDEX

D

Y